A Long Line

of Cells

A Long Line of Cells

COLLECTED ESSAYS

Lewis Thomas

Book-of-the-Month Club
New York

Many of these essays originally appeared in *Discover*. Essays 1 through 29 originally appeared in *The New England Journal of Medicine*. Copyright © Massachusetts Medical Society, 1971, 1972, 1973.

"Medical Lessons from History" originally appeared in *Daedalus, Journal of the American Academy of Arts and Sciences*, Boston, MA, Summer 1977, under the title "Biomedical Science and Human Health: The Long-Range Prospect." Reprinted by permission of *Daedalus*.

"The Youngest and Brightest Thing Around" appeared in different form in *The New York Times* on July 2, 1978, and is reprinted by permission. Copyright © 1978 by The New York Times.

"The Unforgettable Fire" ("Unacceptable Damage") originally appeared in *The New York Review of Books*.

Excerpt from "The Man with the Blue Guitar" from *The Collected Poems of Wallace Stevens*, copyright 1936 by Wallace Stevens; renewed 1964 by Holly Stevens. Reprinted by permission of Alfred A. Knopf, Inc.

This edition was specially created in 1990 for Book-of-the-Month Club by arrangement with Viking Penguin, a division of Penguin Books USA, Inc. All rights reserved.

Design and composition by The Sarabande Press

Printed in the United States of America

Contents

Introduction

A Long Line of Cells

IT SHOULD BE EASIER, CERTAINLY SHORTER WORK TO COMPOSE A memoir than an autobiography, and surely it is easier to sit and listen to the one than to the other. An autobiography, I take it, is a linear account of one thing after another, leading—progressively, one hopes—to one's personal state of affairs at the moment of writing. In my case this would run to over seventy years, one after the other, discounting maybe twenty-five of the seventy spent sleeping, leaving around forty-five to be dealt with. Even so, a lot of time to be covered if all the events were to be recalled and laid out.

But discount again the portion of those 16,500 days, 264,000 waking hours, spent doing not much of anything—reading the papers, staring at blank sheets of paper, walking from one room to the next, speaking a great deal of small talk and listening to still more, waiting around for the next thing to happen, whatever. Delete all this as irrelevant, then line up what's left in the proper linear order without fudging. There you are with an autobiography, now relieved of an easy three-fourths of the time lived, leaving only eleven years, or 4,000 days, or 64,000 hours. Not much to remember, but still too much to write down.

But now take out all the blurred memories, all the recollections you suspect may have been dressed up by your mind in your favor, leaving only the events you can't get out of your head, the notions that keep leaping to the top of your mind, the ideas you're stuck with, the images that won't come unstuck, including the ones you'd just as soon do without. Edit these down sharply enough to reduce 64,000 hours to around thirty minutes, and there's your memoir.

In my case, going down this shortened list of items, I find that most of what I've got left are not real memories of my own experience, but mainly the remembrances of other people's thoughts, things I've read or been told, metamemories. A surprising number turn out to be wishes rather than recollections, hopes that the place really did work the way everyone said it was supposed to work, hankerings that the one thing leading to another has a direction of some kind, and a hope for a pattern from the jumble—an epiphany out of entropy.

To begin personally on a confessional note, I was at one time, at my outset, a single cell. I have no memory of this stage of my life, but I know it to be true because everyone says so. There was of course a sort of half-life before that, literally half, when the two half-endowed, haploid gametes, each carrying half my chromosomes, were off on their own looking to bump into each other and did so, by random chance, sheer luck, for better or worse, richer or poorer, et cetera, and I got under way.

I do not remember this, but I know that I began dividing. I have probably never worked so hard, and never again with such skill and certainty. At a certain stage, very young, a matter of hours of youth, I sorted myself out and became a system of cells, each labeled for what it was to become—brain cells, limbs, liver, the lot—all of them signaling to each other, calculating their territories, laying me out. At one stage I possessed an excellent kidney, good enough for any higher fish; then I thought better and destroyed it all at once, installing in its place a neater pair for living on land. I didn't plan on this when it was going on, but my cells, with a better memory, did.

Thinking back, I count myself lucky that I was not in charge at the time. If it had been left to me to do the mapping of my cells I would have got it wrong, dropped something, forgotten where to assemble my neural crest, confused it. Or I might have been stopped in my tracks, panicked by the massive deaths, billions of my embryonic cells being killed off systematically to make room for their more senior successors, death on a scale so vast that I can't think of it without wincing. By the time I was born, more of me had died than survived. It is no wonder I can't remember; during that time I went through brain after brain for nine months, finally contriving the one model that could be human, equipped for language.

It is because of language that I am able now to think farther back into my lineage. By myself, I can only remember two parents, one grandmother and the family stories of Welshmen, back into the shadows when all the Welsh were kings, but no farther. From there on I must rely on reading the texts.

They instruct me that I go back to the first of my immediate line, the beginner, the earliest *Homo sapiens,* human all the way through, or not quite human if you measure humanness as I do by the property of language and *its* property, the consciousness of an indisputably singular, unique self. I'm not sure how far back that takes me, and no one has yet told me about this convincingly. When did my relations begin speaking?

Writing is easier to trace, having started not more than a few years back, maybe 10,000 years, not much more. Tracking speech requires guesswork. If we were slow learners, as slow as we seem to be in solving today's hard problems, my guess is that we didn't begin talking until sometime within the last 100,000 years, give or take 50,000. That is what's called a rough scientific guess. But no matter, it is an exceedingly short time ago, and I am embarrassed at the thought that so many of my ancestors, generations of them—all the way back to the very first ones a million-odd years ago—may have been speechless. I am modestly proud to have come from a family of tool makers, bone scratchers, grave diggers, cave painters. Humans all. But it hurts to think of them as so literally dumb, living out their lives without metaphors, deprived of conversation, even small talk. I would prefer to have had them arrive fully endowed, talking their heads off, the moment evolution provided them with braincases large enough to contain words, so to speak. But it was not so, I must guess, and language came late. I will come back to this matter.

What sticks in the top of my mind is another, unavoidable aspect of my genealogy, far beyond my memory, but remembered still, I suspect, by all my cells. It is a difficult and delicate fact to mention. To face it squarely, I come from a line that can be traced straight back, with some accuracy, into a near-infinity of years before my first humanoid ancestors turned up. I go back, and so do you, like it or not, to a single Ur-ancestor whose remains are on display in rocks dated approximately 3.5 thousand million years ago, born a billion or so years after the earth itself took shape and began cooling down. That first of the line, our n-granduncle, was unmistakably a bacterial cell.

I cannot get this out of my head. It has become, for the moment, the most important thing I know, the obligatory beginning of any memoir, the long-buried source of language. We derive from a lineage of bacteria, and a very long line at that. Never mind our embarrassed indignation when we were first told, last century, that we came from a family of apes and had chimps as near-cousins. That was relatively easy to accommodate, having at least the distant look of a set of relatives. But this new connection, already fixed by recent science beyond any hope of disowning the parentage, is something else again. At first encounter the news must come as a kind of humiliation. Humble origins indeed.

But then, it is some comfort to acknowledge that we've had an etymological hunch about such an origin since the start of our language. Our word "human" comes from the Proto-Indo-European root *dhghem,* meaning simply "earth." The most telling cognate word is "humus," the primary product of microbial industry. Also, for what it's worth, "humble." Also "humane." It gives a new sort of English, in the sense of a strange spin, to the old cliché for an apology: "Sorry, I'm only human."

Where did that first microorganism, parent of us all, come from? Nobody knows, and in the circumstance it's anyone's guess, and the guesses abound. Francis Crick suggests that the improbability of its forming itself here on earth is so high that we must suppose it drifted in from outer space, shifting the problem to scientists in some other part of the galaxy or beyond. Others assert that it happened here indeed, piecing itself together molecule by molecule, over a billion years of chance events under the influence of sunlight and lightning, finally achieving by pure luck the exactly right sequence of nucleotides, inside the exactly right sort of membrane, and we were on our way.

No doubt the first success occurred in water. And not much doubt that the first event, however it happened, was the only such event, the only success. It was the biological equivalent of the Big Bang of the cosmophysicists, very likely a singular phenomenon, a piece of un- precedented good luck never to be repeated. If the sheer improbability of the thing taking place more than once, spontaneously and by chance, were not enough, consider the plain fact that all the cells that came later, right up to our modern brain cells, carry the same strings of DNA and work by essentially the same genetic code. It is the plainest evidence of direct inheritance from a single parent. We are all in the same family— grasses, seagulls, fish, fleas and voting citizens of the republic.

I ought to be able to remember the family tie, since all my cells are alive with reminders. In almost everything they do to carry me along from one day to the next, they use the biochemical devices of their microbial forebears. Jesse Roth and his colleagues at the National Insti- tutes of Health have shown that the kingdom of bacteria had already learned, long before nucleated cells like ours came on the scene, how to signal to each other by chemical messages, inventing for this purpose molecules like insulin and a brilliant array of the same peptides that I make use of today for instructing my brain cells in proper behavior.

More than this, I could not be here, blinking in the light, without the help of an immense population of specialized bacteria that swam into cells like mine around a billion years ago and stayed there, as indispens- able lodgers, ever since, replicating on their own, generation after generation. These are my mitochondria, the direct descendants of the first bacteria that learned how to make use of oxygen for energy. They occupy all my cells, swarming from one part to another wherever there is work to do. I could not lift a finger without them, nor think a thought, nor can they live without me. We are symbionts, my mitochondria and I, bound together for the advance of the biosphere, living together in harmony, maybe even affection. For sure, I am fond of my microbial engines, and I assume they are pleased by the work they do for me.

Or is it necessarily that way, or the other way round? It could be, I suppose, that all of me is a sort of ornamented carapace for colonies of bacteria that decided, long ago, to make a try at real evolutionary novelty. Either way, the accommodation will do.

The plants are in the same situation. They have the same swarms of mitochondria in all their cells, and other foreign populations as well. Their chloroplasts, which do the work of tapping solar energy to make all sugar, are the offspring of ancient pigmented microorganisms called cyanobacteria, once known as blue-green algae. These were the first creatures to learn—at least 2.5 billion years ago—how to use carbon dioxide from the air and plain water, and sunlight, to manufacture food for the market.

I am obsessed by bacteria, not just my own and those of the horse chestnut tree in my backyard, but bacteria in general. We would not have nitrogen for the proteins of the biosphere without the nitrogen-fixing bacteria, most of them living like special tissues in the roots of legumes. We would never have decay; dead trees would simply lie there forever, and so would we, and nothing on earth would be recycled. We couldn't keep cows, for cattle can't absorb their kind of food until their intestinal bacteria have worked it over, and for the same reason there would be no termites to cycle the wood; they are, literally, alive with bacteria. We would not have luminous fish for our aquariums, for the source of that spectacular light around their eyes is their private colonies of luminescent bacteria. And we would never have obtained oxygen to breathe, for all the oxygen in our air is exhaled for our use by the photosynthetic microbes in the upper waters of the seas and lakes and in the leaves of forests.

It was not that we invented a sophisticated new kind of cell with a modern nucleus and then invited in the more primitive and simpler forms of life as migrant workers. More likely, the whole assemblage came together by the joining up of different kinds of bacteria; the larger cell, the original "host," may have been one that had lost its rigid wall and swelled because of this defect. Lynn Margulis has proposed that the spirochetes were part of the original committee, becoming the progenitors of the cilia on modern cells, also the organizers of meiosis and mitosis, the lining up of chromosomes, the allocation of DNA to progeny—in effect, the reading of all wills. If she is right about this, the spirochetes were the inventors of biological sex and all that, including conclusive death.

The modern cell is not the single entity we thought it was a few years ago. It is an organism in its own right, a condominium, run by trustees.

If all this is true, as I believe it to be, the life of the earth is more intimately connected than I used to think. This is another thing on my mind, so much in my head these days that it crowds out other thoughts I used to have, making me sit up straight now, bringing me to my feet and then knocking me off them. The world works. The whole earth is alive, all of a piece, one living thing, a creature.

It breathes for us and for itself, and what's more it regulates the breathing with exquisite precision. The oxygen in the air is not placed there at random, any old way; it is maintained at precisely the optimal concentration for the place to be livable. A few percentage points more than the present level and the forests would burst into flames; a few less and most life would strangle. It is held there, constant, by feedback loops of information from the conjoined life of the planet. Carbon dioxide, inhaled by the plants, is held at precisely the low level that would be wildly improbable on any lifeless planet. And this happens to be the right concentration for keeping the earth's temperature, including the heat of the oceans, exactly right. Methane, almost all of it the product of bacterial metabolism, contributes also to the greenhouse effect, and methane is held steady. Statesmen must keep a close eye on the numbers these days — we are already pushing up the level of CO_2 by burning too much fuel and cutting too much forest, and the earth may be in for a climatic catastrophe within the next century.

But there it is: except for our meddling, the earth is the most stable organism we can know about — a complex system, a vast intelligence, turning in the warmth of the sun, running its internal affairs with the near-infallibility of a huge computer. Not entirely infallible, however, on the paleontological record. Natural catastrophes occur, crashes, breakdowns in the system: ice ages, meteor collisions, volcanic eruptions, global clouding, extinctions of great masses of its living tissue. It goes *down,* as we say of computers, but never out, always up again with something new to display to itself.

The newest of all things, the latest novelty among its working parts, seems to be us — language-speaking, song-singing, tool-making, fire-warming, comfortable, warfaring mankind, and I am of that ilk.

I can't remember anything about learning language as a child. I do have a few memories of studying to read and write, age four or five, I think, but I have no earlier recollection at all of learning speech. This surprises me. You'd think that the first word, the first triumphant finished sentence, would have been such a stunning landmark to remain fixed in memory forever, the biggest moment in life. But I have forgotten. Or perhaps it never embedded itself in my mind. Being human, I may have known all along about language, from the time of my first glimpse of human faces, and speech just came, as natural a thing to do as breathing. The reason I can't remember the learning process, the early mistakes, may be that at that time they were not mistakes at all, just the normal speech of childhood, no more memorable than the first drawn breath.

All my adult life I have hoped to speak French one day like a Frenchman, but I am near to giving up, troubled. Why should any small French child, knee high, be able to do so quickly something that I will never learn to do? Or, for that matter, any English or Turkish child living for a few months in Paris? I know the answer, but I don't much like to hear it, implying as it does that there are other knacks that I have lost as well. Childhood is the time for language, no doubt about it. Young children, the younger the better, are good at it, it is child's play; it is a one-time gift to the species, withdrawn sometime in adolescence, switched off, never to be regained. I must have had it once and spent it all on ordinary English.

I possessed a splendid collection of neurons, nested in a center somewhere in my left hemisphere, probably similar to the center in a songbird's brain—also on his left side—used for learning the species' song while he was still a nestling. Like mine, the bird's center is only there for studying in childhood; if he hears the proper song at that stage he will have it in mind for life, ornamenting it later with brief arpeggios so that it becomes his own particular, self-specific song, slightly but perceptibly different from the song of all his relatives. But if he can't hear it as a young child, the center can't compose it on its own, and what comes out later when he is ready for singing and mating is an unmelodious buzzing noise. This is one of the saddest tales in experimental biology.

Children may do more than simply pick up the language, easily as breathing. Perhaps they make it in the first place, and then change it around as time goes by, so that today's speech will, as always, be needing scholars as translators centuries hence. Derek Bickerton, professor of linguistics at the University of Hawaii, has studied the emergence of a brand-new language called Hawaiian Creole, which spread across the islands sometime after 1880, when the plantations were opened up for sugar export and large numbers of polyglot workers came from abroad to work the fields. The languages brought in were Japanese, Chinese, Portuguese, Spanish and Korean, all added to the native Hawaiian and the then-dominant English speech. For a while nobody could understand anyone else. Then, as always happens in such language crises, a form of pidgin English developed (pidgin is the mispronunciation of "business" English), not really a language, more a crude system for naming objects and pointing at work to be done, lacking structure and syntactical rules.

Within the next generation, between 1880 and the turn of the century, Hawaiian Creole appeared. This was a proper language, flexible and fluent, capable of saying anything that popped into the head, filled with subtle metaphors and governed by its own tight grammatical rules for sentence structure. It was a new language, borrowing its vocabulary from the original words in the various tongues but arranging them in novel strings and sentences. According to Bickerton, the new grammar resembles that of creoles in other places—the Seychelles, for instance, and places in New Guinea—formed by other multilanguage communities. It also resembles, he asserts, the kind of sentence structure used by all children as they grow up in the acquisition of their native speech.

Hawaiian Creole was entirely new to the islands, in the important sense that it could not be understood or spoken by the adults of the community. Bickerton's conclusion, logically enough, is that it had to be a language invented *de novo* by the young children of Hawaii. He uses this observation for the deduction that children must possess in their brains what he calls a "bioprogram" for language, a neural mechanism for generating grammar (and a confirmation, on the facts, of Noam Chomsky's insight three decades ago).

If Bickerton is right, the way is open for a new kind of speculation about one of humanity's deepest secrets: How did language first develop? Who started all the talking, and under what circumstances? The story, I believe, tells itself.

I imagine a time, thousands of years ago, when there were only a million or so humans on the earth, mostly scattered and out of touch, traveling in families from place to place in search of food—hunters and gatherers. Nobody spoke, but there were human sounds everywhere: grunts, outcries imitating animals and birds, expletives with explanatory gestures. Very likely, our ancestors were an impatient, frantic lot, always indignant with each other for lacking understanding. Only recently down from the trees, admiring their apposing thumbs, astonished by intelligence, already studying fire, they must have been wondering what was missing and what was coming next. Probably they had learned to make the sounds needed for naming things—trees, plants, animals, fish—but no real speech, nothing like language.

Then they began settling down in places for longer stays, having invented the beginnings of agriculture. More families gathered together, settled in communities. More children were born, and ways had to be found to keep the youngest ones safe from predators and out of the way of the adults. Corrals were constructed, fenced in, filled with children at play.

I imagine one special early evening, the elders sitting around the fire, grunting monosyllables, pointing at the direction of the next day's hunt or the next field to be slashed, thinking as hard as human beings can think when they are at a permanent loss for words. Then more noise than usual from the children's quarters, interrupting the thought. A rising surf of voices, excited, high-pitched, then louder and louder, exultant, totally incomprehensible to all the adults. Language.

It must have been resisted at first, regarded as nonsense. Perhaps resented, even feared, seeing it work so beautifully for communication but only among the children. Magic. Then, later on, accepted as useful magic, parts of it learned by some of the adults from their own children, broken creole. Words became magical, sentences were miraculous, grammar was sacred. (The thought hangs on: the Scottish cognate for grammar is "glamour," with the under-meaning of magic with words.)

"Kwei," said a Proto-Indo-European child, meaning "make something," and the word became, centuries later, our word "poem."

But how did the children get it? I imagine they had it all the time, and have it still, latent in their brains, ready to make the words and join them together—to articulate, as we say. What was needed at the outset was a sufficient concentration of young children, a critical mass, at each other day after day, experimenting, trying words out for sense.

Whatever happened in the human brain to make this talent a possibility remains a mystery. It might have been a mutation, a new set of instructions in our DNA for the construction of a new kind of center, absent in all earlier primates. Or it could have been a more general list of specifications: i.e., don't stop now, keep making more columnar modules of neurons, build a bigger brain. Perhaps any brain with a rich enough cortex can become a speaking brain, with a self-conscious mind.

It is a satisfying notion for a memoir. I come from ancestors whose brains evolved so far beyond those of all their relatives that speech was the result, and with this in hand they became the masters of the earth, God's image, self-aware, able to remember generations back and to think generations ahead, able to write things like "In the beginning was the word." Nothing lies any longer beyond reach, not even the local solar system or out into the galaxy and even, given time, beyond that for colonizing the Universe. In charge of everything.

But this kind of talk is embarrassing; it is the way children talk before they've looked around. I must mend the ways of my mind. This is a very big place, and I don't know how it works, nor how I fit in. I am a member of a fragile species, still new to the earth, the youngest creatures of any scale, here only a few moments as evolutionary time is measured, a juvenile species, a child of a species. We are only tentatively set in place, error-prone, at risk of fumbling, in real danger at the moment of leaving behind only a thin layer of our fossils, radioactive at that.

With so much more to learn, looking around, we should be more embarrassed than we are. We are different, to be sure, but not so much because of our brains as because of our discomfiture, mostly with each other. All the other parts of the earth's life seem to get along, to fit in with each other, to accommodate, even to concede when the stakes are high. They live off each other, devour each other, scramble for ecological niches, but always within set limits, with something like restraint. It is a rough world, by some of our standards, but not the winner-take-all game that it seemed to us a while back. If we look over our shoulders as far as we can see, all the way past trillions of other species to those fossil stromatolites built by enormous communities of collaborating microorganisms, we can see no evidences of meanness or vandalism in nature. It is, on balance, an equable, generally amiable place — good-natured, as we say.

We are the anomalies for the moment, the self-conscious children at the edge of the crowd, unsure of our place, unwilling to join up, tending to grabbiness. We have much more to learn than language.

But we are not as bad a lot as some of us say. I don't agree with this century's fashion of running down the human species as a failed try, a doomed sport. At our worst, we may be going through the early stages of a species' adolescence, and everyone remembers what that is like. Growing up is hard times for an individual but sustained torment for a whole species, especially one as brainy and nervous as ours. If we can last it out, get through the phase, shake off the memory of this century, wait for a break, we may find ourselves off and running again.

This is an optimistic, Panglossian view, and I'm quick to say that I could be all wrong. Perhaps we have indeed come our full evolutionary distance, stuck forever with our present behavior, as mature as we ever will be for as long as we last. I doubt it. We are not out of options.

I am just enough persuaded by the sociobiologists to believe that our attitudes toward each other are influenced by genes, and by more than just the genes for making grammar. If these alone were our only wired-in guides to behavior, we would be limited to metaphor and ambiguity for our most important messages to each other. I think we do some other things, by nature.

From earliest infancy on, we can smile and laugh without taking lessons, we recognize faces and facial expressions, and we hanker for friends and company. It goes too far to say that we have genes for liking each other, but we tend in that direction because of being a biologically social species. I am sure of that point: we are more compulsively social, more interdependent and more inextricably attached to each other than any of the celebrated social insects. We are not, I fear, even marginally so committed to altruism as a way of life as the bees or ants, but at least we are able to sense, instinctively, certain obligations to one another.

One human trait, urging us on by our nature, is the drive to be useful, perhaps the most fundamental of all our biological necessities. We make mistakes with it, get it wrong, confuse it with self-regard, even try to fake it, but it is there in our genes, needing only a better set of definitions for usefulness than we have yet agreed on.

So we are not entirely set in our ways. Some of us may have more dominant genes for getting along than others. I suspect, glancing around my life, that we are also endowed with other, inhibitory alleles, widely spread for the enhancement of anomie. Most of us are a mixture. If we like, we can sit tight, trusting nature for the best of possible worlds to come. Or we can hope for better breeding, in both senses of the term, as our evolution proceeds.

Our microbial ancestors made use of quicker ways for bypassing long stretches of evolutionary time, and I envy them. They have always had an abundance of viruses, darting from one cell to another across species lines, doing no damage most of the time ("temperate" viruses, as they are called), but always picking up odds and ends of DNA from their hosts and then passing these around, as though at a great party. The bits are then used by the recipients for their betterment—new tricks for coping with new contingencies.

I hope our species has a mechanism like this. Come to think of it, maybe we do. After all, we live in a sea of our own viruses, most of which seem to be there for no purpose, not even to make us sick. We can hope that some of them might be taking hold of useful items of genetic news from time to time, then passing these along for the future of the species.

It makes a cheerful footnote, anyway: next time you feel a cold coming on, reflect on the possibility that you may be giving a small boost to evolution.

A Long Line
of Cells

CHAPTER ONE

The Lives of a Cell

WE ARE TOLD THAT THE TROUBLE WITH MODERN MAN IS THAT HE HAS been trying to detach himself from nature. He sits in the topmost tiers of polymer, glass, and steel, dangling his pulsing legs, surveying at a distance the writhing life of the planet. In this scenario, Man comes on as a stupendous lethal force, and the earth is pictured as something delicate, like rising bubbles at the surface of a country pond, or flights of fragile birds.

But it is illusion to think that there is anything fragile about the life of the earth; surely this is the toughest membrane imaginable in the universe, opaque to probability, impermeable to death. We are the delicate part, transient and vulnerable as cilia. Nor is it a new thing for man to invent an existence that he imagines to be above the rest of life; this has been his most consistent intellectual exertion down the millennia. As illusion, it has never worked out to his satisfaction in the past, any more than it does today. Man is embedded in nature.

The biologic science of recent years has been making this a more urgent fact of life. The new, hard problem will be to cope with the dawning, intensifying realization of just how interlocked we are. The old, clung-to notions most of us have held about our special lordship are being deeply undermined.

Item. A good case can be made for our nonexistence as entities. We are not made up, as we had always supposed, of successively enriched packets of our own parts. We are shared, rented, occupied. At the interior of our cells, driving them, providing the oxidative energy that sends us out for the improvement of each shining day, are the mitochondria, and in a strict sense they are not ours. They turn out to be little separate creatures, the colonial posterity of migrant prokaryocytes, probably primitive bacteria that swam into ancestral precursors of our eukaryotic cells and stayed there. Ever since, they have maintained themselves and their ways, replicating in their own fashion, privately, with their own DNA and RNA quite different from ours. They are as much symbionts as the rhizobial bacteria in the roots of beans. Without them, we would not move a muscle, drum a finger, think a thought.

Mitochondria are stable and responsible lodgers, and I choose to trust them. But what of the other little animals, similarly established in my cells, sorting and balancing me, clustering me together? My centrioles, basal bodies, and probably a good many other more obscure tiny beings at work inside my cells, each with its own special genome, are as foreign, and as essential, as aphids in anthills. My cells are no longer the pure line entities I was raised with; they are ecosystems more complex than Jamaica Bay.

I like to think that they work in my interest, that each breath they draw for me, but perhaps it is they who walk through the local park in the early morning, sensing my senses, listening to my music, thinking my thoughts.

I am consoled, somewhat, by the thought that the green plants are in the same fix. They could not be plants, or green, without their chloroplasts, which run the photosynthetic enterprise and generate oxygen for the rest of us. As it turns out, chloroplasts are also separate creatures with their own genomes, speaking their own language.

We carry stores of DNA in our nuclei that may have come in, at one time or another, from the fusion of ancestral cells and the linking of ancestral organisms in symbiosis. Our genomes are catalogues of instructions from all kinds of sources in nature, filed for all kinds of contingencies. As for me, I am grateful for differentiation and speciation, but I cannot feel as separate an entity as I did a few years ago, before I was told these things, nor, I should think, can anyone else.

Item. The uniformity of the earth's life, more astonishing than its diversity, is accountable by the high probability that we derived, originally, from some single cell, fertilized in a bolt of lightning as the earth cooled. It is from the progeny of this parent cell that we take our looks; we still share genes around, and the resemblance of the enzymes of grasses to those of whales is a family resemblance.

The viruses, instead of being single-minded agents of disease and death, now begin to look more like mobile genes. Evolution is still an infinitely long and tedious biologic game, with only the winners staying at the table, but the rules are beginning to look more flexible. We live in a dancing matrix of viruses; they dart, rather like bees, from organism to organism, from plant to insect to mammal to me and back again, and into the sea, tugging along pieces of this genome, strings of genes from that, transplanting grafts of DNA, passing around heredity as though at a great party. They may be a mechanism for keeping new, mutant kinds of DNA in the widest circulation among us. If this is true, the odd virus disease, on which we must focus so much of our attention in medicine, may be looked on as an accident, something dropped.

Item. I have been trying to think of the earth as a kind of organism, but it is no go. I cannot think of it this way. It is too big, too complex, with too many working parts lacking visible connections. The other night, driving through a hilly, wooded part of southern New England, I wondered about this. If not like an organism, what is it like, what is it *most* like? Then, satisfactorily for that moment, it came to me: it is *most* like a single cell.

CHAPTER TWO

Thoughts for a Countdown

THERE IS AMBIGUITY, AND SOME SYMBOLISM, IN THE ELABORATE RIT-
ual observed by each returning expedition of astronauts from the moon.
They celebrate first of all the inviolability of the earth, and they re-enact,
each time, in stereotyped choreography, our long anxiety about the
nature of life. They do not, as one might expect, fall to their knees and
kiss the carrier deck; this would violate, intrude upon, contaminate the
deck, the vessel, the sea around, the whole earth. Instead, they wear
surgical masks. They walk briskly, arms up, untouching, into a sterile
box. They wave enigmatically, gnotobiotically, to the President from
behind glass panes, so as not to breathe moondust on him. They are
levitated to another sealed box in Houston, to wait out their days in
quarantine, while inoculated animals and tissue cultures are squinted at
for omens.

It is only after the long antiseptic ceremony has been completed that
they are allowed out into the sun, for the ride up Broadway.

A visitor from another planet, or another century, would view the
exercise as precisely lunatic behavior, but no one from outside would
understand it. We must do things this way, these days. If there should be
life on the moon, we must begin by fearing it. We must guard against it,
lest we catch something.

It might be a microbe, a strand of lost nucleic acid, a molecule of
enzyme, or a nameless hairless little being with sharp gray eyes. Whatever, once we have imagined it, foreign and therefore hostile, it is not to
be petted. It must be locked up. I imagine the debate would turn on how
best to kill it.

It is remarkable that we have all accepted this, without hooting, as though it simply conformed to a law of nature. It says something about our century, our attitude toward life, our obsession with disease and death, our human chauvinism.

There are pieces of evidence that we have had it the wrong way round. Most of the associations between the living things we know about are essentially cooperative ones, symbiotic in one degree or another; when they have the look of adversaries, it is usually a standoff relation, with one party issuing signals, warnings, flagging the other off. It takes long intimacy, long and familiar interliving, before one kind of creature can cause illness in another. If there were to be life on the moon, it would have a lonely time waiting for acceptance to membership here. We do not have solitary beings. Every creature is, in some sense, connected to and dependent on the rest.

It has been estimated that we probably have real knowledge of only a small proportion of the microbes of the earth, because most of them cannot be cultivated alone. They live together in dense, interdependent communities, feeding and supporting the environment for each other, regulating the balance of populations between different species by a complex system of chemical signals. With our present technology, we can no more isolate one from the rest, and rear it alone, than we can keep a single bee from drying up like a desquamated cell when removed from his hive.

The bacteria are beginning to have the aspect of social animals; they should provide nice models for the study of interactions between forms of life at all levels. They live by collaboration, accommodation, exchange, and barter. They, and the fungi, probably with help from a communication system laid on by the viruses, comprise the parenchyma of the soil (someone has suggested that humic acid, to which the microbes contribute, is a sort of counterpart for the ground substance of our own connective tissue). They live on each other. Sometimes they live inside each other; the *Bdellovibrio* penetrate the walls of other bacteria, tuck themselves up inside, replicate, and burst out again as though they thought themselves phages. Some microbial communities extend so deeply into the affairs of higher forms of life as to seem like new kinds of tissue in plants and animals. The rhizobial bacteria that swarm over the root hairs of leguminous plants have the look of voracious, invasive pathogens, but the root nodules that they then construct, in collaboration with the plant cells, become the earth's chief organ for nitrogen fixation. The production of leghemoglobin in the membrane-lined space between plant and bacterial cells is an example of the high technology of symbiosis; the protein is synthesized by the plant, but only on instructions from the bacteria, and it is possible that the plant DNA for coding this substance came originally from the microbe, early in the evolution of the arrangement.

The bacteria that live in the tissues of insects, like those incorporated into the mycetocytes of cockroaches and termites, have the appearance of specialized organs in their hosts. It is not yet clear what they accomplish for the insect, but it is known that the species cannot survive long without them. They are transmitted, like mitochondria, from generation to generation of eggs.

It has been proposed that symbiotic linkages between prokaryotic cells were the origin of eukaryotes, and that fusion between different sorts of eukaryotes (e.g., motile, ciliated cells joined to phagocytic ones) led to the construction of the communities that eventually turned out to be metazoan creatures. If this is true, the marks of identity, distinguishing self from non-self, have long since been blurred. Today, in the symbiotic associations that dominate so much of the life of the sea, there is rarely a question of who is who, even when the combination functions like a single animal. The anemones that fasten themselves to the shells, even to the claws, of certain crabs are capable of recognizing precisely the molecular configurations that identify those surfaces: the crab, for his part, can recognize his own anemone, and will sometimes seek him out and attach him to the shell like an ornament. The damsel fish that have become, from their point of view, functioning parts of certain species of anemones adapt themselves when very young to life among the lethal tentacles of their host; they cannot just swim in forthwith—they must dart around the edges until labeled at their surfaces by markers acceptable to the anemone.

Sometimes, in the course of the modulation of relations between animals, there are inventions that seem to have been thought up on the spur of the moment, like propositions to be submitted for possible evolution. Some are good-humored, even witty. Certain Australian surf bathers, several years ago, were stung by tiny creatures that turned out to be nudibranchs armed with the stingers of Portuguese men-of-war. Having fed on jellyfish, the Glaucus community had edited their meal and allowed the stinging cells to make their way to the surface of their new host, thus creating, for the time, a sort of instant hybrid with, allowing for some asymmetry, the essential attributes of each partner.

Even when circumstances require that there be winners and losers, the transaction is not necessarily a combat. The aloofness displayed for each other by members of the marine coelenterate species of Gorgonaceae suggests that mechanisms for preserving individuality must have existed long before the evolution of immunity. The gorgonians tend to grow in closely packed, branching masses, but they do not fuse to each other; if they did, their morphogenesis would doubtless become a shambles. Theodor, in a series of elegant experiments, has shown that when two individuals of the same species are placed in close contact, the smaller of the two will always begin to disintegrate. It is autodestruction due to lytic mechanisms entirely under the governance of the smaller partner. He is not thrown out, not outgamed, not outgunned; he simply chooses to bow out. It is not necessarily a comfort to know that such things go on in biology, but it is at least an agreeable surprise.

The oxygen in the atmosphere is the exhalation of the chloroplasts living in plants (also, for our amazement, in the siphons of giant clams and lesser marine animals). It is a natural tendency for genetically unrelated cells in tissue culture to come together, ignoring species differences, and fuse to form hybrid cells. Inflammation and immunology must indeed be powerfully designed to keep us apart; without such mechanisms, involving considerable effort, we might have developed as a kind of flowing syncytium over the earth, without the morphogenesis of even a flower.

Perhaps we will find it possible to accommodate other forms of life, from other planets, out of sheer good nature. We are, after all, a planet where the rain contains vitamin B_{12}! There is enough of it, by Parker's calculation, when convective windstorms occur at the time of farmland cultivation and swirl it from the soil into the upper atmosphere, to produce a visible bloom of Euglena in a fair-sized pond.

CHAPTER THREE

On Societies as Organisms

VIEWED FROM A SUITABLE HEIGHT, THE AGGREGATING CLUSTERS OF medical scientists in the bright sunlight of the boardwalk at Atlantic City, swarmed there from everywhere for the annual meetings, have the look of assemblages of social insects. There is the same vibrating, ionic movement, interrupted by the darting back and forth of jerky individuals to touch antennae and exchange small bits of information; periodically, the mass casts out, like a trout-line, a long single file unerringly toward Childs's. If the boards were not fastened down, it would not be a surprise to see them put together a nest of sorts.

It is permissible to say this sort of thing about humans. They do resemble, in their most compulsively social behavior, ants at a distance. It is, however, quite bad form in biological circles to put it the other way round, to imply that the operation of insect societies has any relation at all to human affairs. The writers of books on insect behavior generally take pains, in their prefaces, to caution that insects are like creatures from another planet, that their behavior is absolutely foreign, totally unhuman, unearthly, almost unbiological. They are more like perfectly tooled but crazy little machines, and we violate science when we try to read human meanings in their arrangements.

It is hard for a bystander not to do so. Ants are so much like human beings as to be an embarrassment. They farm fungi, raise aphids as livestock, launch armies into wars, use chemical sprays to alarm and confuse enemies, capture slaves. The families of weaver ants engage in child labor, holding their larvae like shuttles to spin out the thread that sews the leaves together for their fungus gardens. They exchange information ceaselessly. They do everything but watch television.

What makes us most uncomfortable is that they, and the bees and termites and social wasps, seem to live two kinds of lives: they are individuals, going about the day's business without much evidence of thought for tomorrow, and they are at the same time component parts, cellular elements, in the huge, writhing, ruminating organism of the Hill, the nest, the hive. It is because of this aspect, I think, that we most wish for them to be something foreign. We do not like the notion that there can be collective societies with the capacity to behave like organisms. If such things exist, they can have nothing to do with us.

Still, there it is. A solitary ant, afield, cannot be considered to have much of anything on his mind; indeed, with only a few neurons strung together by fibers, he can't be imagined to have a mind at all, much less a thought. He is more like a ganglion on legs. Four ants together, or ten, encircling a dead moth on a path, begin to look more like an idea. They fumble and shove, gradually moving the food toward the Hill, but as though by blind chance. It is only when you watch the dense mass of thousands of ants, crowded together around the Hill, blackening the ground, that you begin to see the whole beast, and now you observe it thinking, planning, calculating. It is an intelligence, a kind of live computer, with crawling bits for its wits.

At a stage in the construction, twigs of a certain size are needed, and all the members forage obsessively for twigs of just this size. Later, when outer walls are to be finished, thatched, the size must change, and as though given new orders by telephone, all the workers shift the search to the new twigs. If you disturb the arrangement of a part of the Hill, hundreds of ants will set it vibrating, shifting, until it is put right again. Distant sources of food are somehow sensed, and long lines, like tentacles, reach out over the ground, up over walls, behind boulders, to fetch it in.

Termites are even more extraordinary in the way they seem to accumulate intelligence as they gather together. Two or three termites in a chamber will begin to pick up pellets and move them from place to place, but nothing comes of it; nothing is built. As more join in, they seem to reach a critical mass, a quorum, and the thinking begins. They place pellets atop pellets, then throw up columns and beautiful, curving, symmetrical arches, and the crystalline architecture of vaulted chambers is created. It is not known how they communicate with each other, how the chains of termites building one column know when to turn toward the crew on the adjacent column, or how, when the time comes, they manage the flawless joining of the arches. The stimuli that set them off at the outset, building collectively instead of shifting things about, may be pheromones released when they reach committee size. They react as if alarmed. They become agitated, excited, and then they begin working, like artists.

Bees live lives of organisms, tissues, cells, organelles, all at the same time. The single bee, out of the hive retrieving sugar (instructed by the dancer: "south-southeast for seven hundred meters, clover—mind you make corrections for the sundrift") is still as much a part of the hive as if attached by a filament. Building the hive, the workers have the look of embryonic cells organizing a developing tissue; from a distance they are like the viruses inside a cell, running off row after row of symmetrical polygons as though laying down crystals. When the time for swarming comes, and the old queen prepares to leave with her part of the population, it is as though the hive were involved in mitosis. There is an agitated moving of bees back and forth, like granules in cell sap. They distribute themselves in almost precisely equal parts, half to the departing queen, half to the new one. Thus, like an egg, the great, hairy, black and golden creature splits in two, each with an equal share of the family genome.

The phenomenon of separate animals joining up to form an organism is not unique in insects. Slime-mold cells do it all the time, of course, in each life cycle. At first they are single amebocytes swimming around, eating bacteria, aloof from each other, untouching, voting straight Republican. Then, a bell sounds, and acrasin is released by special cells toward which the others converge in stellate ranks, touch, fuse together, and construct the slug, solid as a trout. A splendid stalk is raised, with a fruiting body on top, and out of this comes the next generation of amebocytes, ready to swim across the same moist ground, solitary and ambitious.

Herring and other fish in schools are at times so closely integrated, their actions so coordinated, that they seem to be functionally a great multi-fish organism. Flocking birds, especially the seabirds nesting on the slopes of offshore islands in Newfoundland, are similarly attached, connected, synchronized.

Although we are by all odds the most social of all social animals— more interdependent, more attached to each other, more inseparable in our behavior than bees—we do not often feel our conjoined intelligence. Perhaps, however, we are linked in circuits for the storage, processing, and retrieval of information, since this appears to be the most basic and universal of all human enterprises. It may be our biological function to build a certain kind of Hill. We have access to all the information of the biosphere, arriving as elementary units in the stream of solar photons. When we have learned how these are rearranged against randomness, to make, say, springtails, quantum mechanics, and the late quartets, we may have a clearer notion how to proceed. The circuitry seems to be there, even if the current is not always on.

The system of communications used in science should provide a neat, workable model for studying mechanisms of information-building in human society. Ziman, in a recent *Nature* essay, points out, "the invention of a mechanism for the systematic publication of *fragments* of scientific work may well have been the key event in the history of modern science." He continues:

> A regular journal carries from one research worker to another the various . . . observations which are of common interest. . . . A typical scientific paper has never pretended to be more than another little piece in a larger jigsaw — not significant in itself but as an element in a grander scheme. *This technique, of soliciting many modest contributions to the store of human knowledge, has been the secret of Western science since the seventeenth century, for it achieves a corporate, collective power that is far greater than any one individual can exert* [italics mine].

With some alternation of terms, some toning down, the passage could describe the building of a termite nest.

It is fascinating that the word "explore" does not apply to the searching aspect of the activity, but has its origins in the sounds we make while engaged in it. We like to think of exploring in science as a lonely, meditative business, and so it is in the first stages, but always, sooner or later, before the enterprise reaches completion, as we explore, we call to each other, communicate, publish, send letters to the editor, present papers, cry out on finding.

CHAPTER FOUR

A Fear of Pheromones

WHAT ARE WE GOING TO DO IF IT TURNS OUT THAT WE HAVE PHE-
romones? What on earth would we be doing with such things? With the
richness of speech, and all our new devices for communication, why
would we want to release odors into the air to convey information about
anything? We can send notes, telephone, whisper cryptic invitations,
announce the giving of parties, even bounce words off the moon and
make them carom around the planets. Why a gas, or droplets of moisture made to be deposited on fence posts?

Comfort has recently reviewed the reasons for believing that we are,
in fact, in possession of anatomic structures for which there is no
rational explanation except as sources of pheromones—tufts of hair,
strategically located apocrine glands, unaccountable areas of moisture.
We even have folds of skin here and there designed for the controlled
nurture of bacteria, and it is known that certain microbes eke out a
living, like eighteenth-century musicians, producing chemical signals
by ornamenting the products of their hosts.

Most of the known pheromones are small, simple molecules, active in
extremely small concentrations. Eight or ten carbon atoms in a chain
are all that are needed to generate precise, unequivocal directions about
all kinds of matters—when and where to cluster in crowds, when to
disperse, how to behave to the opposite sex, how to ascertain what *is* the
opposite sex, how to organize members of a society in the proper
ranking orders of dominance, how to mark out exact boundaries of real
estate, and how to establish that one is, beyond argument, one's self.
Trails can be laid and followed, antagonists frightened and confused,
friends attracted and enchanted.

The messages are urgent, but they may arrive, for all we know, in a fragrance of ambiguity. "At home, 4 p.m. today," says the female moth, and releases a brief explosion of bombykol, a single molecule of which will tremble the hairs of any male within miles and send him driving upwind in a confusion of ardor. But it is doubtful if he has an awareness of being caught in an aerosol of chemical attractant. On the contrary, he probably finds suddenly that it has become an excellent day, the weather remarkably bracing, the time appropriate for a bit of exercise of the old wings, a brisk turn upwind. En route, traveling the gradient of bombykol, he notes the presence of other males, heading in the same direction, all in a good mood, inclined to race for the sheer sport of it. Then, when he reaches his destination, it may seem to him the most extraordinary of coincidences, the greatest piece of luck: "Bless my soul, what have we here!"

It has been soberly calculated that if a single female moth were to release all the bombykol in her sac in a single spray, all at once, she could theoretically attract a trillion males in the instant. This is, of course, not done.

Fish make use of chemical signals for the identification of individual members of a species, and also for the announcement of changes in the status of certain individuals. A catfish that has had a career as a local leader smells one way, but as soon as he is displaced in an administrative reorganization, he smells differently, and everyone recognizes the loss of standing. A bullhead can immediately identify the water in which a recent adversary has been swimming, and he can distinguish between this fish and all others in the school.

There is some preliminary, still fragmentary evidence for important pheromones in primates. Short-chain aliphatic compounds are elaborated by female monkeys in response to estradiol, and these are of consuming interest to the males. Whether there are other sorts of social communication by pheromones among primates is not known.

The possibility that human beings are involved in this sort of thing has not attracted much attention until recently. It is still too early to say how it will come out. Perhaps we have inherited only vestiges of the organs needed, only antique and archaic traces of the fragrance, and the memory may be forever gone. We may remain safe from this new challenge to our technology, and, while the twentieth century continues to run out in concentric circles down the drain, we may be able to keep our attention concentrated on how to get energy straight from the sun.

But there are just the slightest suggestions, hints of what may be ahead. Last year it was observed that young women living at close quarters in dormitories tended to undergo spontaneous synchronization of their menstrual cycles. A paper in *Nature* reported the personal experience of an anonymous, quantitatively minded British scientist who lived for long stretches in isolation on an offshore island, and discovered, by taking the dry weight of the hairs trapped by his electric razor every day, that his beard grew much more rapidly each time he returned to the mainland and encountered girls. Schizophrenic patients are reported to have a special odor to their sweat, traced to trans-3-methylhexanoic acid.

The mind, already jelled by the advances in modern communication so that further boggling is impossible, twitches. One can imagine whole new industries springing up to create new perfumes ("A Scientific Combination of Primer and Releaser"), and other, larger corporations raising new turrets with flames alight at their tops on the Jersey flats, for the production of phenolic, anesthetic, possibly bright green sprays to cover, mask, or suppress all pheromones ("Don't Let On"). Gas chromatography of air samples might reveal blips of difference between substances released over a Glasgow football match, a committee meeting on academic promotions, and a summer beach on Saturday afternoon, all highly important. One can even imagine agitated conferences in the Pentagon, new agreements in Geneva.

It is claimed that a well-trained tracking hound can follow with accuracy the trail of a man in shoes, across open ground marked by the footsteps of any number of other people, provided the dog is given an item of the man's clothing to smell beforehand. If one had to think up an R&D program for a National Institute of Human Fragrance (to be created by combining the budgets of the FDA and FCC), this would be a good problem to start with. It might also provide the kind of secondary, spin-off items of science that we like to see in federally supported research. If it is true, as the novels say, that an intelligent dog can tell the difference between one human being and any other by detecting differences in their scents, an explanation might be geometric differences in 10-carbon molecules, or perhaps differences in the relative concentrations of several pheromones in a medley. If this is a fact, it should be of interest to the immunologic community, which has long since staked out claims on the mechanisms involved in the discrimination between self and non-self. Perhaps the fantastically sensitive and precise immunologic mechanisms for the detection of small molecules such as haptenes represent another way of sensing the same markers. Man's best friend might be used to sniff out histocompatible donors. And so forth. If we could just succeed in maintaining the research activity at this level, perhaps diverting everyone's attention from all other aspects by releasing large quantities of money, we might be able to stay out of trouble.

CHAPTER FIVE

The Music of
This Sphere

IT IS ONE OF OUR PROBLEMS THAT AS WE BECOME CROWDED TO-
gether, the sounds we make to each other, in our increasingly complex
communication systems, become more random-sounding, accidental
or incidental, and we have trouble selecting meaningful signals out of
the noise. One reason is, of course, that we do not seem able to restrict
our communication to information-bearing, relevant signals. Given
any new technology for transmitting information, we seem bound to
use it for great quantities of small talk. We are only saved by music from
being overwhelmed by nonsense.

It is a marginal comfort to know that the relatively new science of
bioacoustics must deal with similar problems in the sounds made by
other animals to each other. No matter what sound-making device is
placed at their disposal, creatures in general do a great deal of gabbling,
and it requires long patience and observation to edit out the parts
lacking syntax and sense. Light social conversation, designed to keep
the party going, prevails. Nature abhors a long silence.

Somewhere, underlying all the other signals, is a continual music.
Termites make percussive sounds to each other by beating their heads
against the floor in the dark, resonating corridors of their nests. The
sound has been described as resembling, to the human ear, sand falling
on paper, but spectrographic analysis of sound records has recently
revealed a high degree of organization in the drumming; the beats occur
in regular, rhythmic phrases, differing in duration, like notes for a
tympani section.

From time to time, certain termites make a convulsive movement of their mandibles to produce a loud, high-pitched clicking sound, audible ten meters off. So much effort goes into this one note that it must have urgent meaning, at least to the sender. He cannot make it without such a wrench that he is flung one or two centimeters into the air by the recoil.

There is obvious hazard in trying to assign a particular meaning to this special kind of sound, and problems like this exist throughout the field of bioacoustics. One can imagine a woolly-minded Visitor from Outer Space, interested in human beings, discerning on his spectrograph the click of that golf ball on the surface of the moon, and trying to account for it as a call of warning (unlikely), a signal of mating (out of the question), or an announcement of territory (could be).

Bats are obliged to make sounds almost ceaselessly, to sense, by sonar, all the objects in their surroundings. They can spot with accuracy, on the wing, small insects, and they will home onto things they like with infallibility and speed. With such a system for the equivalent of glancing around, they must live in a world of ultrasonic bat-sound, most of it with an industrial, machinery sound. Still, they communicate with each other as well, by clicks and high-pitched greetings. Moreover, they have been heard to produce, while hanging at rest upside down in the depths of woods, strange, solitary, and lovely bell-like notes.

Almost anything that an animal can employ to make a sound is put to use. Drumming, created by beating the feet, is used by prairie hens, rabbits, and mice; the head is banged by woodpeckers and certain other birds; the males of deathwatch beetles make a rapid ticking sound by percussion of a protuberance on the abdomen against the ground; a faint but audible ticking is made by the tiny beetle *Lepinotus inquilinus,* which is less than two millimeters in length. Fish make sounds by clicking their teeth, blowing air, and drumming with special muscles against tuned inflated air bladders. Solid structures are set to vibrating by toothed bows in crustaceans and insects. The proboscis of the death's-head hawk moth is used as a kind of reed instrument, blown through to make high-pitched, reedy notes.

Gorillas beat their chests for certain kinds of discourse. Animals with loose skeletons rattle them, or, like rattlesnakes, get sounds from externally placed structures. Turtles, alligators, crocodiles, and even snakes make various more or less vocal sounds. Leeches have been heard to tap rhythmically on leaves, engaging the attention of other leeches, which tap back, in synchrony. Even earthworms make sounds, faint staccato notes in regular clusters. Toads sing to each other, and their friends sing back in antiphony.

Birdsong has been so much analyzed for its content of business communication that there seems little time left for music, but it is there. Behind the glossaries of warning calls, alarms, mating messages, pronouncements of territory, calls for recruitment, and demands for dispersal, there is redundant, elegant sound that is unaccountable as part of the working day. The thrush in my backyard sings down his nose in meditative, liquid runs of melody, over and over again, and I have the strongest impression that he does this for his own pleasure. Some of the time he seems to be practicing, like a virtuoso in his apartment. He starts a run, reaches a midpoint in the second bar where there should be a set of complex harmonics, stops, and goes back to begin over, dissatisfied. Sometimes he changes his notation so conspicuously that he seems to be improvising sets of variations. It is a meditative, questioning kind of music, and I cannot believe that he is simply saying, "thrush here."

The robin sings flexible songs, containing a variety of motifs that he rearranges to his liking; the notes in each motif constitute the syntax, and the possibilities for variation produce a considerable repertoire. The meadow lark, with three hundred notes to work with, arranges these in phrases of three to six notes and elaborates fifty types of song. The nightingale has twenty-four basic songs, but gains wild variety by varying the internal arrangement of phrases and the length of pauses. The chaffinch listens to other chaffinches, and incorporates into his memory snatches of their songs.

The need to make music, and to listen to it, is universally expressed by human beings. I cannot imagine, even in our most primitive times, the emergence of talented painters to make cave paintings without there having been, near at hand, equally creative people making song. It is, like speech, a dominant aspect of human biology.

The individual parts played by other instrumentalists—crickets or earthworms, for instance—may not have the sound of music by themselves, but we hear them out of context. If we could listen to them all at once, fully orchestrated, in their immense ensemble, we might become aware of the counterpoint, the balance of tones and timbres and harmonics, the sonorities. The recorded songs of the humpback whale, filled with tensions and resolutions, ambiguities and allusions, incomplete, can be listened to as a *part* of music, like an isolated section of an orchestra. If we had better hearing, and could discern the descants of sea birds, the rhythmic tympani of schools of mollusks, or even the distant harmonics of midges hanging over meadows in the sun, the combined sound might lift us off our feet.

There are, of course, other ways to account for the songs of whales. They might be simple, down-to-earth statements about navigation, or sources of krill, or limits of territory. But the proof is not in, and until it is shown that these long, convoluted, insistent melodies, repeated by different singers with ornamentations of their own, are the means of sending through several hundred miles of undersea such ordinary information as "whale here," I shall believe otherwise. Now and again, in the intervals between songs, the whales have been seen to breach, leaping clear out of the sea and landing on their backs, awash in the turbulence of their beating flippers. Perhaps they are pleased by the way the piece went, or perhaps it is celebration at hearing one's own song returning after circumnavigation; whatever, it has the look of jubilation.

I suppose that my extraterrestrial Visitor might puzzle over my records in much the same way, on first listening. The 14th Quartet might, for him, be a communication announcing, "Beethoven here," answered, after passage through an undersea of time and submerged currents of human thought, by another long signal a century later, "Bartók here."

If, as I believe, the urge to make a kind of music is as much a characteristic of biology as our other fundamental functions, there ought to be an explanation for it. Having none at hand, I am free to make one up. The rhythmic sounds might be the recapitulation of something else—an earliest memory, a score for the transformation of inanimate, random matter in chaos into the improbable, ordered dance of living forms. Morowitz has presented the case, in thermodynamic terms, for the hypothesis that a steady flow of energy from the inexhaustible source of the sun to the unfillable sink of outer space, by way of the earth, is mathematically destined to cause the organization of matter into an increasingly ordered state. The resulting balancing act involves a ceaseless clustering of bonded atoms into molecules of higher and higher complexity, and the emergence of cycles for the storage and release of energy. In a nonequilibrium steady state, which is postulated, the solar energy would not just flow to the earth and radiate away; it is thermodynamically inevitable that it must rearrange matter into symmetry, away from probability, against entropy, lifting it, so to speak, into a constantly changing condition of rearrangement and molecular ornamentation. In such a system, the outcome is a chancy kind of order, always on the verge of descending into chaos, held taut against probability by the unremitting, constant surge of energy from the sun.

If there were to be sounds to represent this process, they would have the arrangement of the Brandenburg Concertos for my ear, but I am open to wonder whether the same events are recalled by the rhythms of insects, the long, pulsing runs of birdsong, the descants of whales, the modulated vibrations of a million locusts in migration, the tympani of gorilla breasts, termite heads, drumfish bladders. A "grand canonical ensemble" is, oddly enough, the proper term for a quantitative model system in thermodynamics, borrowed from music by way of mathematics. Borrowed back again, provided with notation, it would do for what I have in mind.

CHAPTER SIX

An Earnest Proposal

THERE WAS A QUARTER-PAGE ADVERTISEMENT IN THE LONDON *Observer* for a computer service that will enmesh your name in an electronic network of fifty thousand other names, sort out your tastes, preferences, habits, and deepest desires and match them up with opposite numbers, and retrieve for you, within a matter of seconds, and for a very small fee, friends. "Already," it says, "it [the computer] has given very real happiness and lasting relationships to thousands of people, and it can do the same for you!"

Without paying a fee, or filling out a questionnaire, all of us are being linked in similar circuits, for other reasons, by credit bureaus, the census, the tax people, the local police station, or the Army. Sooner or later, if it keeps on, the various networks will begin to touch, fuse, and then, in their coalescence, they will start sorting and retrieving each other, and we will all become bits of information on an enormous grid.

I do not worry much about the computers that are wired to help me find a friend among fifty thousand. If errors are made, I can always beg off with a headache. But what of the vaster machines that will be giving instructions to cities, to nations? If they are programmed to regulate human behavior according to today's view of nature, we are surely in for apocalypse.

The men who run the affairs of nations today are, by and large, our practical men. They have been taught that the world is an arrangement of adversary systems, that force is what counts, aggression is what drives us at the core, only the fittest can survive, and only might can make more might. Thus, it is in observance of nature's law that we have planted, like perennial tubers, the numberless nameless missiles in the soil of Russia and China and our Midwestern farmlands, with more to come, poised to fly out at a nanosecond's notice, and meticulously engineered to ignite, in the centers of all our cities, artificial suns. If we let fly enough of them at once, we can even burn out the one-celled green creatures in the sea, and thus turn off the oxygen.

Before such things are done, one hopes that the computers will contain every least bit of relevant information about the way of the world. I should think we might assume this, in fairness to all. Even the nuclear realists, busy as their minds must be with calculations of acceptable levels of megadeath, would not want to overlook anything. They should be willing to wait, for a while anyway.

I have an earnest proposal to make. I suggest that we defer further action until we have acquired a really complete set of information concerning at least one living thing. Then, at least, we shall be able to claim that we know what we are doing. The delay might take a decade; let us say a decade. We and the other nations might set it as an objective of international, collaborative science to achieve a complete understanding of a single form of life. When this is done, and the information programmed into all our computers, I for one would be willing to take my chances.

As to the subject, I propose a simple one, easily solved within ten years. It is the protozoan *Myxotricha paradoxa,* which inhabits the inner reaches of the digestive tract of Australian termites.

It is not as though we would be starting from scratch. We have a fair amount of information about this creature already—not enough to understand him, of course, but enough to inform us that he means something, perhaps a great deal. At first glance, he appears to be an ordinary, motile protozoan, remarkable chiefly for the speed and directness with which he swims from place to place, engulfing fragments of wood finely chewed by his termite host. In the termite ecosystem, an arrangement of Byzantine complexity, he stands at the epicenter. Without him, the wood, however finely chewed, would never get digested; he supplies the enzymes that break down cellulose to edible carbohydrate, leaving only the nondegradable lignin, which the termite then excretes in geometrically tidy pellets and uses as building blocks for the erection of arches and vaults in the termite nest. Without him there would be no termites, no farms of the fungi that are cultivated by termites and will grow nowhere else, and no conversion of dead trees to loam.

The flagellae that beat in synchrony to propel myxotricha with such directness turn out, on closer scrutiny with the electron microscope, not to be flagellae at all. They are outsiders, in to help with the business: fully formed, perfect spirochetes that have attached themselves at regularly spaced intervals all over the surface of the protozoan.

Then, there are oval organelles, embedded in the surface close to the point of attachment of the spirochetes, and other similar bodies drifting through the cytoplasm with the particles of still undigested wood. These, under high magnification, turn out to be bacteria, living in symbiosis with the spirochetes and the protozoan, probably contributing enzymes that break down the cellulose.

The whole animal, or ecosystem, stuck for the time being halfway along in evolution, appears to be a model for the development of cells like our own. Margulis has summarized the now considerable body of data indicating that the modern nucleated cell was made up, part by part, by the coming together of just such prokaryotic animals. The blue-green algae, the original inventors of photosynthesis, entered partnership with primitive bacterial cells, and became the chloroplasts of plants; their descendants remain as discrete separate animals inside plant cells, with their own DNA and RNA, replicating on their own. Other bacteria with oxidative enzymes in their membranes, makers of ATP, joined up with fermenting bacteria and became the mitochondria of the future; they have since deleted some of their genes but retain personal genomes and can only be regarded as symbionts. Spirochetes, like the ones attached to *M. paradoxa,* joined up and became the cilia of eukaryotic cells. The centrioles, which hoist the microtubules on which chromosomes are strung for mitosis, are similar separate creatures; when not busy with mitosis, they become the basal bodies to which cilia are attached. And there are others, not yet clearly delineated, whose existence in the cell is indicated by the presence of cytoplasmic genes.

There is an underlying force that drives together the several creatures comprising myxotricha, and then drives the assemblage into union with the termite. If we could understand this tendency, we would catch a glimpse of the process that brought single separate cells together for the construction of metazoans, culminating in the invention of roses, dolphins, and, of course, ourselves. It might turn out that the same tendency underlies the joining of organisms into communities, communities into ecosystems, and ecosystems into the biosphere. If this is, in fact, the drift of things, the way of the world, we may come to view immune reactions, genes for the chemical marking of self, and perhaps all reflexive responses of aggression and defense as secondary developments in evolution, necessary for the regulation and modulation of symbiosis, not designed to break into the process, only to keep it from getting out of hand.

If it is in the nature of living things to pool resources, to fuse when possible, we would have a new way of accounting for the progressive enrichment and complexity of form in living things.

I take it on faith that computers, although lacking souls, are possessed of a kind of intelligence. At the end of the decade, therefore, I am willing to predict that the feeding in of all the information then available will result, after a few seconds of whirring, in something like the following message, neatly and speedily printed out: "Request more data. How are spirochetes attached? Do not fire."

CHAPTER SEVEN

The Technology
of Medicine

TECHNOLOGY ASSESSMENT HAS BECOME A ROUTINE EXERCISE FOR THE scientific enterprises on which the country is obliged to spend vast sums for its needs. Brainy committees are continually evaluating the effectiveness and cost of doing various things in space, defense, energy, transportation, and the like, to give advice about prudent investments for the future.

Somehow medicine, for all the $80-odd billion that it is said to cost the nation, has not yet come in for much of this analytical treatment. It seems taken for granted that the technology of medicine simply exists, take it or leave it, and the only major technologic problem which policy-makers are interested in is how to deliver today's kind of health care, with equity, to all the people.

When, as is bound to happen sooner or later, the analysts get around to the technology of medicine itself, they will have to face the problem of measuring the relative cost and effectiveness of all the things that are done in the management of disease. They make their living at this kind of thing, and I wish them well, but I imagine they will have a bewildering time. For one thing, our methods of managing disease are constantly changing—partly under the influence of new bits of information brought in from all corners of biologic science. At the same time, a great many things are done that are not so closely related to science, some not related at all.

In fact, there are three quite different levels of technology in medicine, so unlike each other as to seem altogether different undertakings.

Practitioners of medicine and the analysts will be in trouble if they are not kept separate.

1. First of all, there is a large body of what might be termed "non-technology," impossible to measure in terms of its capacity to alter either the natural course of disease or its eventual outcome. A great deal of money is spent on this. It is valued highly by the professionals as well as the patients. It consists of what is sometimes called "supportive therapy." It tides patients over through diseases that are not, by and large, understood. It is what is meant by the phrases "caring for" and "standing by." It is indispensable. It is not, however, a technology in any real sense, since it does not involve measures directed at the underlying mechanism of disease.

It includes the large part of any good doctor's time that is taken up with simply providing reassurance, explaining to patients who fear that they have contracted one or another lethal disease that they are, in fact, quite healthy.

It is what physicians used to be engaged in at the bedside of patients with diphtheria, meningitis, poliomyelitis, lobar pneumonia, and all the rest of the infectious diseases that have since come under control.

It is what physicians must now do for patients with intractable cancer, severe rheumatoid arthritis, multiple sclerosis, stroke, and advanced cirrhosis. One can think of at least twenty major diseases that require this kind of supportive medical care because of the absence of an effective technology. I would include a large amount of what is called mental disease, and most varieties of cancer, in this category.

The cost of this nontechnology is very high, and getting higher all the time. It requires not only a great deal of time but also very hard effort and skill on the part of physicians; only the very best of doctors are good at coping with this kind of defeat. It also involves long periods of hospitalization, lots of nursing, lots of involvement of nonmedical professionals in and out of the hospital. It represents, in short, a substantial segment of today's expenditures for health.

2. At the next level up is a kind of technology best termed "halfway technology." This represents the kinds of things that must be done after the fact, in efforts to compensate for the incapacitating effects of certain diseases whose course one is unable to do very much about. It is a technology designed to make up for disease, or to postpone death.

The outstanding examples in recent years are the transplantations of hearts, kidneys, livers, and other organs, and the equally spectacular inventions of artificial organs. In the public mind, this kind of technology has come to seem like the equivalent of the high technologies of the physical sciences. The media tend to present each new procedure as though it represented a breakthrough and therapeutic triumph, instead of the makeshift that it really is.

In fact, this level of technology is, by its nature, at the same time highly sophisticated and profoundly primitive. It is the kind of thing that one must continue to do until there is a genuine understanding of the mechanisms involved in disease. In chronic glomerulonephritis, for example, a much clearer insight will be needed into the events leading to the destruction of glomeruli by the immunologic reactants that now appear to govern this disease, before one will know how to intervene intelligently to prevent the process, or turn it round. But when this level of understanding has been reached, the technology of kidney replacement will not be much needed and should no longer pose the huge problems of logistics, cost, and ethics that it poses today.

An extremely complex and costly technology for the management of coronary heart disease has evolved—involving specialized ambulances and hospital units, all kinds of electronic gadgetry, and whole platoons of new professional personnel—to deal with the end results of coronary thrombosis. Almost everything offered today for the treatment of heart disease is at this level of technology, with the transplanted and artificial hearts as ultimate examples. When enough has been learned to know what really goes wrong in heart disease, one ought to be in a position to figure out ways to prevent or reverse the process, and when this happens the current elaborate technology will probably be set to one side.

Much of what is done in the treatment of cancer, by surgery, irradiation, and chemotherapy, represents halfway technology, in the sense that these measures are directed at the existence of already established cancer cells, but not at the mechanisms by which cells become neoplastic.

It is a characteristic of this kind of technology that it costs an enormous amount of money and requires a continuing expansion of hospital facilities. There is no end to the need for new, highly trained people to run the enterprise. And there is really no way out of this, at the present state of knowledge. If the installation of specialized coronary-care units can result in the extension of life for only a few patients with coronary disease (and there is no question that this technology is effective in a few cases), it seems to me an inevitable fact of life that as many of these as can be will be put together, and as much money as can be found will be spent. I do not see that anyone has much choice in this. The only thing that can move medicine away from this level of technology is new information, and the only imaginable source of this information is research.

3. The third type of technology is the kind that is so effective that it

seems to attract the least public notice; it has come to be taken for granted. This is the genuinely decisive technology of modern medicine, exemplified best by modern methods for immunization against diphtheria, pertussis, and the childhood virus diseases, and the contemporary use of antibiotics and chemotherapy for bacterial infections. The capacity to deal effectively with syphilis and tuberculosis represents a milestone in human endeavor, even though full use of this potential has not yet been made. And there are, of course, other examples: the treatment of endocrinologic disorders with appropriate hormones, the prevention of hemolytic disease of the newborn, the treatment and prevention of various nutritional disorders, and perhaps just around the corner the management of Parkinsonism and sickle-cell anemia. There are other examples, and everyone will have his favorite candidates for the list, but the truth is that there are nothing like as many as the public has been led to believe.

The point to be made about this kind of technology—the real high technology of medicine—is that it comes as the result of a genuine understanding of disease mechanisms, and when it becomes available, it is relatively inexpensive, relatively simple, and relatively easy to deliver.

Offhand, I cannot think of any important human disease for which medicine possesses the outright capacity to prevent or cure where the cost of the technology is itself a major problem. The price is never as high as the cost of managing the same diseases during the earlier stages of no-technology or halfway technology. If a case of typhoid fever had to be managed today by the best methods of 1935, it would run to a staggering expense. At, say, around fifty days of hospitalization, requiring the most demanding kind of nursing care, with the obsessive concern for details of diet that characterized the therapy of that time, with daily laboratory monitoring, and, on occasion, surgical intervention for abdominal catastrophe, I should think $10,000 would be a conservative estimate for the illness, as contrasted with today's cost of a bottle of chloramphenicol and a day or two of fever. The halfway technology that was evolving for poliomyelitis in the early 1950s, just before the emergence of the basic research that made the vaccine possible, provides another illustration of the point. Do you remember Sister Kenny, and the cost of those institutes for rehabilitation, with all those ceremonially applied hot fomentations, and the debates about whether the affected limbs should be totally immobilized or kept in passive motion as frequently as possible, and the masses of statistically tormented data mobilized to support one view or the other? It is the cost of that kind of technology, and its relative effectiveness, that must be compared with the cost and effectiveness of the vaccine.

Pulmonary tuberculosis had similar episodes in its history. There was a sudden enthusiasm for the surgical removal of infected lung tissue in the early 1950s, and elaborate plans were being made for new and expensive installations for major pulmonary surgery in tuberculosis hospitals, and then INH and streptomycin came along and the hospitals themselves were closed up.

It is when physicians are bogged down by their incomplete technologies, by the innumerable things they are obliged to do in medicine when they lack a clear understanding of disease mechanisms, that the deficiencies of the health-care system are most conspicuous. If I were a policy-maker, interested in saving money for health care over the long haul, I would regard it as an act of high prudence to give high priority to a lot more basic research in biologic science. This is the only way to get the full mileage that biology owes to the science of medicine, even though it seems, as used to be said in the days when the phrase still had some meaning, like asking for the moon.

CHAPTER EIGHT

Vibes

WE LEAVE TRACES OF OURSELVES WHEREVER WE GO, ON WHATEVER WE touch. One of the odd discoveries made by small boys is that when two pebbles are struck sharply against each other they emit, briefly, a curious smoky odor. The phenomenon fades when the stones are immaculately cleaned, vanishes when they are heated to furnace temperature, and reappears when they are simply touched by the hand again before being struck.

An intelligent dog with a good nose can track a man across open ground by his smell and distinguish that man's tracks from those of others. More than this, the dog can detect the odor of a light human fingerprint on a glass slide, and he will remember that slide and smell it out from others for as long as six weeks, when the scent fades away. Moreover, this animal can smell the identity of identical twins, and will follow the tracks of one or the other as though they had been made by the same man.

We are marked as self by the chemicals we leave beneath the soles of our shoes, as unmistakably and individually as by the membrane surface antigens detectable in homografts of our tissues.

Other animals are similarly endowed with signaling mechanisms. Columns of ants can smell out the differences between themselves and other ants on their trails. The ants of one species, proceeding jerkily across a path, leave trails that can be followed by their own relatives but not by others. Certain ants, predators, have taken unfair advantage of the system; they are born with an ability to sense the trails of the species they habitually take for slaves, follow their victims to their nests, and release special odorants that throw them into disorganized panic.

Minnows and catfish can recognize each member of their own species by his particular, person-specific odor. It is hard to imagine a solitary, independent, existentialist minnow, recognizable for himself alone;

minnows in a school behave like interchangeable, identical parts of an organism. But there it is.

The problem of olfactory sensing shares some of the current puzzles and confusions of immunology, apart from the business of telling self from non-self. A rabbit, it has been calculated, has something like 100 million olfactory receptors. There is a constant and surprisingly rapid turnover of the receptor cells, with new ones emerging from basal cells within a few days. The theories to explain olfaction are as numerous and complex as those for immunologic sensing. It seems likely that the shape of the smelled molecule is what matters most. By and large, odorants are chemically small, Spartan compounds. In a rose garden, a rose is a rose because of geraniol, a 10-carbon compound, and it is the geometric conformation of atoms and their bond angles that determine the unique fragrance. The special vibrations of atoms or groups of atoms within the molecules of odorants, or the vibratory song of the entire molecule, have been made the basis for several theories, with postulated "osmic frequencies" as the source of odor. The geometry of the molecule seems to be more important than the names of the atoms themselves; any set of atoms, if arranged in precisely the same configuration, by whatever chemical name, might smell as sweet. It is not known how the olfactory cells are fired by an odorant. According to one view, a hole is poked in the receptor membrane, launching depolarization, but other workers believe that the substance may become bound to the cells possessing specific receptors for it and then may just sit there, somehow displaying its signal from a distance, after the fashion of antigens on immune cells. Specific receptor proteins have been proposed, with different olfactory cells carrying specific receptors for different "primary" odors, but no one has yet succeeded in identifying the receptors or naming the "primary" odors.

Training of cells for olfactory sensing appears to be an everyday phenomenon. Repeated exposure of an animal to the same odorant, in small doses, leads to great enhancement of acuity, suggesting the possibility that new receptor sites are added to the cells. It is conceivable that new clones of cells with a particular receptor are stimulated to emerge in the process of training. The guinea pig, that immunologically famous animal, can be trained to perceive fantastically small amounts of nitrobenzene by his nose, without the help of Freund's adjuvants or haptene carriers. Minnows have been trained to recognize phenol, and distinguish it from p-chlorophenol, in concentrations of five parts per billion. Eels have been taught to smell two or three molecules of phenylethyl alcohol. And, of course, eels and salmon must be able to remember by nature, as the phrase goes, the odor of the waters in which they were hatched, so as to sniff their way back from the open sea for spawning. Electrodes in the olfactory bulbs of salmon will fire when the olfactory epithelium is exposed to water from their spawning grounds, whereas water from other streams causes no response.

We feel somehow inferior and left out of things by all the marvelous sensory technology in the creatures around us. We sometimes try to diminish our sense of loss (or loss of sense) by claiming to ourselves that we have put such primitive mechanisms behind us in our evolution. We like to regard the olfactory bulb as a sort of archeologic find, and we speak of the ancient olfactory parts of the brain as though they were elderly, dotty relatives in need of hobbies.

But we may be better at it than we think. An average man can detect just a few molecules of butyl mercaptan, and most of us can sense the presence of musk in vanishingly small amounts. Steroids are marvelously odorous, emitting varieties of musky, sexy smells. Women are acutely aware of the odor of a synthetic steroid named exaltolide, which most men are unable to detect. All of us are able to smell ants, for which the great word pismire was originally coined.

There may even be odorants that fire off receptors in our olfactory epithelia without our being conscious of smell, including signals exchanged involuntarily between human beings. Wiener has proposed, on intuitive grounds, that defects and misinterpretations in such a communication system may be an unexplored territory for psychiatry. The schizophrenic, he suggests, may have his problems with identity and reality because of flawed perceptions of his own or others' signals. And, indeed, there may be something wrong with the apparatus in schizophrenics; they have, it is said, an unfamiliar odor, recently attributed to trans-3-methylhexanoic acid, in their sweat.

Olfactory receptors for communication between different creatures are crucial for the establishment of symbiotic relations. The crab and anemone recognize each other as partners by molecular configurations, as do the anemones and their symbiotic damsel fish. Similar devices are employed for defense, as with the limpet, which defends itself against starfish predators by everting its mantle and thus precluding a starfish foothold; the limpet senses a special starfish protein, which is, perhaps in the name of fairness, elaborated by all starfish into their environment. The system is evidently an ancient one, long antedating the immunologic sensing of familiar or foreign forms of life by the antibodies on which we now depend so heavily for our separateness. It has recently been learned that the genes for the marking of self by cellular antigens and those for making immunologic responses by antibody formation are closely linked. It is possible that the invention of antibodies evolved from the earlier sensing mechanisms needed for symbiosis, perhaps designed, in part, to keep the latter from getting out of hand.

A very general system of chemical communication between living things of all kinds, plant and animal, has been termed "allelochemics" by Whittaker. Using one signal or another, each form of life announces its proximity to the others around it, setting limits on encroachment or spreading welcome to potential symbionts. The net effect is a coordinated mechanism for the regulation of rates of growth and occupations of territory. It is evidently designed for the homeostasis of the earth.

Jorge Borges, in his recent bestiary of mythical creatures, notes that the idea of round beasts was imagined by many speculative minds, and Johannes Kepler once argued that the earth itself is such a being. In this immense organism, chemical signals might serve the function of global hormones, keeping balance and symmetry in the operation of various interrelated working parts, informing tissues in the vegetation of the Alps about the state of eels in the Sargasso Sea, by long, interminable relays of interconnected messages between all kinds of other creatures.

This is an interesting kind of problem, made to order for computers if they came in sizes big enough to store in nearby galaxies. It is nice to think that there are so many unsolved puzzles ahead for biology, although I wonder whether we will ever find enough graduate students.

CHAPTER NINE

Ceti

TAU CETI IS A RELATIVELY NEARBY STAR THAT SUFFICIENTLY RESEM-
bles our sun to make its solar system a plausible candidate for the
existence of life. We are, it appears, ready to begin getting in touch with
Ceti, and with any other interested celestial body in more remote places,
out to the edge. CETI is also, by intention, the acronym of the First
International Conference on Communication with Extraterrestrial Intelligence, held in 1972 in Soviet Armenia under the joint sponsorship
of the National Academy of Sciences of the United States and the Soviet
Academy, which involved eminent physicists and astronomers from
various countries, most of whom are convinced that the odds for the
existence of life elsewhere are very high, with a reasonable probability
that there are civilizations, one place or another, with technologic
mastery matching or exceeding ours.

On this assumption, the conferees thought it likely that radioastron-
omy would be the generally accepted mode of interstellar communication, on grounds of speed and economy. They made a formal
recommendation that we organize an international cooperative program, with new and immense radio telescopes, to probe the reaches of
deep space for electromagnetic signals making sense. Eventually, we
would plan to send out messages on our own and receive answers, but at
the outset it seems more practical to begin by catching snatches of
conversation between others.

So, the highest of all our complex technologies in the hardest of our
sciences will soon be engaged, full scale, in what is essentially biologic
research—and with some aspects of social science, at that.

The earth has become, just in the last decade, too small a place. We
have the feeling of being confined—shut in; it is something like out-
growing a small town in a small county. The views of the dark, pocked
surface of Mars, still lifeless to judge from the latest photographs, do not

seem to have extended our reach; instead, they bring closer, too close, another unsatisfactory feature of our local environment. The blue noonday sky, cloudless, has lost its old look of immensity. The word is out that the sky is not limitless; it is finite. It is, in truth, only a kind of local roof, a membrane under which we live, luminous but confusingly refractile when suffused with sunlight; we can sense its concave surface a few miles over our heads. We know that it is tough and thick enough so that when hard objects strike it from the outside they burst into flames. The color photographs of the earth are more amazing than anything outside: we live inside a blue chamber, a bubble of air blown by ourselves. The other sky beyond, absolutely black and appalling, is wide-open country, irresistible for exploration.

Here we go, then. An extraterrestrial embryologist, having a close look at us from time to time, would probably conclude that the morphogenesis of the earth is coming along well, with the beginnings of a nervous system and fair-sized ganglions in the form of cities, and now with specialized, dish-shaped sensory organs, miles across, ready to receive stimuli. He may well wonder, however, how we will go about responding. We are evolving into the situation of a Skinner pigeon in a Skinner box, peering about in all directions, trying to make connections, probing.

When the first word comes in from outer space, finally, we will probably be used to the idea. We can already provide a quite good explanation for the origin of life, here or elsewhere. Given a moist planet with methane, formaldehyde, ammonia, and some usable minerals, all of which abound, exposed to lightning or ultraviolet irradiation at the right temperature, life might start off almost anywhere. The tricky, unsolved thing is how to get the polymers to arrange in membranes and invent replication. The rest is clear going. If they follow our protocol, it will be anaerobic life at first, then photosynthesis and the first exhalation of oxygen, then respiring life and the great burst of variation, then speciation, and, finally, some kind of consciousness. It is easy, in the telling.

I suspect that when we have recovered from the first easy acceptance of signs of life from elsewhere, and finished nodding at each other, and finished smiling, we will be in for shock. We have had it our way, relatively speaking, being unique all these years, and it will be hard to deal with the thought that the whole, infinitely huge, spinning, clocklike apparatus around us is itself animate, and can sprout life whenever the conditions are right. We will respond, beyond doubt, by making connections after the fashion of established life, floating out our filaments, extending pili, but we will end up feeling smaller than ever, as small as a single cell, with a quite new sense of continuity. It will take some getting used to.

The immediate problem, however, is a much more practical, down-to-earth matter, and must be giving insomnia to the CETI participants. Let us assume that there is, indeed, sentient life in one or another part of remote space, and that we will be successful in getting in touch with it. What on earth are we going to talk about? If, as seems likely, it is a hundred or more light years away, there are going to be some very long pauses. The barest amenities, on which we rely for opening conversations—Hello, are you there?, from us, followed by Yes, hello, from them—will take two hundred years at least. By the time we have our party we may have forgotten what we had in mind.

We could begin by gambling on the rightness of our technology and just send out news of ourselves, like a mimeographed Christmas letter, but we would have to choose our items carefully, with durability of meaning in mind. Whatever information we provide must still make sense to us two centuries later, and must still seem important, or the conversation will be an embarrassment to all concerned. In two hundred years it is, as we have found, easy to lose the thread.

Perhaps the safest thing to do at the outset, if technology permits, is to send music. This language may be the best we have for explaining what we are like to others in space, with least ambiguity. I would vote for Bach, all of Bach, streamed out into space, over and over again. We would be bragging, of course, but it is surely excusable for us to put the best possible face on at the beginning of such an acquaintance. We can tell the harder truths later. And, to do ourselves justice, music would give a fairer picture of what we are really like than some of the other things we might be sending, like *Time,* say, or a history of the U.N. or Presidential speeches. We could send out our science, of course, but just think of the wincing at this end when the polite comments arrive two hundred years from now. Whatever we offer as today's items of liveliest interest are bound to be out of date and irrelevant, maybe even ridiculous. I think we should stick to music.

Perhaps, if the technology can be adapted to it, we should send some paintings. Nothing would better describe what this place is like, to an outsider, than the Cézanne demonstrations that an apple is really part fruit, part earth.

What kinds of questions should we ask? The choices will be hard, and everyone will want his special question first. What are your smallest particles? Did you think yourselves unique? Do you have colds? Have you anything quicker than light? Do you always tell the truth? Do you cry? There is no end to the list.

Perhaps we should wait a while, until we are sure we know what we want to know, before we get down to detailed questions. After all, the main question will be the opener: Hello, are you there? If the reply should turn out to be Yes, hello, we might want to stop there and think about that, for quite a long time.

CHAPTER TEN

The Long Habit

WE CONTINUE TO SHARE WITH OUR REMOTEST ANCESTORS THE MOST tangled and evasive attitudes about death, despite the great distance we have come in understanding some of the profound aspects of biology. We have as much distaste for talking about personal death as for thinking about it; it is an indelicacy, like talking in mixed company about venereal disease or abortion in the old days. Death on a grand scale does not bother us in the same special way: we can sit around a dinner table and discuss war, involving 60 million volatilized human deaths, as though we were talking about bad weather; we can watch abrupt bloody death every day, in color, on films and television, without blinking back a tear. It is when the numbers of dead are very small, and very close, that we begin to think in scurrying circles. At the very center of the problem is the naked cold deadness of one's own self, the only reality in nature of which we can have absolute certainty, and it is unmentionable, unthinkable. We may be even less willing to face the issue at first hand than our predecessors because of a secret new hope that maybe it will go away. We like to think, hiding the thought, that with all the marvelous ways in which we seem now to lead nature around by the nose, perhaps we can avoid the central problem if we just become, next year, say, a bit smarter.

"The long habit of living," said Thomas Browne, "indisposeth us to dying." These days, the habit has become an addiction: we are hooked on living; the tenacity of its grip on us, and ours on it, grows in intensity. We cannot think of giving it up, even when living loses its zest—even when we have lost the zest for zest.

We have come a long way in our technologic capacity to put death off, and it is imaginable that we might learn to stall it for even longer periods, perhaps matching the life-spans of the Abkhasian Russians, who are said to go on, springily, for a century and a half. If we can rid ourselves of some of our chronic, degenerative diseases, and cancer, strokes, and coronaries, we might go on and on. It sounds attractive and reasonable, but it is no certainty. If we became free of disease, we would make a much better run of it for the last decade or so, but might still terminate on about the same schedule as now. We may be like the genetically different lines of mice, or like Hayflick's different tissue-culture lines, programmed to die after a predetermined number of days, clocked by their genomes. If this is the way it is, some of us will continue to wear out and come unhinged in the sixth decade, and some much later, depending on genetic timetables.

If we ever do achieve freedom from most of today's diseases, or even complete freedom from disease, we will perhaps terminate by drying out and blowing away on a light breeze, but we will still die.

Most of my friends do not like this way of looking at it. They prefer to take it for granted that we only die because we get sick, with one lethal ailment or another, and if we did not have our diseases we might go on indefinitely. Even biologists choose to think this about themselves, despite the evidences of the absolute inevitability of death that surround their professional lives. Everything dies, all around, trees, plankton, lichens, mice, whales, flies, mitochondria. In the simplest creatures it is sometimes difficult to see it as death, since the strands of replicating DNA they leave behind are more conspicuously the living parts of themselves than with us (not that it is fundamentally any different, but it seems so). Flies do not develop a ward round of diseases that carry them off, one by one. They simply age, and die, like flies.

We hanker to go on, even in the face of plain evidence that long, long lives are not necessarily pleasurable in the kind of society we have arranged thus far. We will be lucky if we can postpone the search for new technologies for a while, until we have discovered some satisfactory things to do with the extra time. Something will surely have to be found to take the place of sitting on the porch re-examining one's watch.

Perhaps we would not be so anxious to prolong life if we did not detest so much the sickness of withdrawal. It is astonishing how little information we have about this universal process, with all the other dazzling advances in biology. It is almost as though we wanted not to know about it. Even if we could imagine the act of death in isolation, without any preliminary stage of being struck down by disease, we would be fearful of it.

There are signs that medicine may be taking a new interest in the process, partly from curiosity, partly from an embarrassed realization that we have not been handling this aspect of disease with as much skill as physicians once displayed, back in the days before they became convinced that disease was their solitary and sometimes defeatable enemy. It used to be the hardest and most important of all the services of a good doctor to be on hand at the time of death and to provide comfort, usually in the home. Now it is done in hospitals, in secrecy (one of the reasons for the increased fear of death these days may be that so many people are totally unfamiliar with it; they never actually see it happen in real life). Some of our technology permits us to deny its existence, and we maintain flickers of life for long stretches in one community of cells or another, as though we were keeping a flag flying. Death is not a sudden-all-at-once affair; cells go down in sequence, one by one. You can, if you like, recover great numbers of them many hours after the lights have gone out, and grow them out in cultures. It takes hours, even days, before the irreversible word finally gets around to all the provinces.

We may be about to rediscover that dying is not such a bad thing to do after all. Sir William Osler took this view: he disapproved of people who spoke of the agony of death, maintaining that there was no such thing.

In a nineteenth-century memoir on an expedition in Africa, there is a story by David Livingston about his own experience of near-death. He was caught by a lion, crushed across the chest in the animal's great jaws, and saved in the instant by a lucky shot from a friend. Later, he remembered the episode in clear detail. He was so amazed by the extraordinary sense of peace, calm, and total painlessness associated with being killed that he constructed a theory that all creatures are provided with a protective physiologic mechanism, switched on at the verge of death, carrying them through in a haze of tranquillity.

I have seen agony in death only once, in a patient with rabies; he remained acutely aware of every stage in the process of his own disintegration over a twenty-four-hour period, right up to his final moment. It was as though, in the special neuropathology of rabies, the switch had been prevented from turning.

We will be having new opportunities to learn more about the physiology of death at first hand, from the increasing numbers of cardiac patients who have been through the whole process and then back again. Judging from what has been found out thus far, from the first generation of people resuscitated from cardiac standstill (already termed the Lazarus syndrome), Osler seems to have been right. Those who remember parts or all of their episodes do not recall any fear, or anguish. Several people who remained conscious throughout, while appearing to have been quite dead, could only describe a remarkable sensation of detachment. One man underwent coronary occlusion with cessation of the heart and dropped for all practical purposes dead, in front of a hospital; within a few minutes his heart had been restarted by electrodes and he breathed his way back into life. According to his account, the strangest thing was that there were so many people around him, moving so urgently, handling his body with such excitement, while all his awareness was of quietude.

In a recent study of the reaction to dying in patients with obstructive disease of the lungs, it was concluded that the process was considerably more shattering for the professional observers than the observed. Most of the patients appeared to be preparing themselves with equanimity for death, as though intuitively familiar with the business. One elderly woman reported that the only painful and distressing part of the process was in being interrupted; on several occasions she was provided with conventional therapeutic measures to maintain oxygenation or restore fluids and electrolytes, and each time she found the experience of coming back harrowing; she deeply resented the interference with her dying.

I find myself surprised by the thought that dying is an all-right thing to do, but perhaps it should not surprise. It is, after all, the most ancient and fundamental of biologic functions, with its mechanisms worked out with the same attention to detail, the same provision for the advantage of the organism, the same abundance of genetic information for guidance through the stages, that we have long since become accustomed to finding in all the crucial acts of living.

Very well. But even so, if the transformation is a coordinated, integrated physiologic process in its initial, local stages, there is still that permanent vanishing of consciousness to be accounted for. Are we to be stuck forever with this problem? Where on earth does it go? Is it simply stopped dead in its tracks, lost in humus, wasted? Considering the tendency of nature to find uses for complex and intricate mechanisms, this seems to me unnatural. I prefer to think of it as somehow separated off at the filaments of its attachment, and then drawn like an easy breath back into the membrane of its origin, a fresh memory for a biospherical nervous system, but I have no data on the matter.

This is for another science, another day. It may turn out, as some scientists suggest, that we are forever precluded from investigating consciousness by a sort of indeterminacy principle that stipulates that the very act of looking will make it twitch and blur out of sight. If this is true, we will never learn. I envy some of my friends who are convinced about telepathy; oddly enough, it is my European scientist acquaintances who believe it most freely and take it most lightly. All their aunts have received Communications, and there they sit, with proof of the motility of consciousness at their fingertips, and the making of a new science. It is discouraging to have had the wrong aunts, and never the ghost of a message.

CHAPTER ELEVEN

Antaeus in Manhattan

INSECTS AGAIN.

When social animals are gathered together in groups, they become qualitatively different creatures from what they were when alone or in pairs. Single locusts are quiet, meditative, sessile things, but when locusts are added to other locusts, they become excited, change color, undergo spectacular endocrine revisions, and intensify their activity until, when there are enough of them packed shoulder to shoulder, they vibrate and hum with the energy of a jet airliner and take off.

Watson, Nel, and Hewitt have collected large numbers of termites in the field and placed them together for observation, in groups and pairs. The grouped termites become increasingly friendly and active, but show no inclination to lay eggs or mate; instead, they cut down on their water intake, watching their weight, and the mitochondria of their flight muscles escalate in metabolic activity. Grouped termites keep touching each other incessantly with their antennae, and this appears to be the central governing mechanism. It is the being touched that counts, rather than the act of touching. Deprived of antennae, any termite can become a group termite if touched frequently enough by the others.

Isolated, paired termites are something else again. As soon as they are removed from the group, and the touching from all sides comes to an end, they become aggressive, standoffish; they begin drinking compulsively, and abstain from touching each other. Sometimes, they even bite off the distal halves of each other's antennae, to eliminate the temptation. Irritably, settling down to make the best of a poor situation, they begin preparations for the laying of eggs and the taking care of the brood. Meanwhile, the mitochondria in their flight muscles go out of business.

The most intensely social animals can only adapt to group behavior. Bees and ants have no option when isolated, except to die. There is really no such creature as a single individual; he has no more life of his own than a cast-off cell marooned from the surface of your skin.

Ants are more like the parts of an animal than entities on their own. They are mobile cells, circulating through a dense connective tissue of other ants in a matrix of twigs. The circuits are so intimately woven that the anthill meets all the essential criteria of an organism.

It would be wonderful to understand how the anthill communication system works. Somehow, by touching each other continually, by exchanging bits of white stuff carried about in their mandibles like money, they manage to inform the whole enterprise about the state of the world outside, the location of food, the nearness of enemies, the maintenance requirements of the Hill, even the direction of the sun; in the Alps, mountaineers are said to use the ameboid configurations of elongated ant nests as pointers to the south. The Hill, for its part, responds by administering the affairs of the institution, coordinating and synchronizing the movements of its crawling parts, aerating and cleaning the nest so that it can last for as long as forty years, fetching food in by long tentacles, rearing broods, taking slaves, raising crops, and, at one time or another, budding off subcolonies in the near vicinity, as progeny.

The social insects, especially ants, have been sources of all kinds of parables, giving lessons in industry, interdependence, altruism, humility, frugality, patience. They have been employed to instruct us in the whole range of our institutional virtues, from the White House to your neighborhood savings bank.

And now, at last, they have become an Art Form. A gallery in New York exhibited a collection of 2 million live army ants, on loan from Central America, in a one-colony show entitled "Patterns and Structures." They were displayed on sand in a huge square bin, walled by plastic sides high enough to prevent them from crawling over and out into Manhattan. The inventor of the work, Alan Sonfist, arranged and rearranged the location of food sources in different places, according to his inspiration and their taste, and they formed themselves into long, black, ropy patterns, extended like writhing limbs, hands, fingers, across the sand in crescents, crisscrosses, and long ellipses, from one station to another. Thus deployed, they were watched with intensity by the crowds of winter-carapaced people who lined up in neat rows to gaze down at them. The ants were, together with the New Yorkers, an abstraction, a live mobile, an action painting, a piece of found art, a happening, a parody, depending on the light.

I can imagine the people moving around the edges of the plastic barrier, touching shoulder to shoulder, sometimes touching hands, exchanging bits of information, nodding, smiling sometimes, prepared as New Yorkers always are to take flight at a moment's notice, their mitochondria fully stoked and steaming. They move in orderly lines around the box, crowding one another precisely, without injury, peering down, nodding, and then backing off to let new people in. Seen from a distance, clustered densely around the white plastic box containing the long serpentine lines of army ants, turning to each other and murmuring repetitively, they seem an absolute marvel. They might have dropped here from another planet.

I am sad that I did not see any of this myself. By the time I had received the communication on television and in my morning paper, felt the tugging pull toward Manhattan, and made my preparations to migrate, I learned that the army ants had all died.

The Art Form simply disintegrated, all at once, like one of those exploding, vanishing faces in paintings by the British artist Francis Bacon.

There was no explanation, beyond the rumored, unproved possibility of cold drafts in the gallery over the weekend. Monday morning they were sluggish, moving with less precision, dully. Then, the death began, affecting first one part and then another, and within a day all 2 million were dead, swept away into large plastic bags and put outside for engulfment and digestion by the sanitation truck.

It is a melancholy parable. I am unsure of the meaning, but I do think it has something to do with all that plastic — that, and the distance from the earth. It is a long, long way from the earth of a Central American jungle to the ground floor of a gallery, especially when you consider that Manhattan itself is suspended on a kind of concrete platform, propped up by a meshwork of wires, pipes, and water mains. But I think it was chiefly the plastic, which seems to me the most unearthly of all man's creations so far. I do not believe you can suspend army ants away from the earth, on plastic, for any length of time. They will lose touch, run out of energy, and die for lack of current.

One steps on ants, single ants or small clusters, every day without giving it a thought, but it is impossible to contemplate the death of so vast a beast as these 2 million ants without feeling twinges of sympathy, and something else. Nervously, thinking this way, thinking especially about Manhattan and the plastic platform, I laid down my newspaper and reached for the book on my shelf that contained, I knew, precisely the paragraph of reassurance required by the moment:

It is not surprising that many analogies have been drawn between the social insects and human societies. Fundamentally, however, these are misleading or meaningless, for the behavior of insects is rigidly stereotyped and determined by innate instructive mechanisms; they show little or no insight or capacity for learning, and they lack the ability to develop a social tradition based on the accumulated experience of many generations.

It is, of course, an incomplete comfort to read this sort of thing to one's self. For full effect, it needs reading aloud by several people at once, moving the lips in synchrony.

CHAPTER TWELVE

The MBL

ONCE YOU HAVE BECOME PERMANENTLY STARTLED, AS I AM, BY THE realization that we are a social species, you tend to keep an eye out for pieces of evidence that this is, by and large, a good thing for us. You look around for the enterprises that we engage in collectively and unconsciously, the things we build like wasp nests, individually unaware of what we are doing. Most of the time, these days, it is a depressing exercise. The joint building activity that consumes most of our energy and binds us together is, of course, language, but this is so overwhelming a structure and grows so slowly that none of us can feel a personal sense of participating in the work.

The less immense, more finite items, of a size allowing the mind to get a handhold, like nations, or space technology, or New York, are hard to think about without drifting toward heartsink.

It is in our very small enterprises that we can find encouragement, here and there. The Marine Biological Laboratory in Woods Hole is a paradigm, a human institution possessed of a life of its own, self-regenerating, touched all around by human meddle but constantly improved, embellished by it. The place was put together, given life, sustained into today's version of its maturity and prepared for further elaboration and changes in its complexity, by what can only be described as a bunch of people. Neither the spectacularly eminent men who have served as directors down through the century nor the numberless committees by which it is seasonally raddled, nor the six-hundred-man corporation that nominally owns and operates it, nor even the trustees, have ever been able to do more than hold the lightest reins over this institution; it seems to have a mind of its own, which it makes up in its own way.

Successive generations of people in bunches, never seeming very well organized, have been building the MBL since it was chartered in 1888. It actually started earlier, in 1871, when Woods Hole, Massachusetts, was selected for a Bureau of Fisheries Station and the news got round that all sorts of marine and estuarine life could be found here in the collisions between the Gulf Stream and northern currents offshore, plus birds to watch. Academic types drifted down from Boston, looked around, began explaining things to each other, and the place was off and running.

The MBL has grown slowly but steadily from the outset, sprouting new buildings from time to time, taking on new functions, expanding, drawing to itself by a sort of tropism greater numbers of biological scientists each summer, attracting students from all parts of the world. Today, it stands as the uniquely national center for biology in this country; it is the National Biological Laboratory without being officially designated (or yet funded) as such. Its influence on the growth and development of biologic science has been equivalent to that of many of the country's universities combined, for it has had its pick of the world's scientific talent for each summer's research and teaching. If you ask around, you will find that any number of today's leading figures in biology and medicine were informally ushered into their careers by the summer course in physiology; a still greater number picked up this or that idea for their key experiments while spending time as summer visitors in the laboratories, and others simply came for a holiday and got enough good notions to keep their laboratories back home busy for a full year. Someone has counted thirty Nobel Laureates who have worked at the MBL at one time or another.

It is amazing that such an institution, exerting so much influence on academic science, has been able to remain so absolutely autonomous. It has, to be sure, linkages of various kinds, arrangements with outside universities for certain graduate programs, and it adheres delicately, somewhat ambiguously, to the Woods Hole Oceanographic Institute just up the street. But it has never come under the domination of any outside institution or governmental agency, nor has it ever been told what to do by any outside group. Internally, the important institutional decisions seem to have been made by a process of accommodation and adaptation, with resistible forces always meeting movable objects.

The invertebrate eye was invented into an optical instrument at the MBL, opening the way to modern visual physiology. The giant axon of the Woods Hole squid became the apparatus for the creation of today's astonishing neurobiology. Developmental and reproductive biology were recognized and defined as sciences here, beginning with sea-urchin eggs and working up. Marine models were essential in the early days of research on muscle structure and function, and research on muscle has become a major preoccupation at the MBL. Ecology was a sober, industrious science here long ago, decades before the rest of us discovered the term. In recent years there have been expansion and strengthening in new fields; biologic membranes, immunology, genetics, and cell regulatory mechanisms are currently booming.

You can never tell when new things may be starting up from improbable lines of work. The amebocytes of starfish were recently found to contain a material that immobilizes the macrophages of mammals, resembling a product of immune lymphocytes in higher forms. Aplysia, a sea slug that looks as though it couldn't be good for anything, has been found by neurophysiologists to be filled with truth. Limulus, one of the world's conservative beasts, has recently been in the newspapers; it was discovered to contain a reagent for the detection of vanishingly small quantities of endotoxin from gram-negative bacteria, and the pharmaceutical industry has already sniffed commercial possibilities for the monitoring of pyrogen-free materials; horseshoe crabs may soon be as marketable as lobsters.

There is no way of predicting what the future will be like for an institution such as the MBL. One way or another, it will evolve. It may shift soon into a new phase, with a year-round program for teaching and research and a year-round staff, but it will have to accomplish this without jeopardizing the immense power of its summer programs, or all institutional hell will break loose. It will have to find new ways for relating to the universities, if its graduate programs are to expand as they should. It will have to develop new symbiotic relations with the Oceanographic Institute, since both places have so much at stake. And it will have to find more money, much more — the kind of money that only federal governments possess — without losing any of its own initiative.

It will be an interesting place to watch, in the years ahead. In a rational world, things ought to go as well for the MBL as they have in the past, and it should become an even larger and more agile collective intelligence. If you can think of good questions to ask about the life of the earth, it should be as good a place as any to go for answers.

It is now, in fact. You might begin at the local beach, which functions as a sort of ganglion. It is called Stony Beach, because it used to be covered, painfully, by small stones. Long ago, somehow, some committee of scientists, prodded by footsore wives, found enough money to cover it with a layer of sand. It is the most minor of beaches, hardly big enough for a committee, but close enough to the laboratories so that the investigators can walk down for a sandwich lunch with their children on sunny weekdays. From time to time, pure physicists turn up, with only a few minutes to spare from a meeting at the National Academy summer headquarters, tired from making forecasts on classifiedly obscure matters, wearing the look of doom. The physicists are another species, whiter-skinned, towel-draped against the sun, unearthly, the soles of their feet so sensitive that they limp on sand.

A small boy, five-ish, with myopia and glasses, emerges from the water; characteristically, although his hair is dripping his glasses are bone dry; he has already begun to master technique. As he picks his way between the conversations, heading for his mother, who is explaining homology between DNA in chloroplasts and bacteria, he is shaking his head slowly in wonderment, looking at something brown and gelatinous held in his hand, saying, "That is very interesting water." At Stony Beach the water is regarded as primarily interesting, even by small boys.

On weekends, in hot midsummer, you can see how the governing mechanisms work. It is so crowded that one must pick one's way on tiptoe to find a hunching place, but there is always a lot of standing up anyway; biologists seem to prefer standing on beaches, talking at each other, gesturing to indicate the way things are assembled, bending down to draw diagrams in the sand. By the end of the day, the sand is crisscrossed with a mesh of ordinates, abscissas, curves to account for everything in nature.

You can hear the sound from the beach at a distance, before you see the people. It is that most extraordinary noise, half-shout, half-song, made by confluent, simultaneously raised human voices, explaining things to each other.

You hear a similar sound at the close of the Friday Evening Lecture, the MBL's weekly grand occasion, when the guest lecturers from around the world turn up to present their most stunning pieces of science. As the audience flows out of the auditorium, there is the same jubilant descant, the great sound of crowded people explaining things to each other as fast as their minds will work. You cannot make out individual words in the mass, except that the recurrent phrase, "But look—" keeps bobbing above the surf of language.

Not many institutions can produce this spontaneous music at will, summer after summer, year after year. It takes a special gift, and the MBL appears to have been born with it. Perhaps this is an aspect of the way we build language after all. The scale is very small, and it is not at all clear how it works, but it makes a nice thought for a time when we can't seem to get anything straight or do anything right.

CHAPTER THIRTEEN

Autonomy

WORKING A TYPEWRITER BY TOUCH, LIKE RIDING A BICYCLE OR strolling on a path, is best done by not giving it a glancing thought. Once you do, your fingers fumble and hit the wrong keys. To do things involving practiced skills, you need to turn loose the systems of muscles and nerves responsible for each maneuver, place them on their own, and stay out of it. There is no real loss of authority in this, since you get to decide whether to do the thing or not, and you can intervene and embellish the technique any time you like; if you want to ride a bicycle backward, or walk with an eccentric loping gait giving a little skip every fourth step, whistling at the same time, you can do that. But if you concentrate your attention on the details, keeping in touch with each muscle, thrusting yourself into a free fall with each step and catching yourself at the last moment by sticking out the other foot in time to break the fall, you will end up immobilized, vibrating with fatigue.

It is a blessing to have options for choice and change in the learning of such unconsciously coordinated acts. If we were born with all these knacks inbuilt, automated like ants, we would surely miss the variety. It would be a less interesting world if we all walked and skipped alike, and never fell from bicycles. If we were all genetically programmed to play the piano deftly from birth, we might never learn to understand music.

The rules are different for the complicated, coordinated, fantastically skilled manipulations we perform with our insides. We do not have to learn anything. Our smooth-muscle cells are born with complete instructions, in need of no help from us, and they work away on their own schedules, modulating the lumen of blood vessels, moving things through intestines, opening and closing tubules according to the requirements of the entire system. Secretory cells elaborate their products in privacy; the heart contracts and relaxes; hormones are sent off to react silently with cell membranes, switching adenyl cyclase, prostaglandin, and other signals on and off; cells communicate with each other by simply touching; organelles send messages to other organelles; all this goes on continually, without ever a personal word from us. The arrangement is that of an ecosystem, with the operation of each part being governed by the state and function of all the other parts. When things are going well, as they generally are, it is an infallible mechanism.

But now the autonomy of this interior domain, long regarded as inviolate, is open to question. The experimental psychologists have recently found that visceral organs can be taught to do various things, as easily as a boy learns to ride a bicycle, by the instrumental techniques of operant conditioning. If a thing is done in the way the teacher wants, at a signal, and a suitable reward given immediately to reinforce the action, it becomes learned. Rats, rewarded by stimulation of their cerebral "pleasure centers," have been instructed to speed up or slow down their hearts at a signal, or to alter their blood pressures, or switch off certain waves in their electroencephalograms and switch on others.

The same technology has been applied to human beings, with other kinds of rewards, and the results have been startling. It is claimed that you can teach your kidneys to change the rate of urine formation, raise or lower your blood pressure, change your heart rate, write different brain waves, at will.

There is already talk of a breakthrough in the prevention and treatment of human disease. According to proponents, when the technology is perfected and extended it will surely lead to new possibilities for therapy. If a rat can be trained to dilate the blood vessels of one of his ears more than those of the other, as has been reported, what rich experiences in self-control and self-operation may lie just ahead for man? There are already cryptic advertisements in the Personal columns of literary magazines, urging the purchase of electronic headsets for the training and regulation of one's own brain waves, according to one's taste.

You can have it.

Not to downgrade it. It is extremely important, I know, and one ought to feel elated by the prospect of taking personal charge, calling the shots, running one's cells around like toy trains. Now that we know that viscera can be taught, the thought comes naturally that we've been neglecting them all these years, and by judicious application of human intelligence, these primitive structures can be trained to whatever standards of behavior we wish to set for them.

My trouble, to be quite candid, is a lack of confidence in myself. If I were informed tomorrow that I was in direct communication with my liver, and could now take over, I would become deeply depressed. I'd sooner be told, forty thousand feet over Denver, that the 747 jet in which

I had a coach seat was now mine to operate as I pleased; at least I would have the hope of bailing out, if I could find a parachute and discover quickly how to open a door. Nothing would save me and my liver, if I were in charge. For I am, to face the facts squarely, considerably less intelligent than my liver. I am, moreover, constitutionally unable to make hepatic decisions, and I prefer not to be obliged to, ever. I would not be able to think of the first thing to do.

I have the same feeling about the rest of my working parts. They are all better off without my intervention, in whatever they do. It might be something of a temptation to take over my brain, on paper, but I cannot imagine doing so in real life. I would lose track, get things mixed up, turn on wrong cells at wrong times, drop things. I doubt if I would ever be able to think up my own thoughts. My cells were born, or differentiated anyway, knowing how to do this kind of thing together. If I moved in to organize them they would resent it, perhaps become frightened, perhaps swarm out into my ventricles like bees.

Although it is, as I say, a temptation. I have never really been satisfied with the operation of my brain, and it might be fun to try running it myself, just once. There are several things I would change, given the opportunity: certain memories that tend to slip away unrecorded, others I've had enough of and would prefer to delete, certain notions I'd just as soon didn't keep popping in, trains of thought that go round and round without getting anywhere, rather like this one. I've always suspected that some of the cells in there are fluffing off much of the time, and I'd like to see a little more attention and real work. Also, while I'm about it, I could do with a bit more respect.

On balance, however, I think it best to stay out of this business. Once you began, there would be no end to the responsibilities. I'd rather leave all my automatic functions with as much autonomy as they please, and hope for the best. Imagine having to worry about running leukocytes, keeping track, herding them here and there, listening for signals. After the first flush of pride in ownership, it would be exhausting and debilitating, and there would be no time for anything else.

What to do, then? It cannot simply be left there. If we have learned anything at all in this century, it is that all new technologies will be put to use, sooner or later, for better or worse, as it is in our nature to do. We cannot expect an exception for the instrumental conditioning of autonomic functions. We will be driven to make use of it, trying to communicate with our internal environment, to meddle, and it will consume so much of our energy that we will end up even more cut off from things outside, missing the main sources of the sensation of living.

I have a suggestion for a way out. Given the capacity to control autonomic functions, modulate brain waves, run cells, why shouldn't it be possible to employ exactly the same technology to go in precisely the opposite direction? Instead of getting in there and taking things over, couldn't we learn to disconnect altogether, uncouple, detach, and float free? You would only need to be careful, if you tried it, that you let go of the right end.

Of course, people have been trying to do this sort of thing for a long time, by other techniques and with varying degrees of luck. This is what Zen archery seems to be about, come to think of it. You learn, after long months of study under a master, to release the arrow without releasing it yourself. Your fingers must do the releasing, on their own, remotely, like the opening of a flower. When you have learned this, no matter where the arrow goes, you have it made. You can step outside for a look around.

CHAPTER FOURTEEN

Organelles as Organisms

WE SEEM TO BE LIVING THROUGH THE BIOLOGIC REVOLUTION, SO FAR anyway, without being upheaved or even much disturbed by it. Even without being entirely clear about just what it is, we are all learning to take it for granted. It is a curious, peaceful sort of revolution, in which there is no general apprehension that old views are being outraged and overturned. Instead, whole, great new blocks of information are being brought in almost daily and put precisely down in what were previously empty spaces. The news about DNA and the genetic code did not displace an earlier dogma; there was nothing much there to be moved aside. Molecular biology did not drive out older, fixed views about the intimate details of cell function. We seem to be starting at the beginning, from scratch.

We not only take it for granted—we tend to talk about the biologic revolution as though expecting to make profits from it, rather like a version of last century's industrial revolution. All sorts of revolutionary changes in technology are postulated for the future, ranging from final control of human disease to solutions of the world food and population problems. We are even beginning to argue about which futures we like and which we prefer to cancel. Questions about the merits of genetic engineering, the cloning of desirable human beings from single cells, and even, I suppose, the possibility that two heads might actually be better than one, are already being debated at seminars.

So far, we don't seem to have been really shocked by anything among the items of new knowledge. There is surprise, even astonishment, but not yet dismay. Perhaps it is still too early to expect this, and it may lie just ahead.

It is not too early to begin looking for trouble. I can sense some, for myself anyway, in what is being learned about organelles. I was raised in the belief that these were obscure little engines inside my cells, owned and operated by me or my cellular delegates, private, submicroscopic bits of my intelligent flesh. Now, it appears, some of them, and the most important ones at that, are total strangers.

The evidence is strong, and direct. The membranes lining the inner compartment of mitochondria are unlike other animal cell membranes, and resemble most closely the membranes of bacteria. The DNA of mitochondria is qualitatively different from the DNA of animal cell nuclei and strikingly similar to bacterial DNA; moreover, like microbial DNA, it is closely associated with membranes. The RNA of mitochondria matches the organelles' DNA, but not that of the nucleus. The ribosomes inside the mitochondria are similar to bacterial ribosomes, and different from animal ribosomes. The mitochondria do not arise *de novo* in cells; they are always there, replicating on their own, independently of the replication of the cell. They travel down from egg to newborn; a few come in with the sperm, but most are maternal passengers.

The chloroplasts in all plants are, similarly, independent and self-replicating lodgers, with their own DNA and RNA and ribosomes. In structure and pigment content they are the images of prokaryotic blue-green algae. It has recently been reported that the nucleic acid of chloroplasts is, in fact, homologous with that of certain photosynthetic microorganisms.

There may be more. It has been suggested that flagellae and cilia were once spirochetes that joined up with the other prokaryotes when nucleated cells were being pieced together. The centrioles and basal bodies are believed in some quarters to be semiautonomous organisms with their own separate genomes. Perhaps there are others, still unrecognized.

I only hope I can retain title to my nuclei.

It is surprising that we take information like this so calmly, as though it fitted in nicely with notions we've had all along. Actually, the suggestion that chloroplasts and mitochondria might be endosymbionts was made as long ago as 1885, but one might expect, nevertheless, that confirmation of the suggestion would have sent the investigators out into the streets, hallooing. But this is a sober, industrious field, and the work goes on methodically, with special interest just now in the molecular genetics of organelles. There is careful, restrained speculation on how they got there in the first place, with a consensus that they were probably engulfed by larger cells more than a billion years ago and have simply stayed there ever since.

The usual way of looking at them is as enslaved creatures, captured to supply ATP for cells unable to respire on their own, or to provide carbohydrate and oxygen for cells unequipped for photosynthesis. This master-slave arrangement is the common view of full-grown biologists, eukaryotes all. But there is the other side. From their own standpoint, the organelles might be viewed as having learned early how to have the best of possible worlds, with least effort and risk to themselves and their progeny. Instead of evolving as we have done, manufacturing longer and elaborately longer strands of DNA, and running ever-increasing risks of mutating into evolutionary cul-de-sacs, they elected to stay small and stick to one line of work. To accomplish this, and to assure themselves the longest possible run, they got themselves inside all the rest of us.

It is a good thing for the entire enterprise that mitochondria and chloroplasts have remained small, conservative, and stable, since these two organelles are, in a fundamental sense, the most important living things on earth. Between them they produce the oxygen and arrange for its use. In effect, they run the place.

My mitochondria comprise a very large proportion of me. I cannot do the calculation, but I suppose there is almost as much of them in sheer dry bulk as there is the rest of me. Looked at in this way, I could be taken for a very large, motile colony of respiring bacteria, operating a complex system of nuclei, microtubules, and neurons for the pleasure and sustenance of their families, and running, at the moment, a typewriter.

I am intimately involved, and obliged to do a great deal of essential work for my mitochondria. My nuclei code out the outer membranes of each, and a good many of the enzymes attached to the cristae must be synthesized by me. Each of them, by all accounts, makes only enough of its own materials to get along on, and the rest must come from me. And I am the one who has to do the worrying.

Now that I know about the situation, I can find all kinds of things to worry about. Viruses, for example. If my organelles are really symbiotic bacteria, colonizing me, what's to prevent them from catching a virus, or if they have such a thing as lysogeny, from conveying a phage to other organelles? Then there is the question of my estate. Do my mitochondria all die with me, or did my children get some of mine along with their mother's; this sort of thing should not worry me, I know, but it does.

Finally, there is the whole question of my identity, and, more than that, my human dignity. I did not mind it when I first learned of my descent from lower forms of life. I had in mind an arboreal family of beetle-browed, speechless, hairy sub-men, ape-like, and I've never objected to them as forebears. Indeed, being Welsh, I feel the better for it, having clearly risen above them in my time of evolution. It is a source of satisfaction to be part of the improvement of the species.

But not these things. I had never bargained on descent from single cells without nuclei. I could even make my peace with that, if it were all, but there is the additional humiliation that I have not, in a real sense, descended at all. I have brought them all along with me, or perhaps they have brought me.

It is no good standing on dignity in a situation like this, and better not to try. It is a mystery. There they are, moving about in my cytoplasm, breathing for my own flesh, but strangers. They are much less closely related to me than to each other and to the free-living bacteria out under the hill. They feel like strangers, but the thought comes that the same creatures, precisely the same, are out there in the cells of sea gulls, and whales, and dune grass, and seaweed, and hermit crabs, and further inland in the leaves of the beech in my backyard, and in the family of skunks beneath the back fence, and even in that fly on the window. Through them, I am connected; I have close relatives, once removed, all over the place. This is a new kind of information, for me, and I regret somewhat that I cannot be in closer touch with my mitochondria. If I concentrate, I can imagine that I feel them; they do not quite squirm, but there is, from time to time, a kind of tingle. I cannot help thinking that if only I knew more about them, and how they maintain our synchrony, I would have a new way to explain music to myself.

There is something intrinsically good-natured about all symbiotic relations, necessarily, but this one, which is probably the most ancient and most firmly established of all, seems especially equable. There is nothing resembling predation, and no pretense of an adversary stance on either side. If you were looking for something like natural law to take the place of the "social Darwinism" of a century ago, you would have a hard time drawing lessons from the sense of life alluded to by chloroplasts and mitochondria, but there it is.

CHAPTER FIFTEEN

Germs

WATCHING TELEVISION, YOU'D THINK WE LIVED AT BAY, IN TOTAL jeopardy, surrounded on all sides by human-seeking germs, shielded against infection and death only by a chemical technology that enables us to keep killing them off. We are instructed to spray disinfectants everywhere, into the air of our bedrooms and kitchens and with special energy into bathrooms, since it is our very own germs that seem the worst kind. We explode clouds of aerosol, mixed for good luck with deodorants, into our noses, mouths, underarms, privileged crannies — even into the intimate insides of our telephones. We apply potent antibiotics to minor scratches and seal them with plastic. Plastic is the new protector; we wrap the already plastic tumblers of hotels in more plastic, and seal the toilet seats like state secrets after irradiating them with ultraviolet light. We live in a world where the microbes are always trying to get at us, to tear us cell from cell, and we only stay alive and whole through diligence and fear.

We still think of human disease as the work of an organized, modernized kind of demonology, in which the bacteria are the most visible and centrally placed of our adversaries. We assume that they must somehow relish what they do. They come after us for profit, and there are so many of them that disease seems inevitable, a natural part of the human condition; if we succeed in eliminating one kind of disease there will always be a new one at hand, waiting to take its place.

These are paranoid delusions on a societal scale, explainable in part by our need for enemies, and in part by our memory of what things used to be like. Until a few decades ago, bacteria were a genuine household threat, and although most of us survived them, we were always aware of the nearness of death. We moved, with our families, in and out of death. We had lobar pneumonia, meningococcal meningitis, streptococcal infections, diphtheria, endocarditis, enteric fevers, various septicemias, syphilis, and, always, everywhere, tuberculosis. Most of these have now left most of us, thanks to antibiotics, plumbing, civilization, and money, but we remember.

In real life, however, even in our worst circumstances we have always been a relatively minor interest of the vast microbial world. Pathogenicity is not the rule. Indeed, it occurs so infrequently and involves such a relatively small number of species, considering the huge population of bacteria on the earth, that it has a freakish aspect. Disease usually results from inconclusive negotiations for symbiosis, an overstepping of the line by one side or the other, a biologic misinterpretation of borders.

Some bacteria are only harmful to us when they make exotoxins, and they only do this when they are, in a sense, diseased themselves. The toxins of diphtheria bacilli and streptococci are produced when the organisms have been infected by bacteriophage; it is the virus that provides the code for toxin. Uninfected bacteria are uninformed. When we catch diphtheria it is a virus infection, but not of us. Our involvement is not that of an adversary in a straightforward game, but more like blundering into someone else's accident.

I can think of a few microorganisms, possibly the tubercle bacillus, the syphilis spirochete, the malarial parasite, and a few others, that have a selective advantage in their ability to infect human beings, but there is nothing to be gained, in an evolutionary sense, by the capacity to cause illness or death. Pathogenicity may be something of a disadvantage for most microbes, carrying lethal risks more frightening to them than to us. The man who catches a meningococcus is in considerably less danger for his life, even without chemotherapy, than meningococci with the bad luck to catch a man. Most meningococci have the sense to stay out on the surface, in the rhinopharynx. During epidemics this is where they are to be found in the majority of the host population, and it generally goes well. It is only in the unaccountable minority, the "cases," that the line is crossed, and then there is the devil to pay on both sides, but most of all for the meningococci.

Staphylococci live all over us, and seem to have adapted to conditions in our skin that are uncongenial to most other bacteria. When you count them up, and us, it is remarkable how little trouble we have with the relation. Only a few of us are plagued by boils, and we can blame a large part of the destruction of tissues on the zeal of our own leukocytes. Hemolytic streptococci are among our closest intimates, even to the extent of sharing antigens with the membranes of our muscle cells; it is our reaction to their presence, in the form of rheumatic fever, that gets us into trouble. We can carry brucella for long periods in the cells of our reticuloendothelial system without any awareness of their existence; then cyclically, for reasons not understood but probably related to immunologic reactions on our part, we sense them, and the reaction of sensing is the clinical disease.

Most bacteria are totally preoccupied with browsing, altering the configurations of organic molecules so that they become usable for the energy needs of other forms of life. They are, by and large, indispensable to each other, living in interdependent communities in the soil or sea. Some have become symbionts in more specialized, local relations, living as working parts in the tissues of higher organisms. The root nodules of legumes would have neither form nor function without the masses of rhizobial bacteria swarming into root hairs, incorporating themselves with such intimacy that only an electron microscope can detect which membranes are bacterial and which plant. Insects have colonies of bacteria, the mycetocytes, living in them like little glands, doing heaven knows what but being essential. The microfloras of animal intestinal tracts are part of the nutritional system. And then, of course, there are the mitochondria and chloroplasts, permanent residents in everything.

The microorganisms that seem to have it in for us in the worst way — the ones that really appear to wish us ill — turn out on close examination to be rather more like bystanders, strays, strangers in from the cold. They will invade and replicate if given the chance, and some of them will get into our deepest tissues and set forth in the blood, but it is our response to their presence that makes the disease. Our arsenals for fighting off bacteria are so powerful, and involve so many different defense mechanisms, that we are in more danger from them than from the invaders. We live in the midst of explosive devices; we are mined.

It is the information carried by the bacteria that we cannot abide.

The gram-negative bacteria are the best examples of this. They display lipopolysaccharide endotoxin in their walls, and these macromolecules are read by our tissues as the very worst of bad news. When we sense lipopolysaccharide, we are likely to turn on every defense at our disposal; we will bomb, defoliate, blockade, seal off, and destroy all the tissues in the area. Leukocytes become more actively phagocytic, release lysosomal enzymes, turn sticky, and aggregate together in dense masses, occluding capillaries and shutting off the blood supply. Complement is switched on at the right point in its sequence to release chemotactic signals, calling in leukocytes from everywhere. Vessels become hyperreactive to epinephrine so that physiologic concentrations suddenly possess necrotizing properties. Pyrogen is released from leukocytes, adding fever to hemorrhage, necrosis, and shock. It is a shambles.

All of this seems unnecessary, panic-driven. There is nothing intrinsically poisonous about endotoxin, but it must look awful, or feel awful, when sensed by cells. Cells believe that it signifies the presence of gram-negative bacteria, and they will stop at nothing to avoid this threat.

I used to think that only the most highly developed, civilized animals could be fooled in this way, but it is not so. The horseshoe crab is a primitive fossil of a beast, ancient and uncitified, but he is just as vulnerable to disorganization by endotoxin as a rabbit or a man. Bang has shown that an injection of a very small dose into the body cavity will cause the aggregation of hemocytes in ponderous, immovable masses that block the vascular channels, and a gelatinous clot brings the circulation to a standstill. It is now known that a limulus clotting system, perhaps ancestral to ours, is centrally involved in the reaction. Extracts of the hemocytes can be made to jell by adding extremely small amounts of endotoxin. The self-disintegration of the whole animal that follows a systemic injection can be interpreted as a well-intentioned but lethal error. The mechanism is itself quite a good one, when used with precision and restraint, admirably designed for coping with intrusion by a single bacterium: the hemocyte would be attracted to the site, extrude the coagulable protein, the microorganism would be entrapped and immobilized, and the thing would be finished. It is when confronted by the overwhelming signal of free molecules of endotoxin, evoking memories of vibrios in great numbers, that the limulus flies into panic, launches all his defenses at once, and destroys himself.

It is, basically, a response to propaganda, something like the panic-producing pheromones that slave-taking ants release to disorganize the colonies of their prey.

I think it likely that many of our diseases work in this way. Sometimes, the mechanisms used for overkill are immunologic, but often, as in the limulus model, they are more primitive kinds of memory. We tear ourselves to pieces because of symbols, and we are more vulnerable to this than to any host of predators. We are, in effect, at the mercy of our own Pentagons, most of the time.

CHAPTER SIXTEEN

Your Very Good

Health

WE SPEND $80 BILLION A YEAR ON HEALTH, AS WE KEEP REMINDING ourselves, or is it now $90 billion? Whichever, it is a shocking sum, and just to mention it is to suggest the presence of a vast, powerful enterprise, intricately organized and coordinated. It is, however, a bewildering, essentially scatterbrained kind of business, expanding steadily without being planned or run by anyone in particular. Whatever sum we spent last year was only discovered after we'd spent it, and nobody can be sure what next year's bill will be. The social scientists, attracted by problems of this magnitude, are beginning to swarm in from all quarters to take a closer look, and the economists are all over the place, pursing their lips and shaking their heads, shipping more and more data off to the computers, trying to decide whether this is a proper industry or a house of IBM cards. There doesn't seem to be any doubt about the amount of money being spent, but it is less certain where it goes, and for what.

It has become something of a convenience to refer to the whole endeavor as the "Health Industry." This provides the illusion that it is in a general way all one thing, and that it turns out, on demand, a single, unambiguous product, which is health. Thus, health care has become the new name for medicine. Health-care delivery is what doctors now do, along with hospitals and the other professionals who work with doctors, now known collectively as the health providers. The patients have become health consumers. Once you start on this line, there's no stopping. Just recently, to correct some of the various flaws, inequities, logistic defects, and near-bankruptcies in today's health-care delivery system, the government has officially invented new institutions called Health Maintenance Organizations, already known familiarly as HMO's, spreading out across the country like post offices, ready to distribute in neat packages, as though from a huge, newly stocked inventory, health.

Sooner or later, we are bound to get into trouble with this word. It is too solid and unequivocal a term to be used as a euphemism and this seems to be what we are attempting. I am worried that we may be overdoing it, taxing its meaning, to conceal an unmentionable reality that we've somehow agreed not to talk about in public. It won't work. Illness and death still exist and cannot be hidden. We are still beset by plain diseases, and we do not control them; they are loose on their own, afflicting us unpredictably and haphazardly. We are only able to deal with them when they have made their appearance, and we must use the methods of medical care for this, as best we can, for better or worse.

It would be a better world if this were not true, but the fact is that diseases do not develop just because of carelessness about the preservation of health. We do not become sick only because of a failure of vigilance. Most illnesses, especially the major ones, are blind accidents that we have no idea how to prevent. We are really not all that good at preventing disease or preserving health—not yet anyway—and we are not likely to be until we have learned a great deal about disease mechanisms.

There is disagreement on this point, of course. Some of the believers among us are convinced that once we get a health-care delivery system that really works, the country might become a sort of gigantic spa, offering, like the labels on European mineral-water bottles, preventives for everything from weak kidneys to moroseness.

It is a surprise that we haven't already learned that the word is a fallible incantation. Several decades of mental health have not made schizophrenia go away, nor has it been established that a community mental-health center can yet maintain the mental health of a community. These admirable institutions are demonstrably useful for the management of certain forms of mental disease, but that is another matter.

My complaint about the terms is that they sound too much like firm promises. A Health Maintenance Organization, if well organized and financed, will have the best features of a clinic and hospital and should be of value to any community, but the people will expect it to live up to its new name. It will become, with the sign over its door, an official institution for the distribution of health, and if intractable heart disease develops in anyone thereafter, as it surely will (or multiple sclerosis, or rheumatoid arthritis, or the majority of cancers that can neither be prevented nor cured, or chronic nephritis, or stroke, or moroseness), the people will begin looking sidelong and asking questions in a low voice.

Meanwhile, we are paying too little attention, and respect, to the built-in durability and sheer power of the human organism. Its surest tendency is toward stability and balance. It is a distortion, with something profoundly disloyal about it, to picture the human being as a teetering, fallible contraption, always needing watching and patching, always on the verge of flapping to pieces; this is the doctrine that people hear most often, and most eloquently, on all our information media. We ought to be developing a much better system for general education about human health, with more curricular time for acknowledgment, and even some celebration, of the absolute marvel of good health that is the real lot of most of us, most of the time.

The familiar questions about the needs of the future in medicine are still before us. What items should be available, optimally, in an ideal health-care delivery system? How do you estimate the total need, per patient per year, for doctors, nurses, drugs, laboratory tests, hospital beds, x-rays, and so forth, in the best of rational worlds? My suggestion for a new way to develop answers is to examine, in detail, the ways in which the various parts of today's medical-care technology are used, from one day to the next, by the most sophisticated, knowledgeable, and presumably satisfied consumers who now have full access to the system—namely, the well-trained, experienced, middle-aged, married-with-family internists.

I could design the questionnaire myself, I think. How many times in the last five years have the members of your family, including yourself, had any kind of laboratory test? How many complete physical examinations? X-rays? Electrocardiograms? How often, in a year's turning, have you prescribed antibiotics of any kind for yourself or your family? How many hospitalizations? How much surgery? How many consultations with a psychiatrist? How many formal visits to a doctor, any doctor, including yourself?

I will bet that if you got this kind of information, and added everything up, you would find a quite different set of figures from the ones now being projected in official circles for the population at large. I have tried it already, in an unscientific way, by asking around among my friends. My data, still soft but fairly consistent, reveal that none of my internist friends have had a routine physical examination since military service; very few have been x-rayed except by dentists; almost all have resisted surgery; laboratory tests for anyone in the family are extremely rare. They use a lot of aspirin, but they seem to write very few prescriptions and almost never treat family fever with antibiotics. This is not to say that they do not become ill; these families have the same incidence of chiefly respiratory and gastrointestinal illness as everyone else, the same number of anxieties and bizarre notions, and the same number — on balance, a small number — of frightening or devastating diseases.

It will be protested that internists and their households are really full-time captive patients and cannot fairly be compared to the rest of the population. As each member of the family appears at the breakfast table, the encounter is, in effect, a house-call. The father is, in the liveliest sense, a family doctor. This is true, but all the more reason for expecting optimal use to be made of the full range of medicine's technology. There is no problem of access, the entire health-care delivery system is immediately at hand, and the cost of all items is surely less than that for nonmedical families. All the usual constraints that limit the use of medical care by the general population are absent.

If my hunch, based on the small sample of professional friends, is correct, these people appear to use modern medicine quite differently from the ways in which we have systematically been educating the public over the last few decades. It cannot be explained away as an instance of shoemakers' children going without shoes. Doctors' families do tend to complain that they receive less medical attention than their friends and neighbors, but they seem a normal, generally healthy lot, with a remarkably low incidence of iatrogenic illness.

The great secret, known to internists and learned early in marriage by internists' wives, but still hidden from the general public, is that most things get better by themselves. Most things, in fact, are better by morning.

It is conceivable that we might be able to provide good medical care for everyone needing it, in a new system designed to assure equity, provided we can restrain ourselves, or our computers, from designing a system in which all 200 million of us are assumed to be in constant peril of failed health every day of our lives. In the same sense that our judicial system presumes us to be innocent until proved guilty, a medical-care system may work best if it starts with the presumption that most people are healthy. Left to themselves, computers may try to do it in the opposite way, taking it as given that some sort of direct, continual, professional intervention is required all the time to maintain the health of each citizen, and we will end up spending all our money on nothing but that. Meanwhile, there is a long list of other things to do if we are to change the way we live together, especially in our cities, in time. Social health is another kind of problem, more complex and urgent, and there will be other bills to pay.

CHAPTER SEVENTEEN

Social Talk

NOT ALL SOCIAL ANIMALS ARE SOCIAL WITH THE SAME DEGREE OF commitment. In some species, the members are so tied to each other and interdependent as to seem the loosely conjoined cells of a tissue. The social insects are like this; they move, and live all their lives, in a mass; a beehive is a spherical animal. In other species, less compulsively social, the members make their homes together, pool resources, travel in packs or schools, and share the food, but any single one can survive solitary, detached from the rest. Others are social only in the sense of being more or less congenial, meeting from time to time in committees, using social gatherings as *ad hoc* occasions for feeding and breeding. Some animals simply nod at each other in passing, never reaching even a first-name relationship.

It is not a simple thing to decide where we fit, for at one time or another in our lives we manage to organize in every imaginable social arrangement. We are as interdependent, especially in our cities, as bees or ants, yet we can detach if we wish and go live alone in the woods, in theory anyway. We feed and look after each other, constructing elaborate systems for this, even including vending machines to dispense ice cream in gas stations, but we also have numerous books to tell us how to live off the land. We cluster in family groups, but we tend, unpredictably, to turn on each other and fight as if we were different species. Collectively, we hanker to accumulate all the information in the universe and distribute it around among ourselves as though it were a kind of essential foodstuff, ant-fashion (the faintest trace of real news in science has the action of a pheromone, lifting the hairs of workers in laboratories at the ends of the earth), but each of us also builds a private store of his own secret knowledge and hides it away like untouchable treasure. We have names to label each as self, and we believe without reservation that this system of taxonomy will guarantee the entity, the absolute separateness of each of us, but the mechanism has no discernible function in the center of a crowded city; we are essentially nameless, most of our time.

Nobody wants to think that the rapidly expanding mass of mankind, spreading out over the surface of the earth, blackening the ground, bears any meaningful resemblance to the life of an anthill or a hive. Who would consider for a moment that the more than 3 billion of us are a sort of stupendous animal when we become linked together? We are not mindless, nor is our day-to-day behavior coded out to the last detail by our genomes, nor do we seem to be engaged together, compulsively, in any single, universal, stereotyped task analogous to the construction of a nest. If we were ever to put all our brains together in fact, to make a common mind the way the ants do, it would be an unthinkable thought, way over our heads.

Social animals tend to keep at a particular thing, generally something huge for their size; they work at it ceaselessly under genetic instructions and genetic compulsion, using it to house the species and protect it, assuring permanence.

There are, to be sure, superficial resemblances in some of the things we do together, like building glass and plastic cities on all the land and farming under the sea, or assembling in armies, or landing samples of ourselves on the moon, or sending memoranda into the next galaxy. We do these together without being quite sure why, but we can stop doing one thing and move to another whenever we like. We are not committed or bound by our genes to stick to one activity forever, like the wasps. Today's behavior is no more fixed than when we tumbled out over Europe to build cathedrals in the twelfth century. At that time we were convinced that it would go on forever, that this was the way to live, but it was not; indeed, most of us have already forgotten what it was all about. Anything we do in this transient, secondary social way, compulsively and with all our energies but only for a brief period of our history, cannot be counted as social behavior in the biological sense. If we can turn it on and off, on whims, it isn't likely that our genes are providing the detailed instructions. Constructing Chartres was good for our minds, but we found that our lives went on, and it is no more likely that we will find survival in Rome plows or laser bombs, or rapid mass transport or a Mars lander, or solar power, or even synthetic protein. We do tend to improvise things like this as we go along, but it is clear that we can pick and choose.

For practical purposes, it would probably be best for us not to be biologically social, in the long run. Not that we have a choice, of course, or even a vote. It would not be good news to learn that we are all roped together intellectually, droning away at some featureless, genetically driven collective work, building something so immense that we can never see the outlines. It seems especially hard, even perilous, for this to be the burden of a species with the unique attribute of speech, and argument. Leave this kind of life to the insects and birds, and lesser mammals, and fish.

But there is just that one thing. About human speech.

It begins to look, more and more disturbingly, as if the gift of language is the single human trait that marks us all genetically, setting us apart from all the rest of life. Language is, like nest-building or hive-making, the universal and biologically specific activity of human beings. We engage in it communally, compulsively, and automatically. We cannot be human without it; if we were to be separated from it our minds would die, as surely as bees lost from the hive.

We are born knowing how to use language. The capacity to recognize syntax, to organize and deploy words into intelligible sentences, is innate in the human mind. We are programmed to identify patterns and generate grammar. There are invariant and variable structures in speech that are common to all of us. As chicks are endowed with an innate capacity to read information in the shapes of overhanging shadows, telling hawk from other birds, we can identify the meaning of grammar in a string of words, and we are born this way. According to Chomsky, who has examined it as a biologist looks at live tissue, language "must simply be a biological property of the human mind." The universal attributes of language are genetically set; we do not learn them, or make them up as we go along.

We work at this all our lives, and collectively we give it life, but we do not exert the least control over language, not as individuals or committees or academies or governments. Language, once it comes alive, behaves like an active, motile organism. Parts of it are always being changed, by a ceaseless activity to which all of us are committed; new words are invented and inserted, old ones have their meaning altered or abandoned. New ways of stringing words and sentences together come into fashion and vanish again, but the underlying structure simply grows, enriches itself, expands. Individual languages age away and seem to die, but they leave progeny all over the place. Separate languages can exist side by side for centuries without touching each other, maintaining their integrity with the vigor of incompatible tissues. At other times, two languages may come together, fuse, replicate, and give rise to nests of new tongues.

If language is at the core of our social existence, holding us together, housing us in meaning, it may also be safe to say that art and music are functions of the same universal, genetically determined mechanism. These are not bad things to do together. If we are social creatures because of this, and therefore like ants, I for one (or should I say we for one?) do not mind.

CHAPTER EIGHTEEN

Information

ACCORDING TO THE LINGUISTIC SCHOOL CURRENTLY ON TOP, HUMAN beings are all born with a genetic endowment for recognizing and formulating language. This must mean that we possess genes for all kinds of information, with strands of special, peculiarly human DNA for the discernment of meaning in syntax. We must imagine the morphogenesis of deep structures, built into our minds, for coding out, like proteins, the parts of speech. Correct grammar (correct in the logical, not fashionable, sense) is as much a biologic characteristic of our species as feathers on birds.

If this is true, it would mean that the human mind is preset, in some primary sense, to generate more than just the parts of speech. Since everything else that we recognize as human behavior derives from the central mechanism of language, the same sets of genes are at least indirectly responsible for governing such astonishing behavior as in the concert hall, where hundreds of people crowd together, silent, head-tilted, meditating, listening to music as though receiving instructions, or in a gallery, moving along slowly, peering, never looking at each other, concentrating as though reading directions.

This view of things is compatible with the very old notion that a framework for meaning is somehow built into our minds at birth. We start our lives with templates, and attach to them, as we go along, various things that fit. There are neural centers for generating, spontaneously, numberless hypotheses about the facts of life. We store up information the way cells store energy. When we are lucky enough to find a direct match between a receptor and a fact, there is a deep explosion in the mind; the idea suddenly enlarges, rounds up, bursts with new energy, and begins to replicate. At times there are chains of reverberating explosions, shaking everything: the imagination, as we say, is staggered.

This system seems to be restricted to human beings, since we are the only beings with language, although chimpanzees may have the capability of manipulating symbols with a certain syntax. The great difference between us and the other animals may be the qualitative difference made by speech. We live by making transformations of energy into words, storing it up, and releasing it in controlled explosions.

Speechless animals cannot do this sort of thing, and they are limited to single-stage transactions. They wander, as we do, searching for facts to fit their sparser stock of hypotheses, but when the receptor meets its match, there is only a single thud. Without language, the energy that is encoiled, springlike, inside information can only be used once. The solitary wasp, Sphex, nearing her time of eggs, travels aloft with a single theory about caterpillars. She is, in fact, a winged receptor for caterpillars. Finding one to match the hypothesis, she swoops, pins it, paralyzes it, carries it off, and descends to deposit it precisely in front of the door of the round burrow (which, obsessed by a different version of the same theory, she had prepared beforehand). She drops the beast, enters the burrow, inspects the interior for last-minute irregularities, then comes out to pull it in for the egg-laying. It has the orderly, stepwise look of a well-thought-out business. But if, while she is inside inspecting, you move the caterpillar a short distance, she has a less sensible second thought about the matter. She emerges, searches for a moment, finds it, drags it back to the original spot, drops it again, and runs inside to check the burrow again. If you move the caterpillar again, she will repeat the program, and you can keep her totally preoccupied for as long as you have the patience and the heart for it. It is a compulsive, essentially neurotic kind of behavior, as mindless as an Ionesco character, but the wasp cannot imagine any other way of doing the thing.

Lymphocytes, like wasps, are genetically programmed for exploration, but each of them seems to be permitted a different, solitary idea. They roam through the tissues, sensing and monitoring. Since there are so many of them, they can make collective guesses at almost anything antigenic on the surface of the earth, but they must do their work one notion at a time. They carry specific information in their surface receptors, presented in the form of a question: is there, anywhere out there, my particular molecular configuration? It seems to be in the nature of biologic information that it not only stores itself up as energy but also instigates a search for more. It is an insatiable mechanism.

Lymphocytes are apparently informed about everything foreign around them, and some of them come equipped for fitting with polymers that do not exist until organic chemists synthesize them in their laboratories. The cells can do more than predict reality; they are evidently programmed with wild guesses as well.

Not all animals have lymphocytes with the same range of information, as you might expect. As with language, the system is governed by genes, and there are genetic differences between species and between inbred animals of the same species. There are polymers that will fit the receptors of one line of guinea pigs or mice but not others; there are responders and nonresponders.

When the connection is made, and a particular lymphocyte with a particular receptor is brought into the presence of the particular antigen, one of the greatest small spectacles in nature occurs. The cell enlarges, begins making new DNA at a great rate, and turns into what is termed, appropriately, a blast. It then begins dividing, replicating itself into a new colony of identical cells, all labeled with the same receptor, primed with the same question. The new cluster is a memory, nothing less.

For this kind of mechanism to be useful, the cells are required to stick precisely to the point. Any ambiguity, any tendency to wander from the matter at hand, will introduce grave hazards for the cells, and even more for the host in which they live. Minor inaccuracies may cause reactions in which neighboring cells are recognized as foreign, and done in. There is a theory that the process of aging may be due to the cumulative effect of imprecision, a gradual degrading of information. It is not a system that allows for deviating.

Perhaps it is in this respect that language differs most sharply from other biologic systems for communication. Ambiguity seems to be an essential, indispensable element for the transfer of information from one place to another by words, where matters of real importance are concerned. It is often necessary, for meaning to come through, that there be an almost vague sense of strangeness and askewness. Speechless animals and cells cannot do this. The specifically locked-on antigen at the surface of a lymphocyte does not send the cell off in search of something totally different; when a bee is tracking sugar by polarized light, observing the sun as though consulting his watch, he does not veer away to discover an unimaginable marvel of a flower. Only the human mind is designed to work in this way, programmed to drift away in the presence of locked-on information, straying from each point in a hunt for a better, different point.

If it were not for the capacity for ambiguity, for the sensing of strangeness, that words in all languages provide, we would have no way of recognizing the layers of counterpoint in meaning, and we might be spending all our time sitting on stone fences, staring into the sun. To be sure, we would always have had some everyday use to make of the alphabet, and we might have reached the same capacity for small talk, but it is unlikely that we would have been able to evolve from words to Bach. The great thing about human language is that it prevents us from sticking to the matter at hand.

CHAPTER NINETEEN

Death in the Open

MOST OF THE DEAD ANIMALS YOU SEE ON HIGHWAYS NEAR THE CITIES are dogs, a few cats. Out in the countryside, the forms and coloring of the dead are strange; these are the wild creatures. Seen from a car window they appear as fragments, evoking memories of woodchucks, badgers, skunks, voles, snakes, sometimes the mysterious wreckage of a deer.

It is always a queer shock, part a sudden upwelling of grief, part unaccountable amazement. It is simply astounding to see an animal dead on a highway. The outrage is more than just the location; it is the impropriety of such visible death, anywhere. You do not expect to see dead animals in the open. It is the nature of animals to die alone, off somewhere, hidden. It is wrong to see them lying out on the highway; it is wrong to see them anywhere.

Everything in the world dies, but we only know about it as a kind of abstraction. If you stand in a meadow, at the edge of a hillside, and look around carefully, almost everything you can catch sight of is in the process of dying, and most things will be dead long before you are. If it were not for the constant renewal and replacement going on before your eyes, the whole place would turn to stone and sand under your feet.

There are some creatures that do not seem to die at all; they simply vanish totally into their own progeny. Single cells do this. The cell becomes two, then four, and so on, and after a while the last trace is gone. It cannot be seen as death; barring mutation, the descendants are simply the first cell, living all over again. The cycles of the slime mold have episodes that seem as conclusive as death, but the withered slug, with its stalk and fruiting body, is plainly the transient tissue of a developing animal; the free-swimming amebocytes use this organ collectively in order to produce more of themselves.

There are said to be a billion billion insects on the earth at any moment, most of them with very short life expectancies by our standards. Someone has estimated that there are 25 million assorted insects hanging in the air over every temperate square mile, in a column extending upward for thousands of feet, drifting through the layers of the atmosphere like plankton. They are dying steadily, some by being eaten, some just dropping in their tracks, tons of them around the earth, disintegrating as they die, invisibly.

Who ever sees dead birds, in anything like the huge numbers stipulated by the certainty of the death of all birds? A dead bird is an incongruity, more startling than an unexpected live bird, sure evidence to the human mind that something has gone wrong. Birds do their dying off somewhere, behind things, under things, never on the wing.

Animals seem to have an instinct for performing death alone, hidden. Even the largest, most conspicuous ones find ways to conceal themselves in time. If an elephant missteps and dies in an open place, the herd will not leave him there; the others will pick him up and carry the body from place to place, finally putting it down in some inexplicably suitable location. When elephants encounter the skeleton of an elephant out in the open, they methodically take up each of the bones and distribute them, in a ponderous ceremony, over neighboring acres.

It is a natural marvel. All of the life of the earth dies, all of the time, in the same volume as the new life that dazzles us each morning, each spring. All we see of this is the odd stump, the fly struggling on the porch floor of the summer house in October, the fragment on the highway. I have lived all my life with an embarrassment of squirrels in my backyard, they are all over the place, all year long, and I have never seen, anywhere, a dead squirrel.

I suppose it is just as well. If the earth were otherwise, and all the dying were done in the open, with the dead there to be looked at, we would never have it out of our minds. We can forget about it much of the time, or think of it as an accident to be avoided, somehow. But it does make the process of dying seem more exceptional than it really is, and harder to engage in at the times when we must ourselves engage.

In our way, we conform as best we can to the rest of nature. The obituary pages tell us of the news that we are dying away, while the birth announcements in finer print, off at the side of the page, inform us of our replacements, but we get no grasp from this of the enormity of scale. There are 3 billion of us on the earth, and all 3 billion must be dead, on a schedule, within this lifetime. The vast mortality, involving something over 50 million of us each year, takes place in relative secrecy. We can only really know of the deaths in our households, or among our friends. These, detached in our minds from all the rest, we take to be unnatural events, anomalies, outrages. We speak of our own dead in low voices; struck down, we say, as though visible death can only occur for cause, by disease or violence, avoidably. We send off for flowers, grieve, make ceremonies, scatter bones, unaware of the rest of the 3 billion on the same schedule. All of that immense mass of flesh and bone and consciousness will disappear by absorption into the earth, without recognition by the transient survivors.

Less than a half century from now, our replacements will have more than doubled the numbers. It is hard to see how we can continue to keep the secret, with such multitudes doing the dying. We will have to give up the notion that death is catastrophe, or detestable, or avoidable, or even strange. We will need to learn more about the cycling of life in the rest of the system, and about our connection to the process. Everything that comes alive seems to be in trade for something that dies, cell for cell. There might be some comfort in the recognition of synchrony, in the information that we all go down together, in the best of company.

CHAPTER TWENTY

Natural Science

THE ESSENTIAL WILDNESS OF SCIENCE AS A MANIFESTATION OF HUMAN behavior is not generally perceived. As we extract new things of value from it, we also keep discovering parts of the activity that seem in need of better control, more efficiency, less unpredictability. We'd like to pay less for it and get our money's worth on some more orderly, businesslike schedule. The Washington planners are trying to be helpful in this, and there are new programs for the centralized organization of science all over the place, especially in the biomedical field.

It needs thinking about. There is an almost ungovernable, biologic mechanism at work in scientific behavior at its best, and this should not be overlooked.

The difficulties are more conspicuous when the problems are very hard and complicated and the facts not yet in. Solutions cannot be arrived at for problems of this sort until the science has been lifted through a preliminary, turbulent zone of outright astonishment. Therefore, what must be planned for, in the laboratories engaged in the work, is the totally unforeseeable. If it is centrally organized, the system must be designed primarily for the elicitation of disbelief and the celebration of surprise.

Moreover, the whole scientific enterprise must be arranged so that the separate imaginations in different human minds can be pooled, and this is more a kind of game than a systematic business. It is in the abrupt, unaccountable aggregation of random notions, intuitions, known in science as good ideas, that the high points are made.

The most mysterious aspect of difficult science is the way it is done. Not the routine, not just the fitting together of things that no one had guessed at fitting, not the making of connections; these are merely the workaday details, the methods of operating. They are interesting, but not as fascinating as the central mystery, which is that we do it at all, and that we do it under such compulsion.

I don't know of any other human occupation, even including what I have seen of art, in which the people engaged in it are so caught up, so totally preoccupied, so driven beyond their strength and resources.

Scientists at work have the look of creatures following genetic instructions; they seem to be under the influence of a deeply placed human instinct. They are, despite their efforts at dignity, rather like young animals engaged in savage play. When they are near to an answer their hair stands on end, they sweat, they are awash in their own adrenalin. To grab the answer, and grab it first, is for them a more powerful drive than feeding or breeding or protecting themselves against the elements.

It sometimes looks like a lonely activity, but it is as much the opposite of lonely as human behavior can be. There is nothing so social, so communal, so interdependent. An active field of science is like an immense intellectual anthill; the individual almost vanishes into the mass of minds tumbling over each other, carrying information from place to place, passing it around at the speed of light.

There are special kinds of information that seem to be chemotactic. As soon as a trace is released, receptors at the back of the neck are caused to tremble, there is a massive convergence of motile minds flying upwind on a gradient of surprise, crowding around the source. It is an infiltration of intellects, an inflammation.

There is nothing to touch the spectacle. In the midst of what seems a collective derangement of minds in total disorder, with bits of information being scattered about, torn to shreds, disintegrated, reconstituted, engulfed, in a kind of activity that seems as random and agitated as that of bees in a disturbed part of the hive, there suddenly emerges, with the purity of a slow phrase of music, a single new piece of truth about nature.

In short, it works. It is the most powerful and productive of the things human beings have learned to do together in many centuries, more effective than farming, or hunting and fishing, or building cathedrals, or making money.

It is instinctive behavior, in my view, and I do not understand how it works. It cannot be prearranged in any precise way; the minds cannot be lined up in tidy rows and given directions from printed sheets. You cannot get it done by instructing each mind to make this or that piece, for central committees to fit with the pieces made by other instructed minds. It does not work this way.

What it needs is for the air to be made right. If you want a bee to make honey, you do not issue protocols on solar navigation or carbohydrate chemistry, you put him together with other bees (and you'd better do this quickly, for solitary bees do not stay alive) and you do what you can to arrange the general environment around the hive. If the air is right, the science will come in its own season, like pure honey.

There is something like aggression in the activity, but it differs from other forms of aggressive behavior in having no sort of destruction as the objective. While it is going on, it looks and feels like aggression: get at it, uncover it, bring it out, grab it, it's mine! It is like a primitive running hunt, but there is nothing at the end of it to be injured. More probably, the end is a sigh. But then, if the air is right and the science is going well, the sigh is immediately interrupted, there is a yawping new question, and the wild, tumbling activity begins once more, out of control all over again.

CHAPTER TWENTY-ONE

Natural Man

THE SOCIAL SCIENTISTS, ESPECIALLY THE ECONOMISTS, ARE MOVING deeply into ecology and the environment these days, with disquieting results. It goes somehow against the grain to learn that cost-benefit analyses can be done neatly on lakes, meadows, nesting gannets, even whole oceans. It is hard enough to confront the environmental options ahead, and the hard choices, but even harder when the price tags are so visible. Even the new jargon is disturbing: it hurts the spirit, somehow, to read the word *environments,* when the plural means that there are so many alternatives there to be sorted through, as in a market, and voted on. Economists need cool heads and cold hearts for this sort of work, and they must write in icy, often skiddy prose.

The degree to which we are all involved in the control of the earth's life is just beginning to dawn on most of us, and it means another revolution for human thought.

This will not come easily. We've just made our way through inconclusive revolutions on the same topic, trying to make up our minds how we feel about nature. As soon as we arrived at one kind of consensus, like an enormous committee, we found it was time to think it through all over, and now here we are, at it again.

The oldest, easiest-to-swallow idea was that the earth was man's personal property, a combination of garden, zoo, bank vault, and energy source, placed at our disposal to be consumed, ornamented, or pulled apart as we wished. The betterment of mankind was, as we understood it, the whole point of the thing. Mastery over nature, mystery and all, was a moral duty and social obligation.

In the last few years we were wrenched away from this way of looking at it, and arrived at something like general agreement that we had it wrong. We still argue the details, but it is conceded almost everywhere that we are not the masters of nature that we thought ourselves; we are as dependent on the rest of life as are the leaves or midges or fish. We are part of the system. One way to put it is that the earth is a loosely formed, spherical organism, with all its working parts linked in symbiosis. We are, in this view, neither owners nor operators; at best, we might see ourselves as motile tissue specialized for receiving information — perhaps, in the best of all possible worlds, functioning as a nervous system for the whole being.

There is, for some, too much dependency in this view, and they prefer to see us as a separate, qualitatively different, special species, unlike any other form of life, despite the sharing around of genes, enzymes, and organelles. No matter, there is still the underlying idea that we cannot have a life of our own without concern for the ecosystem in which we live, whether in majesty or not. This idea has been strong enough to launch the new movements for the sustenance of wilderness, the protection of wildlife, the turning off of insatiable technologies, the preservation of "whole earth."

But now, just when the new view seems to be taking hold, we may be in for another wrench, this time more dismaying and unsettling than anything we've come through. In a sense, we shall be obliged to swing back again, still believing in the new way but constrained by the facts of life to live in the old. It may be too late, as things have turned out.

We are, in fact, the masters, like it or not.

It is a despairing prospect. Here we are, practically speaking twenty-first-century mankind, filled to exuberance with our new understanding of kinship to all the family of life, and here we are, still nineteenth-century man, walking bootshod over the open face of nature, subjugating and civilizing it. And we cannot stop this controlling, unless we vanish under the hill ourselves. If there were such a thing as a world mind, it should crack over this.

The truth is, we have become more deeply involved than we ever dreamed. The fact that we sit around as we do, worrying seriously about how best to preserve the life of the earth, is itself the sharpest measure of our involvement. It is not human arrogance that has taken us in this direction, but the most natural of natural events. We developed this way, we grew this way, we are this kind of species.

We have become, in a painful, unwished-for way, nature itself. We have grown into everywhere, spreading like a new growth over the entire surface, touching and affecting every other kind of life, *incorporating* ourselves. The earth risks being eutrophied by us. We are now the dominant feature of our own environment. Humans, large terrestrial metazoans, fired by energy from microbial symbionts lodged in their cells, instructed by tapes of nucleic acid stretching back to the earliest live membranes, informed by neurons essentially the same as all the other neurons on earth, sharing structures with mastodons and lichens, living off the sun, are now in charge, running the place, for better or worse.

Or is it really this way? It could be, you know, just the other way around. Perhaps we are the invaded ones, the subjugated, used.

Certain animals in the sea live by becoming part-animal, part-plant. They engulf algae, which then establish themselves as complex plant tissues, essential for the life of the whole company. I suppose the giant clam, if he had more of a mind, would have moments of dismay on seeing what he has done to the plant world, incorporating so much of it, enslaving green cells, living off the photosynthesis. But the plant cells would take a different view of it, having captured the clam on the most satisfactory of terms, including the small lenses in his tissues that focus sunlight for their benefit; perhaps algae have bad moments about what they may collectively be doing to the world of clams.

With luck, our own situation might be similar, on a larger scale. This might turn out to be a special phase in the morphogenesis of the earth when it is necessary to have something like us, for a time anyway, to fetch and carry energy, look after new symbiotic arrangements, store up information for some future season, do a certain amount of ornamenting, maybe even carry seeds around the solar system. That kind of thing. Handyman for the earth.

I would much prefer this useful role, if I had any say, to the essentially unearthly creature we seem otherwise on the way to becoming. It would mean making some quite fundamental changes in our attitudes toward each other, if we were really to think of ourselves as indispensable elements of nature. We would surely become the environment to worry about the most. We would discover, in ourselves, the sources of wonderment and delight that we have discerned in all other manifestations of nature. Who knows, we might even acknowledge the fragility and vulnerability that always accompany high specialization in biology, and movements might start up for the protection of ourselves as a valuable, endangered species. We couldn't lose.

CHAPTER TWENTY-TWO

The Iks

THE SMALL TRIBE OF IKS, FORMERLY NOMADIC HUNTERS AND gatherers in the mountain valleys of northern Uganda, have become celebrities, literary symbols for the ultimate fate of disheartened, heartless mankind at large. Two disastrously conclusive things happened to them: the government decided to have a national park, so they were compelled by law to give up hunting in the valleys and become farmers on poor hillside soil, and then they were visited for two years by an anthropologist who detested them and wrote a book about them.

The message of the book is that the Iks have transformed themselves into an irreversibly disagreeable collection of unattached, brutish creatures, totally selfish and loveless, in response to the dismantling of their traditional culture. Moreover, this is what the rest of us are like in our inner selves, and we will all turn into Iks when the structure of our society comes all unhinged.

The argument rests, of course, on certain assumptions about the core of human beings, and is necessarily speculative. You have to agree in advance that man is fundamentally a bad lot, out for himself alone, displaying such graces as affection and compassion only as learned habits. If you take this view, the story of the Iks can be used to confirm it. These people seem to be living together, clustered in small, dense villages, but they are really solitary, unrelated individuals with no evident use for each other. They talk, but only to make ill-tempered demands and cold refusals. They share nothing. They never sing. They turn the children out to forage as soon as they can walk, and desert the elders to starve whenever they can, and the foraging children snatch food from the mouths of the helpless elders. It is a mean society.

They breed without love or even casual regard. They defecate on each other's doorsteps. They watch their neighbors for signs of misfortune, and only then do they laugh. In the book they do a lot of laughing, having so much bad luck. Several times they even laughed at the anthropologist, who found this especially repellent (one senses, between the lines, that the scholar is not himself the world's luckiest man). Worse, they took him into the family, snatched his food, defecated on his doorstep, and hooted dislike at him. They gave him two bad years.

It is a depressing book. If, as he suggests, there is only Ikness at the center of each of us, our sole hope for hanging on to the name of humanity will be in endlessly mending the structure of our society, and it is changing so quickly and completely that we may never find the threads in time. Meanwhile, left to ourselves alone, solitary, we will become the same joyless, zestless, untouching lone animals.

But this may be too narrow a view. For one thing, the Iks are extraordinary. They are absolutely astonishing, in fact. The anthropologist has never seen people like them anywhere, nor have I. You'd think, if they were simply examples of the common essence of mankind, they'd seem more recognizable. Instead, they are bizarre, anomalous. I have known my share of peculiar, difficult, nervous, grabby people, but I've never encountered any genuinely, consistently detestable human beings in all my life. The Iks sound more like abnormalities, maladies.

I cannot accept it. I do not believe that the Iks are representative of isolated, revealed man, unobscured by social habits. I believe their behavior is something extra, something laid on. This unremitting, compulsive repellence is a kind of complicated ritual. They must have learned to act this way; they copied it, somehow.

I have a theory, then. The Iks have gone crazy.

The solitary Ik, isolated in the ruins of an exploded culture, has built a new defense for himself. If you live in an unworkable society you can make up one of your own, and this is what the Iks have done. Each Ik has become a group, a one-man tribe on its own, a constituency.

Now everything falls into place. This is why they do seem, after all, vaguely familiar to all of us. We've seen them before. This is precisely the way groups of one size or another, ranging from committees to nations, behave. It is, of course, this aspect of humanity that has lagged behind the rest of evolution, and this is why the Ik seems so primitive. In his absolute selfishness, his incapacity to give anything away, no matter what, he is a successful committee. When he stands at the door of his hut, shouting insults at his neighbors in a loud harangue, he is city addressing another city.

Cities have all the Ik characteristics. They defecate on doorsteps, in rivers and lakes, their own or anyone else's. They leave rubbish. They detest all neighboring cities, give nothing away. They even build institutions for deserting elders out of sight.

Nations are the most Iklike of all. No wonder the Iks seem familiar.

For total greed, rapacity, heartlessness, and irresponsibility there is nothing to match a nation. Nations, by law, are solitary, self-centered, withdrawn into themselves. There is no such thing as affection between nations, and certainly no nation ever loved another. They bawl insults from their doorsteps, defecate into whole oceans, snatch all the food, survive by detestation, take joy in the bad luck of others, celebrate the death of others, live for the death of others.

That's it, and I shall stop worrying about the book. It does not signify that man is a sparse, inhuman thing at his center. He's all right. It only says what we've always known and never had enough time to worry about, that we haven't yet learned how to stay human when assembled in masses. The Ik, in his despair, is acting out this failure, and perhaps we should pay closer attention. Nations have themselves become too frightening to think about, but we might learn some things by watching these people.

CHAPTER TWENTY-THREE

Computers

YOU CAN MAKE COMPUTERS THAT ARE ALMOST HUMAN. IN SOME respects they are superhuman; they can beat most of us at chess, memorize whole telephone books at a glance, compose music of a certain kind and write obscure poetry, diagnose heart ailments, send personal invitations to vast parties, even go transiently crazy. No one has yet programmed a computer to be of two minds about a hard problem, or to burst out laughing, but that may come. Sooner or later, there will be real human hardware, great whirring, clicking cabinets intelligent enough to read magazines and vote, able to think rings around the rest of us.

Well, maybe, but not for a while anyway. Before we begin organizing sanctuaries and reservations for our software selves, lest we vanish like the whales, here is a thought to relax with.

Even when technology succeeds in manufacturing a machine as big as Texas to do everything we recognize as human, it will still be, at best, a single individual. This amounts to nothing, practically speaking. To match what we can do, there would have to be 3 billion of them with more coming down the assembly line, and I doubt that anyone will put up the money, much less make room. And even so, they would all have to be wired together, intricately and delicately, as we are, communicating with each other, talking incessantly, listening. If they weren't *at* each other this way, all their waking hours, they wouldn't be anything like human, after all. I think we're safe, for a long time ahead.

It is in our collective behavior that we are most mysterious. We won't be able to construct machines like ourselves until we've understood this, and we're not even close. All we know is the phenomenon: we spend our time sending messages to each other, talking and trying to listen at the same time, exchanging information. This seems to be our most urgent biological function; it is what we do with our lives. By the time we reach the end, each of us has taken in a staggering store, enough to exhaust any computer, much of it incomprehensible, and we generally manage to put out even more than we take in. Information is our source of energy; we are driven by it. It has become a tremendous enterprise, a kind of energy system on its own. All 3 billion of us are being connected by telephones, radios, television sets, airplanes, satellites, harangues on public-address systems, newspapers, magazines, leaflets dropped from great heights, words got in edgewise. We are becoming a grid, a circuitry around the earth. If we keep at it, we will become a computer to end all computers, capable of fusing all the thoughts of the world into a syncytium.

Already, there are no closed, two-way conversations. Any word you speak this afternoon will radiate out in all directions, around town before tomorrow, out and around the world before Tuesday, accelerating to the speed of light, modulating as it goes, shaping new and unexpected messages, emerging at the end as an enormously funny Hungarian joke, a fluctuation in the money market, a poem, or simply a long pause in someone's conversation in Brazil.

We do a lot of collective thinking, probably more than any other social species, although it goes on in something like secrecy. We don't acknowledge the gift publicly, and we are not as celebrated as the insects, but we do it. Effortlessly, without giving it a moment's thought, we are capable of changing our language, music, manners, morals, entertainment, even the way we dress, all around the earth in a year's turning. We seem to do this by general agreement, without voting or even polling. We simply think our way along, pass information around, exchange codes disguised as art, change our minds, transform ourselves.

Computers cannot deal with such levels of improbability, and it is just as well. Otherwise, we might be tempted to take over the control of ourselves in order to make long-range plans, and that would surely be the end of us. It would mean that some group or other, marvelously intelligent and superbly informed, undoubtedly guided by a computer, would begin deciding what human society ought to be like, say, over the next five hundred years or so, and the rest of us would be persuaded, one way or another, to go along. The process of social evolution would then grind to a standstill, and we'd be stuck in today's rut for a millennium.

Much better we work our way out of it on our own, without governance. The future is too interesting and dangerous to be entrusted to any predictable, reliable agency. We need all the fallibility we can get. Most of all, we need to preserve the absolute unpredictability and total improbability of our connected minds. That way we can keep open all the options, as we have in the past.

It would be nice to have better ways of monitoring what we're up to so that we could recognize change while it is occurring, instead of waking up as we do now to the astonished realization that the whole century just past wasn't what we thought it was, at all. Maybe computers can be used to help in this, although I rather doubt it. You can make simulation models of cities, but what you learn is that they seem to be beyond the reach of intelligent analysis; if you try to use common sense to make predictions, things get more botched up than ever. This is interesting, since a city is the most concentrated aggregation of humans, all exerting whatever influence they can bring to bear. The city seems to have a life of its own. If we cannot understand how this works, we are not likely to get very far with human society at large.

Still, you'd think there would be some way in. Joined together, the great mass of human minds around the earth seems to behave like a coherent, living system. The trouble is that the flow of information is mostly one-way. We are all obsessed by the need to feed information in, as fast as we can, but we lack sensing mechanisms for getting anything much back. I will confess that I have no more sense of what goes on in the mind of mankind than I have for the mind of an ant. Come to think of it, this might be a good place to start.

CHAPTER TWENTY-FOUR

The Planning
of Science

IT IS GENERALLY ACCEPTED THAT THE BIOLOGIC SCIENCES ARE ABSO-lutely splendid. In just the past decade, they have uncovered a huge mass of brand-new information, and there is plenty more ahead; the biologic revolution is evidently still in its early stages. Everyone approves. By contrast, the public view of the progress of medicine during the same period is restrained, qualified, a mixture of hope and worry. For all the new knowledge, we still have formidable diseases, still unsolved, lacking satisfactory explanation, lacking satisfactory treatment. Why, it is asked, does the supply of new miracle drugs lag so far behind, while biology continues to move from strength to strength, elaborating new, powerful technologies for explaining, in fine detail, the very processes of life?

It doesn't seem to help to apply the inclusive term "biomedical" to our science, much as we would like to show that we are all one field of inquiry, share and share alike. There is still the conspicuous asymmetry between molecular biology and, say, the therapy of lung cancer. We may as well face up to it: there is a highly visible difference between the pace of basic science and the application of new knowledge to human problems. It needs explaining.

This is an especially lively problem at the moment, because of the immediate implications for national science policy. It is administratively fashionable in Washington to attribute the delay of applied science in medicine to a lack of systematic planning. Under a new kind of management, it is said, with more businesslike attention to the invention of practical applications, we should arrive at our targets more quickly and, it is claimed as a bonus, more economically. Targeting is the new word. We need more targeted research, more mission-oriented science. And maybe less basic research—maybe considerably less. This is said to be the new drift.

One trouble with this view is that it attributes to biology and medicine a much greater store of usable information, with coherence and connectedness, than actually exists. In real life, the biomedical sciences have not yet reached the stage of any kind of general applicability to disease mechanisms. In some respects we are like the physical sciences of the early twentieth century, booming along into new territory, but without an equivalent for the engineering of that time. It is possible that we are on the verge of developing a proper applied science, but it has to be said that we don't have one yet. The important question before the policy-makers is whether this should be allowed to occur naturally, as a matter of course, or whether it can be ordered up more quickly, under the influence of management and money.

There are risks. We may be asking for more of the kind of trouble with which we are already too familiar. There is a trap here that has enmeshed medicine for all the millennia of its professional existence. It has been our perpetual habit to try anything, on the slimmest of chances, the thinnest of hopes, empirically and wishfully, and we have proved to ourselves over and over again that the approach doesn't work well. Bleeding, cupping, and purging are the classical illustrations, but we have plenty of more recent examples to be embarrassed about. We have been hoaxed along by comparable substitutes for technology right up to the present. There is no question about our good intentions in this matter: we all hanker, collectively, to become applied scientists as soon as we can, overnight if possible.

It takes some doing, however. Everyone forgets how long and hard the work must be before the really important applications become applicable. The great contemporary achievement of modern medicine is the technology for controlling and preventing bacterial infection, but this did not fall into our laps with the appearance of penicillin and the sulfonamides. It had its beginnings in the final quarter of the last century, and decades of the most painstaking and demanding research were required before the etiology of pneumonia, scarlet fever, meningitis, and the rest could be worked out. Generations of energetic and imaginative investigators exhausted their whole lives on the problems. It overlooks a staggering amount of basic research to say that modern medicine began with the era of antibiotics.

We have to face, in whatever discomfort, the real possibility that the level of insight into the mechanisms of today's unsolved diseases—schizophrenia, for instance, or cancer, or stroke—is comparable to the situation for infectious disease in 1875, with similarly crucial bits of information still unencountered. We could be that far away, in the work to be done if not in the years to be lived through. If this is the prospect, or anything like this, all ideas about better ways to speed things up should be given open-minded, close scrutiny.

Long-range planning and organization on a national scale are obviously essential. There is nothing unfamiliar about this; indeed, we've been engaged in a coordinated national effort for over two decades, through the established processes of the National Institutes of Health. Today's question is whether the plans are sharply focused enough, the organization sufficiently tight. Do we need a new system of research management, with all the targets in clear display, arranged to be aimed at?

This would seem reassuring and tidy, and there are some important disease problems for which it has already been done effectively, demonstrating that the direct, frontal approach does work. Poliomyelitis is the most spectacular example. Once it had been learned (from basic research) that there were three antigenic types of virus and that they could be abundantly grown in tissue culture, it became a certainty that a vaccine could be made. Not to say that the job would be easy, or in need of any less rigor and sophistication than the previous research; simply that it could be done. Given the assumption that experiments would be carried out with technical perfection, the vaccine was a sure thing. It was an elegant demonstration of how to organize applied science, and for this reason it would have been a surprise if it had not succeeded.

This is the element that distinguishes applied science from basic. Surprise is what makes the difference. When you are organized to apply knowledge, set up targets, produce a usable product, you require a high degree of certainty from the outset. All the facts on which you base protocols must be reasonably hard facts with unambiguous meaning. The challenge is to plan the work and organize the workers so that it will come out precisely as predicted. For this, you need centralized authority, elaborately detailed time schedules, and some sort of reward system based on speed and perfection. But most of all you need the intelligible basic facts to begin with, and these must come from basic research. There is no other source.

In basic research, everything is just the opposite. What you need at the outset is a high degree of uncertainty; otherwise it isn't likely to be an important problem. You start with an incomplete roster of facts, characterized by their ambiguity; often the problem consists of discovering the connections between unrelated pieces of information. You must plan experiments on the basis of probability, even bare possibility, rather than certainty. If an experiment turns out precisely as predicted, this can be very nice, but it is only a great event if at the same time it is a surprise. You can measure the quality of the work by the intensity of astonishment. The surprise can be because it did turn out as predicted (in some lines of research, 1 per cent is accepted as a high yield), or it can be confoundment because the prediction was wrong and something totally unexpected turned up, changing the look of the problem and requiring a new kind of protocol. Either way, you win.

I believe, on hunch, that an inventory of our major disease problems based on this sort of classification would show a limited number of important questions for which the predictable answers carry certainty. It might be a good idea, when commissions go to work laying out long-range plans for disease-oriented research, for these questions to be identified and segregated from all the rest, and the logic of operations research should be invaluable for this purpose. There will be lots of disputing among the experts over what is certain and what not; perhaps the heat and duration of dispute could be adapted for the measurement of uncertainty. In any case, once a set of suitable questions becomes agreed upon, these can be approached by the most systematic methods of applied science.

However, I have a stronger hunch that the greatest part of the important biomedical research waiting to be done is in the class of basic science. There is an abundance of interesting fact relating to all our major diseases, and more items of information are coming in steadily from all quarters in biology. The new mass of knowledge is still formless, incomplete, lacking the essential threads of connection, displaying misleading signals at every turn, riddled with blind alleys. There are fascinating ideas all over the place, irresistible experiments beyond numbering, all sorts of new ways into the maze of problems. But every next move is unpredictable, every outcome uncertain. It is a puzzling time, but a very good time.

I do not know how you lay out orderly plans for this kind of activity, but I suppose you could find out by looking through the disorderly records of the past hundred years. Somehow, the atmosphere has to be set so that a disquieting sense of being wrong is the normal attitude of the investigators. It has to be taken for granted that the only way in is by riding the unencumbered human imagination, with the special rigor required for recognizing that something can be highly improbable, maybe almost impossible, and at the same time true.

Locally, a good way to tell how the work is going is to listen in the corridors. If you hear the word, "Impossible!" spoken as an expletive, followed by laughter, you will know that someone's orderly research plan is coming along nicely.

CHAPTER TWENTY-FIVE

Some Biomythology

THE MYTHICAL ANIMALS CATALOGUED IN THE BESTIARIES OF THE world seem, at a casual glance, nothing but exotic nonsense. The thought comes that Western civilized, scientific, technologic society is a standing proof of human progress, in having risen above such imaginings. They are as obsolete as the old anecdotes in which they played their puzzling, ambiguous roles, and we have no more need for the beasts than for the stories. The Griffon, Phoenix, Centaur, Sphinx, Manticore, Ganesha, Ch'i-lin, and all the rest are like recurrent bad dreams, and we are well rid of them. So we say.

The trouble is that they are in fact like dreams, and not necessarily bad ones, and we may have a hard time doing without them. They may be as essential for society as mythology itself, as loaded with symbols, and as necessary for the architecture of our collective unconscious. If Lévi-Strauss is right, myths are constructed by a universal logic that, like language itself, is as characteristic for human beings as nest-building is for birds. The stories seem to be different stories, but the underlying structure is always the same, in any part of the world, at any time. They are like engrams, built into our genes. In this sense, bestiaries are part of our inheritance.

There is something basically similar about most of these crazy animals. They are all unbiologic, but unbiologic in the same way. Bestiaries do not contain, as a rule, totally novel creatures of the imagination made up of parts that we have never seen before. On the contrary, they are made up of parts that are entirely familiar. What is novel, and startling, is that they are mixtures of species.

It is perhaps this characteristic that makes the usual bestiary so outlandish to the twentieth-century mind. Our most powerful story, equivalent in its way to a universal myth, is evolution. Never mind that it is true whereas myths are not; it is filled with symbolism, and this is the way it has influenced the mind of society. In our latest enlightenment, the fabulous beasts are worse than improbable — they are impossible, because they violate evolution. They are not species, and they deny the existence of species.

The Phoenix comes the closest to being a conventional animal, all bird for all of its adult life. It is, in fact, the most exuberant, elaborate, and ornamented of all plumed birds. It exists in the mythology of Egypt, Greece, the Middle East, and Europe, and is the same as the vermilion bird of ancient China. It lives for five hundred triumphant years, and when it dies it constructs a sort of egg-shaped cocoon around itself. Inside, it disintegrates and gives rise to a wormlike creature, which then develops into the new Phoenix, ready for the next five hundred years. In other versions the dead bird bursts into flames, and the new one arises from the ashes, but the worm story is very old, told no doubt by an early biologist.

There are so many examples of hybrid beings in bestiaries that you could say that an ardent belief in mixed forms of life is an ancient human idea, or that something else, deeply believed in, is symbolized by these consortia. They are disturbing to look at, nightmarish, but most of them, oddly enough, are intended as lucky benignities. The Ch'i-lin, for instance, out of ancient China, has the body of a deer covered with gleaming scales, a marvelous bushy tail, cloven hooves, and small horns. Whoever saw a Ch'i-lin was in luck, and if you got to ride one, you had it made.

The Ganesha is one of the oldest and most familiar Hindu deities, possessing a fat human body, four human arms, and the head of a cheerful-looking elephant. Prayers to Ganesha are regarded as the quickest way around obstacles.

Not all mythical beasts are friendly, of course, but even the hostile ones have certain amiable redeeming aspects. The Manticore has a lion's body, a man's face, and a tail with a venomous snake's head at the end of it. It bounds around seeking prey with huge claws and three rows of teeth, but it makes the sounds of a beautiful silver flute.

Some of the animal myths have the ring of contemporary biologic theory, if you allow for differences in jargon. An ancient idea in India postulates an initial Being, the first form of life on the earth, analogous to our version of the earliest prokaryotic arrangement of membrane-limited nucleic acid, the initial cell, born of lightning and methane. The Indian Being, undefined and indefinable, finding itself alone, fearing death, yearning for company, began to swell in size, rearranged itself inside, and then split into two identical halves. One of these changed into a cow, the other a bull, and they mated, then changed again to a mare and stallion, and so on, down to the ants, and thus the earth was populated. There is a lot of oversimplification here, and too much shorthand for modern purposes, but the essential myth is recognizable.

The serpent keeps recurring through the earliest cycles of mythology, always as a central symbol for the life of the universe and the continuity of creation. There are two great identical snakes on a Levantine libation vase of around 2000 B.C., coiled around each other in a double helix, representing the original generation of life. They are the replicated parts of the first source of living, and they are wonderfully homologous.

There is a Peruvian deity, painted on a clay pot dating from around A.D. 300, believed to be responsible for guarding farms. His hair is made of snakes, entwined in braids, with wings for his headdress. Plants of various kinds are growing out of his sides and back, and a vegetable of some sort seems to be growing from his mouth. The whole effect is wild and disheveled but essentially friendly. He is, in fact, an imaginary version of a genuine animal, *symbiopholus,* described in *Nature* several years back, a species of weevil in the mountains of northern New Guinea that lives symbiotically with dozens of plants, growing in the niches and clefts in its carapace, rooted all the way down to its flesh, plus a whole ecosystem of mites, rotifers, nematodes, and bacteria attached to the garden. The weevil could be taken for a good-luck omen on its own evidence; it is not attacked by predators, it lives a long, untroubled life, and nothing else will eat it, either because of something distasteful in the system or simply because of the ambiguity. The weevil is only about thirty millimeters long, easily overlooked, but it has the makings of a myth.

Perhaps we should be looking around for other candidates. I suggest the need for a new bestiary, to take the place of the old ones. I can think of several creatures that seem designed for this function, if you will accept a microbestiary, and if you are looking for metaphors.

First of all, there is *Myxotricha paradoxa.* This is the protozoan, not yet as famous as he should be, who seems to be telling us everything about everything, all at once. His cilia are not cilia at all, but individual spirochetes, and at the base of attachment of each spirochete is an oval organelle, embedded in the myxotricha membrane, which is a bacterium. It is not an animal after all—it is a company, an assemblage.

The story told by myxotricha is as deep as any myth, as profoundly allusive. This creature has lagged behind the rest of us, and is still going through the process of being assembled. Our cilia gave up any independent existence long ago, and our organelles are now truly ours, but the genomes controlling separate parts of our cells are still different genomes, lodged in separate compartments; doctrinally, we are still assemblages.

There is another protozoan, called blepharisma, telling a long story about the chanciness and fallibility of complex life. Blepharisma is called that because of a conspicuous fringe of ciliated membranes around the oral cavity, which evidently reminded someone of eyelashes (*blepharidos*). The whole mythlike tale has been related in a book by Giese. Blepharisma has come much further along than myxotricha, but not far enough to be free of slip-ups. There are three different sets of self-duplicating nuclei, with the DNA in each set serving different purposes: a large macronucleus, governing the events in regeneration after injury, a set of eight or more micronuclei containing the parts of the genome needed for reproduction, and great numbers of tiny nuclei from which the cilia arise.

One part of the organism produces a pinkish pigment, now called blepharismin, which is similar to hypericin and certain other photosensitizing plant pigments. Blepharismin causes no trouble unless the animal swims into sunlight, but then the pigment kills it outright. Under certain circumstances, the membrane surrounding blepharisma disintegrates and comes independently loose, like a cast-off shell, leaving the creature a transient albino. At times of famine, a single blepharisma will begin eating its neighbors; it then enlarges to an immense size and turns into a cannibalistic giant, straight out of any Norse fable. Evidently, this creature still has trouble getting along with the several parts of itself, and with the collective parts of other blepharismae.

There are innumerable plant-animal combinations, mostly in the sea, where the green plant cells provide carbohydrate and oxygen for the animal and receive a share of energy in return. It is the fairest of arrangements. When the paramecium bursaria runs out of food, all he needs to do is stay in the sun and his green endosymbionts will keep him supplied as though he were a grain.

Bacteria are the greatest of all at setting up joint enterprises, on which the lives of their hosts are totally dependent. The nitrogen-fixing rhizobia in root nodules, the mycetomes of insects, and the enzyme-producing colonies in the digestive tracts of many animals are variations of this meticulously symmetrical symbiosis.

The meaning of these stories may be basically the same as the meaning of a medieval bestiary. There is a tendency for living things to join up, establish linkages, live inside each other, return to earlier arrangements, get along, whenever possible. This is the way of the world.

The new phenomenon of cell fusion, a laboratory trick on which much of today's science of molecular genetics relies for its data, is the simplest and most spectacular symbol of the tendency. In a way, it is the most unbiologic of all phenomena, violating the most fundamental myth of the last century, for it denies the importance of specificity, integrity, and separateness in living things. Any cell—man, animal, fish, fowl, or insect—given the chance and under the right conditions, brought into contact with any other cell, however foreign, will fuse with it. Cytoplasm will flow easily from one to the other, the nuclei will combine, and it will become, for a time anyway, a single cell with two complete, alien genomes, ready to dance, ready to multiply. It is a Chimera, a Griffon, a Sphinx, a Ganesha, a Peruvian god, a Ch'i-lin, an omen of good fortune, a wish for the world.

CHAPTER TWENTY-SIX

On Various Words

THE IDEA THAT COLONIES OF SOCIAL INSECTS ARE SOMEHOW EQUIVA-
lent to vast, multicreatured organisms, possessing a collective intelligence and a gift for adaptation far superior to the sum of the individual
inhabitants, had its origin in the papers of the eminent entomologist,
William Morton Wheeler, who proposed the term Superorganism to
describe the arrangement. From 1911 to the early 1950s this ranked as a
central notion in entomology, attracting the attention of many fascinated nonentomologists. Maeterlinck and Marais wrote best-selling
books on the presumed soul that must exist somewhere in the nests of
ants and termites.

Then, unaccountably, the whole idea abruptly dropped out of fashion
and sight. During the past quarter-century almost no mention of it is
made in the proliferation of scientific literature in entomology. It is not
talked about. It is not just that the idea has been forgotten; it is as though
it had become unmentionable, an embarrassment.

It is hard to explain. The notion was not shown to be all that
mistaken, nor was it in conflict with any other, more acceptable view of
things. It was simply that nobody could figure out what to do with such
an abstraction. There it sat, occupying important intellectual ground, at
just the time when entomology was emerging as an experimental
science of considerable power, capable of solving matters of intricate
detail, a paradigm of the new reductionism. This huge idea—that
individual organisms might be self-transcending in their relation to a
dense society—was not approachable by the new techniques, nor did it
suggest new experiments or methods. It just sat there, in the way, and
was covered over by leaves and papers. It needed heuristic value to
survive, and this was lacking.

"Holism," a fabricated word, has been applied to concepts like the
Superorganism. One wonders whether this word may not itself have
scared off some investigators; it is a word with an alarming visage.

General Jan Smuts, who invented it out of whole cloth in 1926, might have done better with "Wholism"; it would have served the same etymological purpose and might have been just secular enough to survive this kind of century. As it is, there is doubt for its future. Holism is in some of the scientific glossaries but has not yet made it into most standard dictionaries of English. It got as far as the Supplement volume of the new OED, which is something, but not enough to assure survival. Perhaps it will die away, along with Superorganism.

I cannot quarrel with any of this. If an idea cannot move on its own, pushing it doesn't help; best to let it lie there.

It may be, though, that the pushing was tried in the wrong direction. Colonies of ants or termites, or bees and social wasps, may in fact be Superorganisms by Wheeler's criteria, but perhaps that is the end of that line of information as far as insects are concerned, for the time being. Maybe it would work better if you tried it out on another social species, easier to handle. Us, for one.

It has long troubled the entomologists that the rest of us are always interfering in their affairs by offering explanations of insect behavior in human terms. They take pains to explain that ants are not, emphatically not, tiny mechanical models of human beings. I agree with this. Nothing that we know for sure about human behavior is likely to account for what ants do, and we ought to stay clear of it; this is the business of entomologists. As for the ants themselves, they are plainly not in need of lessons from us.

However, this does not mean that we cannot take it the other way, on the off chance that some of the collective actions of ants may cast light on human problems.

There are lots of possibilities here, but if you think about the construction of the Hill by a colony of a million ants, each one working ceaselessly and compulsively to add perfection to his region of the structure without having the faintest notion of what is being constructed elsewhere, living out his brief life in a social enterprise that extends back into what is for him the deepest antiquity (ants die at the rate of 3–4 per cent per day; in a month or so an entire generation vanishes, while the Hill can go on for sixty years or, given good years, forever), performing his work with infallible, undistracted skill in the midst of a confusion of others, all tumbling over each other to get the twigs and bits of earth aligned in precisely the right configurations for the warmth and ventilation of the eggs and larvae, but totally incapacitated by isolation, there is only one human activity that is like this, and it is language.

We have been working at it for what seems eternity, generation after articulate generation, and still we have no notion how it is done, nor what it will be like when finished, if it is ever to be finished. It is the most compulsively collective, genetically programmed, species-specific, and autonomic of all the things we do, and we are infallible at it. It comes naturally. We have DNA for grammar, neurons for syntax. We can never let up; we scramble our way through one civilization after another, metamorphosing, sprouting tools and cities everywhere, and all the time new words keep tumbling out.

The words themselves are marvels, each one perfectly designed for its use. The older, more powerful ones are membranous, packed with layers of different meaning, like one-word poems. "Articulated," for instance, first indicated a division into small joints, then, effortlessly, signified the speaking of sentences. Some words are gradually altered while we have them in everyday use, without our being aware until the change has been completed: the *ly* in today's adverbs, such as ably and benignly, began to appear in place of "like" just a few centuries ago, and "like" has since worn away to a mere suffix. By a similar process, "love-did" changed itself into "loved."

None of the words are ever made up by anyone we know; they simply turn up in the language when they are needed. Sometimes a familiar word will suddenly be grabbed up and transformed to mean something quite strange: "strange" is itself such a word today, needed by nuclear physicists to symbolize the behavior of particles which decay with peculiar slowness; the technical term for such particles now is "strange particles," and they possess a "strangeness number (S)." The shock of sudden unfamiliarity with an old, familiar word is something we take in stride; it has been going on for thousands of years.

A few words are made up by solitary men in front of our eyes, like Holism out of Smuts, or Quark out of Joyce, but most of these are exotic and transient; it takes a great deal of use before a word can become a word.

Most new words are made up from other, earlier words; language-making is a conservative process, wasting little. When new words unfold out of old ones, the original meaning usually hangs around like an unrecognizable scent, a sort of secret.

"Holism" suggests something biologically transcendental because of "holy," although it was intended more simply to mean a complete assemblage of living units. Originally, it came from the Indo-European root word *kailo*, which meant whole, also intact and uninjured. During passage through several thousand years it transformed into hail, hale, health, hallow, holy, whole, and heal, and all of these still move together through our minds.

"Heuristic" is a more specialized, single-purpose word, derived from the Indo-European *wer*, meaning to find, then taken up in Greek as *heuriskein*, from which Archimedes was provided with Heureka!

There are two immense words from Indo-European, *gene* and *bheu,* each a virtual anthill in itself, from which we have constructed the notion of Everything. At the beginning, or as far back as they are traceable, they meant something like being. *Gene* signified beginning, giving birth, while *bheu* indicated existence and growth. *Gene* turned itself successively into *kundjaz* (Germanic) and *gecynd* (Old English), meaning kin or kind. Kind was at first a family connection, later an elevated social rank, and finally came to rest meaning kindly or gentle. Meanwhile, a branch of *gene* became the Latin *gens,* then gentle itself; it also emerged as genus, genius, genital, and generous; then, still holding on to its inner significance, it became "nature" (out of *gnasci*).

While gene was evolving into "nature" and "kind," *bheu* was moving through similar transformations. One branch became *bowan* in Germanic and *bua* in Old Norse, meaning to live and dwell, and then the English word build. It moved into Greek, as *phuein,* meaning to bring forth and make grow; then as *phusis,* which was another word for nature. *Phusis* became the source of physic, which at first meant natural science and later was the word for medicine. Still later, physic became physics.

Both words, at today's stage of their evolution, can be taken together to mean, literally, everything in the universe. You do not come by words like this easily; they cannot just be made up from scratch. They need long lives before they can signify. "Everything," C. S. Lewis observed in a discussion of the words, "is a subject on which there is not much to be said." The words themselves must show the internal marks of long use; they must contain their own inner conversation.

These days it is reassuring to know that nature and physics, in their present meanings, have been interconnected in our minds, by a sort of hunch, for all these years. The other words clinging to them are a puzzlement, but nice to see. If you let your mind relax, all the words will flow into each other in an amiable sort of nonsense. "Kind" means a relation, but it also means "nature." The word for kind is the same as the word for gentle. Even "physics," save us, is a kind of "nature," by its nature, and is, simultaneously, another kind of kind. There are ancient ideas reverberating through this structure, very old hunches.

It is part of the magic of language that some people can get to the same place by the use of totally different words. Julian of Norwich, a fourteenth-century hermitess, said it so well that a paragraph of hers was used recently by a physicist for his introduction to a hard-science review of contemporary cosmological physics: "He showed me a little thing, the quantity of an hazelnut, in the palm of my hand, and it was as round as a ball. I looked thereupon with the eye of my understanding and thought: What may this be? And it was answered generally thus: it is all that is made."

CHAPTER TWENTY-SEVEN

Living Language

"STIGMERGY" IS A NEW WORD, INVENTED RECENTLY BY GRASSÉ TO explain the nest-building behavior of termites, perhaps generalizable to other complex activities of social animals. The word is made of Greek roots meaning "to incite to work," and Grassé's intention was to indicate that it is the product of work itself that provides both the stimulus and instructions for further work. He arrived at this after long observation of the construction of termite nests, which excepting perhaps a man-made city are the most formidable edifices in nature. When you consider the size of an individual termite, photographed standing alongside his nest, he ranks with the New Yorker and shows a better sense of organization than a resident of Los Angeles. Some of the mound nests of *Macrotermes bellicosus* in Africa measure twelve feet high and a hundred feet across, they contain several millions of termites, and around them are clustered other small and younger mounds, like suburbs.

The interiors of the nests are like a three-dimensional maze, intricate arrangements of spiraling galleries, corridors, and arched vaults, ventilated and air-conditioned. There are great caverns for the gardens of fungi on which the termites depend for their nourishment, perhaps also as a source of heat. There is a rounded vaulted chamber for the queen, called the royal cell. The fundamental structural unit, on which the whole design is based, is the arch.

Grassé needed his word in order to account for the ability of such tiny, blind, and relatively brainless animals to erect structures of such vast size and internal complexity. Does each termite possess a fragment of blueprint, or is the whole design, arch by arch, encoded in his DNA? Or does the whole colony have, by virtue of the interconnections of so many small brains, the collective intellectual power of a huge contractor?

Grassé placed a handful of termites in a dish filled with soil and fecal pellets (these are made of lignin, a sort of micro-lumber) and watched what they did. They did not, in the first place, behave at all like contractors. Nobody stood around in place and gave orders or collected fees; they all simply ran around, picking up pellets at random and dropping them again. Then, by chance, two or three pellets happened to light on top of each other, and this transformed the behavior of everyone. Now they displayed the greatest interest and directed their attention obsessively to the primitive column, adding new pellets and fragments of earth. After reaching a certain height, the construction stopped unless another column was being formed nearby; in this case the structure changed from a column to an arch, bending off in a smooth curve, the arch was joined, and the termites then set off to build another.

Building a language may be something like this. One can imagine primitive proto-Indo-European men finding themselves clustered together, making random sounds, surrounded, say, by bees, and one of them suddenly saying "*bhei,*" and then the rest of them picking it up and repeating "*bhei*" and thus beginning that part of language, but this is a restricted, too mechanistic view of things. It makes pellets out of phonemes, implies that the deep structures of grammar are made of something like cement. I do not care for this.

More likely, language is simply alive, like an organism. We tell each other this, in fact, when we speak of living languages, and I think we mean something more than an abstract metaphor. We mean alive. Words are the cells of language, moving the great body, on legs.

Language grows and evolves, leaving fossils behind. The individual words are like different species of animals. Mutations occur. Words fuse, and then mate. Hybrid words and wild varieties of compound words are the progeny. Some mixed words are dominated by one parent while the other is recessive. The way a word is used this year is its phenotype, but it has a deeply seated, immutable meaning, often hidden, which is the genotype.

The language of genetics might be used in some such way to describe the genetics of language, if we knew more about both.

The separate languages of the Indo-European family were at one time, perhaps five thousand years ago, maybe much longer, a single language. The separation of the speakers by migrations had effects on language comparable to the speciation observed by Darwin on various islands of Galápagos. Languages became different species, retaining enough resemblance to an original ancestor so that the family resemblance can still be seen. Variation has been maintained by occasional contact between different islands of speakers, and perhaps also by random mutations.

But there is something else about words that gives them the look and feel of living motile beings with minds of their own. This is best experienced by looking them up, preferably in one of the dictionaries that provide all the roots back to the original, hypothetical fossil language of proto-Indo-European, and observing their behavior.

Some words started from Indo-European and swarmed into religion over a very large part of the earth. The word *blaghmen,* for example, meant priest. It moved into Latin and Middle English as *flamen,* a pagan word for priest, and into Sanskrit as *brahma,* then "brahman." *Weid,* a word meaning to see, with later connotations of wisdom and wit, entered Germanic as *witan,* and Old English as *wis,* becoming "wisdom." It became *videre* in Latin, hence "vision." Finally, in its suffixed form *woid-o,* it became the Sanskrit word *veda.*

Beudh traveled a similar distance. With the meaning of awareness, it became *beodan* in Old English, meaning "bode," and *bodhati* in Sanskrit, meaning he awakes, is enlightened, and thus Bodhisattva, and Buddha.

The *sattva* part of Bodhisattva came from the Indo-European word *es,* meaning to be, or is, which, on its way into Sanskrit as *sat* and *sant,* also became *esse* in Latin and *einai* in Greek; einai became the -ont in certain words signifying being, such as "symbiont."

The Indo-European word *bhag,* meaning to share, turned into the Greek *phagein,* to eat, and the Old Persian *bakhsh* (yielding "baksheesh," and, in Sanskrit, with the meaning of *bhage,* good fortune, it emerged as Bhagavad-gita (the *gita* from *gei,* a song).

The Hari-Krishna people are chanting something closer to English than it sounds. Krishna, the eighth avatar of Vishnu, has his name from the Sanskrit *Krsnah,* the black one, which came from the Indo-European word for black, *kers* (which also produced "chernozem," black topsoil, by the way of the Russian *chernyi*).

There is obviously no end to this; it can tie up a whole life, and has luckily done just that during the past century for generations of comparative linguists. Their science began properly in 1786 with the discovery of the similarity of Sanskrit to Greek and Latin, by William Jones. In 1817, with a publication by Franz Bopp, it became recognized that Sanskrit, Greek, Latin, Persian, and all the Germanic languages were so closely related to each other that a common ancestor must have existed earlier. Since then, this science has developed in more or less parallel with biology, but more quietly.

It is a field in which the irresponsible amateur can have a continually mystifying sort of fun. Whenever you get the available answer to a straight question, like, say, where does the most famous and worst of the four-letter Anglo-Saxon unprintable words come from, the answer raises new and discomfiting questions. Take that particular word. It comes from *peig,* a crawling, wicked Indo-European word meaning evil and hostile, the sure makings of a curse. It becomes *poikos,* then *gafaihaz* in Germanic and *gefah* in Old English, signifying "foe." It turned from *poik-yos* into *faigjaz* in Germanic, and *faege* in Old English, meaning fated to die, leading to "fey." It went on from *fehida* in Old English to become "feud," and *fokken* in Old Dutch. Somehow, from these beginnings, it transformed itself into one of the most powerful English expletives, meaning something like "Die before your time!" The unspeakable malevolence of the message is now buried deep inside the word, and out on the surface it presents itself as merely an obscenity.

"Leech" is a fascinating word. It is an antique term for physician, and also for the aquatic worm *sanguisugus,* used for leeching. The two words appear to be quite separate, but there is something like biological mimicry going on: leech the doctor means the doctor who uses leech the worm; leech the worm is a symbol for the doctor. Leech the doctor comes from the Indo-European *leg,* which meant to collect, with numerous derivatives meaning to speak. *Leg* became the Germanic *lekjaz,* meaning one who speaks magic words, an enchanter, and also *laece* in Old English, meaning physician. (In Denmark the word for doctor is still *laege,* in Swedish *läkare.*) *Leg* in its senses of gathering, choosing, and speaking gave rise to the Latin *legere,* and thus words like "lecture" and "legible." In Greek, it became *legein,* meaning to gather and to speak; "legal" and "legislator" and other such words derived. *Leg* was further transformed in Greek to *logos,* signifying reason.

All this history seems both plausible and creditable, good reading for doctors, but there is always that other leech, the worm. It is not certain how it came. Somehow it began its descent through the language at the same time as leech the doctor, turning up as both *laece* and *lyce* in Old English, always recognizable as something distinctly the worm and at the same time important in medicine. It also took on the meaning of someone parasitic, living on the flesh of others. Gradually, perhaps under the influence of a Middle English AMA, the worm was given sole rights to the word, and the doctor became the doctor, out of *dek,* meaning to accept, later to teach.

Man is an unchanged word from Indo-European *man,* meaning just that. But two other important words for man have stranger sources. One is *dhghem,* meaning earth; this became *guman* in Germanic, *gumen* in Old English, then *homo* and *humanus* in Latin, from which we have both "human" and "humus." The other word for man contains the same admonition, but turns the message around. It is *wiros,* meaning man in Indo-European, taken as *weraldh* in Germanic and *weorold* in Old English, emerging, flabbergastingly, as "world."

This must be a hard science to work in. You might think that with a word for earth giving rise to one important word for man, and an early word for man turning into the word for the world, you would find a parallel development in other words for the earth. Not so: the Indo-European word *ers,* which later became "earth," has evolved only one animal that I can find mentioned, and it is the aardvark.

I am glad to have a semipermeable memory after getting into this. If you had to speak English with running captions in your mind showing all the roots, all the way back to Indo-European, you'd fall off the bicycle. Speaking is an autonomic business; you may search for words as you go along, but they are found for you by agents in your brain over which you exercise no direct control. You really couldn't be thinking Indo-European at the same time, without going speechless or babbling (from *baba,* meaning indistinct speech, Russian *balalayka,* Latin *balbus,* meaning "booby," Old French *baboue,* leading to "baboon," Greek *barbaros,* meaning foreign or rude, and Sanskrit *babu,* meaning father). That sort of thing.

I got into even more trouble while looking into "Stigmergy." I was looking for other words for inciting and instigating work, and came upon "to egg on." The egg here comes from *ak,* a word for sharp, suffixed to *akjo* in Germanic, meaning "edge," and to *akjan* in Old Norse, meaning "egg," to incite, goad; the same root moves on into Old English as *aehher* and *ear,* for ear of corn. (Corn, if you have a moment, is from *greno,* for grain, which became *korn* in Old High German, *granum* in Latin, and *cyrnel* in Old English, thence "kernel.") But neither the egg nor the ear from *ak* are the real egg or ear. The real egg comes from *awi,* meaning bird, which turned into *avis* and *ovum* in Latin (not known, of course, which came first), into *oion* in Greek, and was compounded with *spek* (to see) to form *awispek,* "watcher of birds" which became *auspex* in Latin, meaning augur.

The real ear began as *ous,* then *auzan* in Germanic, and *eare* in Old English and *auri* in Latin; along the way, it was compounded with *sleg,* meaning slack, and transformed to *lagous,* meaning "with drooping ears," which then became *lagos,* Greek for rabbit.

There is no way to stop, once you've started, not even by trying to round a circle. *Ous* became *aus* became "auscultation," which is what leeches (*leg*) do for a living (*leip*) unless they are legal (*leg*) leeches, which, incidentally, is not the same thing as lawyers *(legh).*

That should be enough (*nek,* to attain, becoming *ganoga* in Germanic and *genog* in Old English, also *onkos* in Greek, meaning burden, hence "oncology") to give you the general (*gene*) idea (*weid* becoming *widesya* then *idea* in Greek). It is easy to lose the thread (from *ter,* to rub, twist — possibly also the root of termite). Are you there?

CHAPTER TWENTY-EIGHT

On Probability
and Possibility

STATISTICALLY, THE PROBABILITY OF ANY ONE OF US BEING HERE IS SO small that you'd think the mere fact of existing would keep us all in a contented dazzlement of surprise. We are alive against the stupendous odds of genetics, infinitely outnumbered by all the alternates who might, except for luck, be in our places.

Even more astounding is our statistical improbability in physical terms. The normal, predictable state of matter throughout the universe is randomness, a relaxed sort of equilibrium, with atoms and their particles scattered around in an amorphous muddle. We, in brilliant contrast, are completely organized structures, squirming with information at every covalent bond. We make our living by catching electrons at the moment of their excitement by solar photons, swiping the energy released at the instant of each jump and storing it up in intricate loops for ourselves. We violate probability, by our nature. To be able to do this systemically, and in such wild varieties of form, from viruses to whales, is extremely unlikely; to have sustained the effort successfully for the several billion years of our existence, without drifting back into randomness, was nearly a mathematical impossibility.

Add to this the biological improbability that makes each member of our own species unique. Everyone is one in 3 billion at the moment, which describes the odds. Each of us is a self-contained, free-standing individual, labeled by specific protein configurations at the surfaces of cells, identifiable by whorls of fingertip skin, maybe even by special medleys of fragrance. You'd think we'd never stop dancing.

Perhaps it is not surprising that we do not live more surprised. After all, we are used to unlikelihood. Being born into it, raised in it, we become acclimated to the altitude, like natives in the Andes. Moreover, we all know that the astonishment is transient, and sooner or later our particles will all go back to being random.

Also, there are reasons to suspect that we are really not the absolute, pure entities that we seem. We have some sense of ordinariness, and it tends to diminish our surprise. Despite all the evidences of biological privacy in our cells and tissues (to the extent that a fragment of cell membrane will be recognized and rejected between any conceivable pairs among the 3 billion, excepting identical twins), there is a certain slippage in our brains. No one, in fact, can lay claim with certainty to his own mind with anything like the specificity stipulated by fingerprints or tissue antigens.

The human brain is the most public organ on the face of the earth, open to everything, sending out messages to everything. To be sure, it is hidden away in bone and conducts internal affairs in secrecy, but virtually all the business is the direct result of thinking that has already occurred in other minds. We pass thoughts around, from mind to mind, so compulsively and with such speed that the brains of mankind often appear, functionally, to be undergoing fusion.

This is, when you think about it, really amazing. The whole dear notion of one's own Self—marvelous old free-willed, free-enterprising, autonomous, independent, isolated island of a Self—is a myth.

We do not yet have a science strong enough to displace the myth. If you could label, by some equivalent of radioactive isotopes, all the bits of human thought that are constantly adrift, like plankton, all around us, it might be possible to discern some sort of systematic order in the process, but, as it is, it seems almost entirely random. There has to be something wrong with this view. It is hard to see how we could be in possession of an organ so complex and intricate and, as it occasionally reveals itself, so powerful, and be using it on such a scale just for the production of a kind of background noise. Somewhere, obscured by the snatches of conversation, pages of old letters, bits of books and magazines, memories of old movies, and the disorder of radio and television, there ought to be more intelligible signals.

Or perhaps we are only at the beginning of learning to use the system, with almost all our evolution as a species still ahead of us. Maybe the thoughts we generate today and flick around from mind to mind, like the jokes that turn up simultaneously at dinner parties in Hong Kong and Boston, or the sudden changes in the way we wear our hair, or all the popular love songs, are the primitive precursors of more complicated, polymerized structures that will come later, analogous to the prokaryotic cells that drifted through shallow pools in the early days of biological evolution. Later, when the time is right, there may be fusion and symbiosis among the bits, and then we will see eukaryotic thought, metazoans of thought, huge interliving coral shoals of thought.

The mechanism is there, and there is no doubt that it is already capable of functioning, even though the total yield thus far seems to consist largely of bits. After all, it has to be said that we've been at it for only the briefest time in evolutionary terms, a few thousand years out of billions, and during most of this time the scattered aggregates of human thought have been located patchily around the earth. There may be some laws about this kind of communication, mandating a critical density and mass before it can function with efficiency. Only in this century have we been brought close enough to each other, in great numbers, to begin the fusion around the earth, and from now on the process may move very rapidly.

There is, if it goes well, quite a lot to look forward to. Already, by luck, we have seen the assembly of particles of exchanged thought into today's structures of art and science. It is done by simply passing the bits around from mind to mind, until something like natural selection makes the final selection, all on grounds of fitness.

The real surprises, which set us back on our heels when they occur, will always be the mutants. We have already had a few of these, sweeping across the field of human thought periodically, like comets. They have slightly different receptors for the information cascading in from other minds, and slightly different machinery for processing it, so that what comes out to rejoin the flow is novel, and filled with new sorts of meaning. Bach was able to do this, and what emerged in the current were primordia in music. In this sense, the Art of Fugue and the St. Matthew Passion were, for the evolving organism of human thought, feathered wings, apposing thumbs, new layers of frontal cortex.

But we may not be so dependent on mutants from here on, or perhaps there are more of them around than we recognize. What we need is more crowding, more unrestrained and obsessive communication, more open channels, even more noise, and a bit more luck. We are simultaneously participants and bystanders, which is a puzzling role to play. As participants, we have no choice in the matter; this is what we do as a species. As bystanders, stand back and give it room is my advice.

CHAPTER TWENTY-NINE

The World's Biggest Membrane

VIEWED FROM THE DISTANCE OF THE MOON, THE ASTONISHING THING about the earth, catching the breath, is that it is alive. The photographs show the dry, pounded surface of the moon in the foreground, dead as an old bone. Aloft, floating free beneath the moist, gleaming membrane of bright blue sky, is the rising earth, the only exuberant thing in this part of the cosmos. If you could look long enough, you would see the swirling of the great drifts of white cloud, covering and uncovering the half-hidden masses of land. If you had been looking for a very long, geologic time, you could have seen the continents themselves in motion, drifting apart on their crustal plates, held afloat by the fire beneath. It has the organized, self-contained look of a live creature, full of information, marvelously skilled in handling the sun.

It takes a membrane to make sense out of disorder in biology. You have to be able to catch energy and hold it, storing precisely the needed amount and releasing it in measured shares. A cell does this, and so do the organelles inside. Each assemblage is poised in the flow of solar energy, tapping off energy from metabolic surrogates of the sun. To stay alive, you have to be able to hold out against equilibrium, maintain imbalance, bank against entropy, and you can only transact this business with membranes in our kind of world.

When the earth came alive it began constructing its own membrane, for the general purpose of editing the sun. Originally, in the time of prebiotic elaboration of peptides and nucleotides from inorganic ingredients in the water on the earth, there was nothing to shield out ultraviolet radiation except the water itself. The first thin atmosphere came entirely from the degassing of the earth as it cooled, and there was only a vanishingly small trace of oxygen in it. Theoretically, there could have been some production of oxygen by photodissociation of water vapor in ultraviolet light, but not much. This process would have been self-limiting, as Urey showed, since the wave lengths needed for photolysis are the very ones screened out selectively by oxygen; the production of oxygen would have been cut off almost as soon as it occurred.

The formation of oxygen had to await the emergence of photosynthetic cells, and these were required to live in an environment with sufficient visible light for photosynthesis but shielded at the same time against lethal ultraviolet. Berkner and Marshall calculate that the green cells must therefore have been about ten meters below the surface of water, probably in pools and ponds shallow enough to lack strong convection currents (the ocean could not have been the starting place).

You could say that the breathing of oxygen into the atmosphere was the result of evolution, or you could turn it around and say that evolution was the result of oxygen. You can have it either way. Once the photosynthetic cells had appeared, very probably counterparts of today's blue-green algae, the future respiratory mechanism of the earth was set in place. Early on, when the level of oxygen had built up to around 1 per cent of today's atmospheric concentration, the anaerobic life of the earth was placed in jeopardy, and the inevitable next stage was the emergence of mutants with oxidative systems and ATP. With this, we were off to an explosive developmental stage in which great varieties of respiring life, including the multicellular forms, became feasible.

Berkner has suggested that there were two such explosions of new life, like vast embryological transformations, both dependent on threshold levels of oxygen. The first, at 1 per cent of the present level, shielded out enough ultraviolet radiation to permit cells to move into the surface layers of lakes, rivers, and oceans. This happened around 600 million years ago, at the beginning of the Paleozoic era, and accounts for the sudden abundance of marine fossils of all kinds in the record of this period. The second burst occurred when oxygen rose to 10 per cent of the present level. At this time, around 400 million years ago, there was a sufficient canopy to allow life out of the water and onto the land. From here on it was clear going, with nothing to restrain the variety of life except the limits of biologic inventiveness.

It is another illustration of our fantastic luck that oxygen filters out the very bands of ultraviolet light that are most devastating for nucleic acids and proteins, while allowing full penetration of the visible light needed for photosynthesis. If it had not been for this semipermeability, we could never have come along.

The earth breathes, in a certain sense. Berkner suggests that there may have been cycles of oxygen production and carbon dioxide consumption, depending on relative abundances of plant and animal life, with the ice ages representing periods of apnea. An overwhelming richness of vegetation may have caused the level of oxygen to rise above today's concentration, with a corresponding depletion of carbon dioxide. Such a drop in carbon dioxide may have impaired the "greenhouse" property of the atmosphere, which holds in the solar heat otherwise lost by radiation from the earth's surface. The fall in temperature would in turn have shut off much of living, and, in a long sigh, the level of oxygen may have dropped by 90 per cent. Berkner speculates that this is what happened to the great reptiles; their size may have been all right for a richly oxygenated atmosphere, but they had the bad luck to run out of air.

Now we are protected against lethal ultraviolet rays by a narrow rim of ozone, thirty miles out. We are safe, well ventilated, and incubated, provided we can avoid technologies that might fiddle with that ozone, or shift the levels of carbon dioxide. Oxygen is not a major worry for us, unless we let fly with enough nuclear explosives to kill off the green cells in the sea; if we do that, of course, we are in for strangling.

It is hard to feel affection for something as totally impersonal as the atmosphere, and yet there it is, as much a part and product of life as wine or bread. Taken all in all, the sky is a miraculous achievement. It works, and for what it is designed to accomplish it is as infallible as anything in nature. I doubt whether any of us could think of a way to improve on it, beyond maybe shifting a local cloud from here to there on occasion. The word "chance" does not serve to account well for structures of such magnificence. There may have been elements of luck in the emergence of chloroplasts, but once these things were on the scene, the evolution of the sky became absolutely ordained. Chance suggests alternatives, other possibilities, different solutions. This may be true for gills and swimbladders and forebrains, matters of detail, but not for the sky. There was simply no other way to go.

We should credit it for what it is: for sheer size and perfection of function, it is far and away the grandest product of collaboration in all of nature.

It breathes for us, and it does another thing for our pleasure. Each day, millions of meteorites fall against the outer limits of the membrane and are burned to nothing by the friction. Without this shelter, our surface would long since have become the pounded powder of the moon. Even though our receptors are not sensitive enough to hear it, there is comfort in knowing that the sound is there overhead, like the random noise of rain on the roof at night.

CHAPTER THIRTY

The Medusa and the Snail

WE'VE NEVER BEEN SO SELF-CONSCIOUS ABOUT OUR SELVES AS WE SEEM to be these days. The popular magazines are filled with advice on things to do with a self: how to find it, identify it, nurture it, protect it, even, for special occasions, weekends, how to lose it transiently. There are instructive books, best sellers on self-realization, self-help, self-development. Groups of self-respecting people pay large fees for three-day sessions together, learning self-awareness. Self-enlightenment can be taught in college electives.

You'd think, to read about it, that we'd only just now discovered selves. Having long suspected that there was *something alive* in there, running the place, separate from everything else, absolutely individual and independent, we've celebrated by giving it a real name. My self.

It is an interesting word, formed long ago in much more social ambiguity than you'd expect. The original root was *se* or *seu,* simply the pronoun of the third person, and most of the descendant words, except "self" itself, were constructed to allude to other, somehow connected people; "sibs" and "gossips," relatives and close acquaintances, came from *seu. Se* was also used to indicate something outside or apart, hence words like "separate," "secret," and "segregate." From an extended root *swedh* it moved into Greek as *ethnos,* meaning people of one's own sort, and *ethos,* meaning the customs of such people. "Ethics" means the behavior of people like one's self, one's own ethics.

We tend to think of our selves as the only wholly unique creations in nature, but it is not so. Uniqueness is so commonplace a property of living things that there is really nothing at all unique about it. A phenomenon can't be unique and universal at the same time. Even individual, free-swimming bacteria can be viewed as unique entities, distinguishable from each other even when they are the progeny of a single clone. Spudich and Koshland have recently reported that motile microorganisms of the same species are like solitary eccentrics in their swimming behavior. When they are searching for food, some tumble in one direction for precisely so many seconds before quitting, while others tumble differently and for different, but characteristic, periods of time. If you watch them closely, tethered by their flagellae to the surface of an antibody-coated slide, you can tell them from each other by the way they twirl, as accurately as though they had different names.

Beans carry self-labels, and are marked by these as distinctly as a mouse by his special smell. The labels are glycoproteins, the lectins, and may have something to do with negotiating the intimate and essential attachment between the bean and the nitrogen-fixing bacteria which live as part of the plant's flesh, embedded in root nodules. The lectin from one line of legume has a special affinity for the surfaces of the particular bacteria which colonize that line, but not for bacteria from other types of bean. The system seems designed for the maintenance of exclusive partnerships. Nature is pieced together by little snobberies like this.

Coral polyps are biologically self-conscious. If you place polyps of the same genetic line together, touching each other, they will fuse and become a single polyp, but if the lines are different, one will reject the other.

Fish can tell each other apart as individuals, by the smell of self. So can mice, and here the olfactory discrimination is governed by the same H2 locus which contains the genes for immunologic self-marking.

The only living units that seem to have no sense of privacy at all are the nucleated cells that have been detached from the parent organism and isolated in a laboratory dish. Given the opportunity, under the right conditions, two cells from wildly different sources, a yeast cell, say, and a chicken erythrocyte, will touch, fuse, and the two nuclei will then fuse as well, and the new hybrid cell will now divide into monstrous progeny. Naked cells, lacking self-respect, do not seem to have any sense of self.

The markers of self, and the sensing mechanisms responsible for detecting such markers, are conventionally regarded as mechanisms for maintaining individuality for its own sake, enabling one kind of creature to defend and protect itself against all the rest. Selfness, seen thus, is for self-preservation.

In real life, though, it doesn't seem to work this way. The self-marking of invertebrate animals in the sea, who must have perfected the business long before evolution got around to us, was set up in order to permit creatures of one kind to locate others, not for predation but to set up symbiotic households. The anemones who live on the shells of crabs are precisely finicky; so are the crabs. Only a single species of anemone will find its way to only a single species of crab. They sense each other exquisitely, and live together as though made for each other.

Sometimes there is such a mix-up about selfness that two creatures, each attracted by the molecular configuration of the other, incorporate the two selves to make a single organism. The best story I've ever heard about this is the tale told of the nudibranch and medusa living in the Bay of Naples. When first observed, the nudibranch, a common sea slug, was found to have a tiny vestigial parasite, in the form of a jellyfish, permanently affixed to the ventral surface near the mouth. In curiosity to learn how the medusa got there, some marine biologists began searching the local waters for earlier developmental forms, and discovered something amazing. The attached parasite, although apparently so specialized as to have given up living for itself, can still produce offspring, for they are found in abundance at certain seasons of the year. They drift through the upper waters, grow up nicely and astonishingly, and finally become full-grown, handsome, normal jellyfish. Meanwhile, the snail produces snail larvae, and these too begin to grow normally, but not for long. While still extremely small, they become entrapped in the tentacles of the medusa and then engulfed within the umbrella-shaped body. At first glance, you'd believe the medusae are now the predators, paying back for earlier humiliations, and the snails the prey. But no. Soon the snails, undigested and insatiable, begin to eat, browsing away first at the radial canals, then the borders of the rim, finally the tentacles, until the jellyfish becomes reduced in substance by being eaten while the snail grows correspondingly in size. At the end, the arrangement is back to the first scene, with a full-grown nudibranch basking, and nothing left of the jellyfish except the round, successfully edited parasite, safely affixed to the skin near the mouth.

It is a confusing tale to sort out, and even more confusing to think about. Both creatures are designed for this encounter, marked as selves so that they can find each other in the waters of the Bay of Naples. The collaboration, if you want to call it that, is entirely specific; it is only this species of medusa and only this kind of nudibranch that can come together and live this way. And, more surprising, they cannot live in any other way; they depend for their survival on each other. They are not really selves, they are specific *others*.

The thought of these creatures gives me an odd feeling. They do not remind me of anything, really. I've never heard of such a cycle before. They are bizarre, that's it, unique. And at the same time, like a vaguely remembered dream, they remind me of the whole earth at once. I cannot get my mind to stay still and think it through.

CHAPTER THIRTY-ONE

The Tucson Zoo

SCIENCE GETS MOST OF ITS INFORMATION BY THE PROCESS OF REDUC-
tionism, exploring the details, then the details of the details, until all the
smallest bits of the structure, or the smallest parts of the mechanism, are
laid out for counting and scrutiny. Only when this is done can the
investigation be extended to encompass the whole organism or the
entire system. So we say.

Sometimes it seems that we take a loss, working this way. Much of
today's public anxiety about science is the apprehension that we may
forever be overlooking the whole by an endless, obsessive preoccupation with the parts. I had a brief, personal experience of this misgiving
one afternoon in Tucson, where I had time on my hands and visited the
zoo, just outside the city. The designers there have cut a deep pathway
between two small artificial ponds, walled by clear glass, so when you
stand in the center of the path you can look into the depths of each pool,
and at the same time you can regard the surface. In one pool, on the right
side of the path, is a family of otters; on the other side, a family of
beavers. Within just a few feet from your face, on either side, beavers
and otters are at play, underwater and on the surface, swimming toward
your face and then away, more filled with life than any creatures I have
ever seen before, in all my days. Except for the glass, you could reach
across and touch them.

I was transfixed. As I now recall it, there was only one sensation in
my head: pure elation mixed with amazement at such perfection. Swept
off my feet, I floated from one side to the other, swiveling my brain,
staring astounded at the beavers, then at the otters. I could hear shouts
across my corpus callosum, from one hemisphere to the other. I remember thinking, with what was left in charge of my consciousness, that I
wanted no part of the science of beavers and otters; I wanted never to
know how they performed their marvels; I wished for no news about the
physiology of their breathing, the coordination of their muscles, their

vision, their endocrine systems, their digestive tracts. I hoped never to have to think of them as collections of cells. All I asked for was the full hairy complexity, then in front of my eyes, of whole, intact beavers and otters in motion.

It lasted, I regret to say, for only a few minutes, and then I was back in the late twentieth century, reductionist as ever, wondering about the details by force of habit, but not, this time, the details of otters and beavers. Instead, me. Something worth remembering had happened in my mind, I was certain of that; I would have put it somewhere in the brain stem; maybe this was my limbic system at work. I became a behavioral scientist, an experimental psychologist, an ethologist, and in the instant I lost all the wonder and the sense of being overwhelmed. I was flattened.

But I came away from the zoo with something, a piece of news about myself: I am coded, somehow, for otters and beavers. I exhibit instinctive behavior in their presence, when they are displayed close at hand behind glass, simultaneously below water and at the surface. I have receptors for this display. Beavers and otters possess a "releaser" for me, in the terminology of ethology, and the releasing was my experience. What was released? Behavior. What behavior? Standing, swiveling flabbergasted, feeling exultation and a rush of friendship. I could not, as the result of the transaction, tell you anything more about beavers and otters than you already know. I learned nothing new about them. Only about me, and I suspect also about you, maybe about human beings at large: we are endowed with genes which code out our reaction to beavers and otters, maybe our reaction to each other as well. We are stamped with stereotyped, unalterable patterns of response, ready to be released. And the behavior released in us, by such confrontations, is, essentially, a surprised affection. It is compulsory behavior and we can avoid it only by straining with the full power of our conscious minds, making up conscious excuses all the way. Left to ourselves, mechanistic and autonomic, we hanker for friends.

Everyone says, stay away from ants. They have no lessons for us; they are crazy little instruments, inhuman, incapable of controlling themselves, lacking manners, lacking souls. When they are massed together, all touching, exchanging bits of information held in their jaws like memoranda, they become a single animal. Look out for that. It is a debasement, a loss of individuality, a violation of human nature, an unnatural act.

Sometimes people argue this point of view seriously and with deep thought. Be individuals, solitary and selfish, is the message. Altruism, a jargon word for what used to be called love, is worse than weakness, it is sin, a violation of nature. Be separate. Do not be a social animal. But this is a hard argument to make convincingly when you have to depend on language to make it. You have to print up leaflets or publish books and get them bought and sent around, you have to turn up on television and catch the attention of millions of other human beings all at once, and then you have to say to all of them, all at once, all collected and paying attention: be solitary; do not depend on each other. You can't do this and keep a straight face.

Maybe altruism is our most primitive attribute, out of reach, beyond our control. Or perhaps it is immediately at hand, waiting to be released, disguised now, in our kind of civilization, as affection or friendship or attachment. I don't see why it should be unreasonable for all human beings to have strands of DNA coiled up in chromosomes, coding out instincts for usefulness and helpfulness. Usefulness may turn out to be the hardest test of fitness for survival, more important than aggression, more effective, in the long run, than grabbiness. If this is the sort of information biological science holds for the future, applying to us as well as to ants, then I am all for science.

One thing I'd like to know most of all: when those ants have made the Hill, and are all there, touching and exchanging, and the whole mass begins to behave like a single huge creature, and *thinks,* what on earth is that thought? And while you're at it, I'd like to know a second thing: when it happens, does any single ant know about it? Does his hair stand on end?

CHAPTER THIRTY-TWO

The Youngest
and Brightest
Thing Around

(Notes for a Medical School Commencement Address)

DOCTORS:

Somewhere, on some remote planet set at precisely the right distance from a star of just the right magnitude and the right temperature, on the other side of our galaxy, there is at this moment a committee nearing the end of a year-long study of our own tiny, provincial solar system. The intelligent beings of that place are putting their signatures (numbers of some sort, no doubt) to a paper which asserts, with finality, that life is out of the question here and the place is not worth an expedition. Their instruments have detected the presence of that most lethal of all gases, oxygen, and that is the end of that. They had planned to come, bringing along mobile factories for manufacturing life-giving ammonia, but what's the use of risking strangulation?

The only part of this scenario that I really believe is that committee. I take it as an article of faith that this is the most fundamental aspect of nature that we know about. If you are going to go looking for evidences of life on other celestial bodies, you need special instruments with delicate sensors for detecting the presence of committees. If there is life there, you will find consortia, collaborating groups, working parties, all over the place.

At least this is true for our kind of life.

Mars, from the look we've had at it thus far, is a horrifying place. It is, by all appearances, stone dead, surely the deadest place any of us has ever seen, hard to look at without flinching. Come to think of it, it is probably the only really dead place of any size we've ever caught a close glimpse of, and the near view is incredibly sad.

Or maybe there is life on Mars, and we've simply missed it so far. The innumerable consultants orbiting around NASA are confounded, just now, by intense arguments, highly technical, over this point. Could there be an island of life at the bottom of one of the Martian ravines? Shouldn't we set down fleets of wheeled vehicles on various parts of the surface, deployed to nose about from place to place, in and out of deep crevices, turning over rocks, sniffing for life? Maybe there is a single spot, just one, where living organisms are holed up.

Maybe so, but if so it would be the strangest thing of all, absolutely incomprehensible. For we are not familiar with this kind of living. We do not have solitary, isolated creatures. It is beyond our imagination to conceive of a single form of life that exists alone and independent, unattached to other forms.

If you dropped a vehicle, or a billion vehicles, for that matter, on our planet you might be able to find one or two lifeless spots, but only if you took very small samples. There are living cells in our hottest deserts and at the tops of our coldest mountains. Even in the ancient frozen rocks recently dug out in Antarctica there are endolithic organisms tucked up comfortably in porous spaces beneath the rock face, as much alive as the petunia in the florist's window.

If you did find a single form of life on Mars, in a single place, how would you go about explaining it? The technical term for this arrangement is a "closed ecosystem," and there is the puzzle. We do not have closed ecosystems here, at all. The only closed ecosystem we know about is the earth itself, and even here the term has to be expanded to include the sun as part of the system, and lord knows what sorts of essential minerals that have drifted onto our surface from outside, at one time or another long ago.

Everything here is alive thanks to the living of everything else. All the forms of life are connected. This is what I meant in proposing the committee as the basis of terrestrial life. The most centrally placed committee, carrying the greatest responsibility, more deeply involved in keeping the whole system running than any other body, or any other working part of the earth's whole body, is the vast community of prokaryotic, nonnucleated microbes. Without bacteria for starters, we would never have had enough oxygen to go around, nor could we have found and fixed the nitrogen for making enzymes, nor could we recycle the solid matter of life for new generations.

One technical definition of a system is as follows: a system is a structure of interacting, intercommunicating components that, as a group, act or operate individually and jointly to achieve a common goal through the concerted activity of the individual parts. This is, of course, a completely satisfactory definition of the earth, except maybe for that last part about a common goal. What on earth is *our* common goal? How did we ever get mixed up in a place like this?

This is the greatest discomfort for our species. Some of us simply write it off by announcing that our situation is ridiculous, that the whole place is ungovernable, and that our responsibilities are therefore to ourselves alone. And yet, there it is: we are components in a dense, fantastically complicated system of life, we are enmeshed in the inter-living, and we really don't know what we're up to.

The earth holds together, its tissues cohere, and it has the look of a structure that really would make comprehensible sense if only we knew enough about it. From a little way off, photographed from the moon, it seems to be a kind of organism. Looked at over its whole time, it is plainly in the process of developing, like an enormous embryo. It is, for all its stupendous size and the numberless units and infinite variety of its life forms, coherent. Every tissue is linked for its viability to every other tissue; it gets along by symbiosis, and the invention of new modes of symbiotic coupling is a fundamental process in its embryogenesis. We have no rules for the evolution of this kind of life. We have learned a lot, and in some biomathematical detail, about the laws governing the evolution of individual species on the earth, but no Darwin has yet emerged to take account of the orderly, coordinated growth and differentiation of the whole astonishing system, much less its seemingly permanent survival. It makes an interesting problem: how do mechanisms that seem to be governed entirely by chance and randomness bring into existence new species which fit so neatly and precisely, and usefully, as though they were the cells of an organism? This is a wonderful puzzle.

And now human beings have swarmed like bees over the whole surface, changing everything, meddling with all the other parts, making believe we are in charge, risking the survival of the entire magnificent creature.

You could forgive us, or excuse us anyway, on grounds of ignorance, and at least it can be said for us that we are, at long last, becoming aware of that. In no other century of our brief existence have human beings learned so deeply, and so painfully, the extent and depth of their ignorance about nature. We are beginning to confront this, and trying to do something about it with science, and this may save us all if we are clever enough, and lucky enough. But we are starting almost from scratch, and we have a long, long way to go.

Mind you, I do not wish to downgrade us; I believe fervently in our species and have no patience with the current fashion of running down the human being as a useful part of nature. On the contrary, we are a spectacular, splendid manifestation of life. We have language and can build metaphors as skillfully and precisely as ribosomes make proteins. We have affection. We have genes for usefulness, and usefulness is about as close to a "common goal" for all of nature as I can guess at. And finally, and perhaps best of all, we have music. Any species capable of producing, at this earliest, juvenile stage of its development—almost instantly after emerging on the earth by any evolutionary standard—the music of Johann Sebastian Bach, cannot be all bad. We ought to be able to feel more secure for our future, with Julian of Norwich at our elbow: "But all shall be well and all shall be well and all manner of thing shall be well." For our times of guilt we have Montaigne to turn to: "If it did not seem crazy to talk to oneself, there is not a day when I would not be heard growling at myself, 'Confounded fool.'"

But security is the last thing we feel entitled to feel. We are, perhaps uniquely among the earth's creatures, the worrying animal. We worry away our lives, fearing the future, discontent with the present, unable to take in the idea of dying, unable to sit still. We deserve a better press, in my view. We have always had a strong hunch about our origin, which does us credit; from the oldest language we know, the Indo-European tongue, we took the word for earth—*Dhghem*—and turned it into "humus" and "human"; "humble" too, which does us more credit. We are by all odds the most persistently and obsessively social of all species, more dependent on each other than the famous social insects, and really, when you look at us, infinitely more imaginative and deft at social living. We are good at this; it is the way we have built all our cultures and the literature of our civilizations. We have high expectations and set high standards for our social behavior, and when we fail at it and endanger the species—as we have done several times in this century— the strongest words we can find to condemn ourselves and our behavior are the telling words "inhuman" and "inhumane."

There is nothing at all absurd about the human condition. We matter. It seems to me a good guess, hazarded by a good many people who have thought about it, that we may be engaged in the formation of something like a mind for the life of this planet. If this is so, we are still at the most primitive stage, still fumbling with language and thinking, but infinitely capacitated for the future. Looked at this way, it is remarkable that we've come as far as we have in so short a period, really no time at all as geologists measure time. We are the newest, the youngest, and the brightest thing around.

CHAPTER THIRTY-THREE

On Magic in

Medicine

MEDICINE HAS ALWAYS BEEN UNDER PRESSURE TO PROVIDE PUBLIC
explanations for the diseases with which it deals, and the formulation of
comprehensive, unifying theories has been the most ancient and willing preoccupation of the profession. In the earliest days, hostile spirits
needing exorcism were the principal pathogens, and the shaman's duty
was simply the development of improved techniques for incantation.
Later on, especially in the Western world, the idea that the distribution
of body fluids among various organs determined the course of all
illnesses took hold, and we were in for centuries of bleeding, cupping,
sweating, and purging in efforts to intervene. Early in this century the
theory of autointoxication evolved, and a large part of therapy was
directed at emptying the large intestine and keeping it empty. Then the
global concept of focal infection became popular, accompanied by the
linked notion of allergy to the presumed microbial pathogens, and no
one knows the resulting toll of extracted teeth, tonsils, gallbladders, and
appendixes: the idea of psychosomatic influences on disease emerged in
the 1930s and, for a while, seemed to sweep the field.

Gradually, one by one, some of our worst diseases have been edited
out of such systems by having their causes indisputably identified and
dealt with. Tuberculosis was the paradigm. This was the most chronic
and inexorably progressive of common human maladies, capable of
affecting virtually every organ in the body and obviously influenced by
crowding, nutrition, housing, and poverty; theories involving the climate in general, and night air and insufficient sunlight in particular,
gave rise to the spa as a therapeutic institution. It was not until the

development of today's effective chemotherapy that it became clear to everyone that the disease had a single, dominant, central cause. If you got rid of the tubercle bacillus you were rid of the disease.

But that was some time ago, and today the idea that complicated diseases can have single causes is again out of fashion. The microbial infections that can be neatly coped with by antibiotics are regarded as lucky anomalies. The new theory is that most of today's human illnesses, the infections aside, are multifactorial in nature, caused by two great arrays of causative mechanisms: 1) the influence of things in the environment and 2) one's personal life-style. For medicine to become effective in dealing with such diseases, it has become common belief that the environment will have to be changed, and personal ways of living will also have to be transformed, and radically.

These things may turn out to be true, for all I know, but it will take a long time to get the necessary proofs. Meanwhile, the field is wide open for magic.

One great difficulty in getting straightforward answers is that so many of the diseases in question have unpredictable courses, and some of them have a substantial tendency toward spontaneous remission. In rheumatoid arthritis, for instance, when such widely disparate therapeutic measures as copper bracelets, a move to Arizona, diets low in sugar or salt or meat or whatever, and even an inspirational book have been accepted by patients as useful, the trouble in evaluation is that approximately 35 percent of patients with this diagnosis are bound to recover no matter what they do. But if you actually have rheumatoid arthritis or, for that matter, schizophrenia, and then get over it, or if you are a doctor and observe this to happen, it is hard to be persuaded that it wasn't *something* you did that was responsible. Hence you need very large numbers of patients and lots of time, and a cool head.

Magic is back again, and in full force. Laetrile cures cancer, acupuncture is useful for deafness and low-back pain, vitamins are good for anything, and meditation, yoga, dancing, biofeedback, and shouting one another down in crowded rooms over weekends are specifics for the human condition. Running, a good thing to be doing for its own sake, has acquired the medicinal value formerly attributed to rare herbs from Indonesia.

There is a recurring advertisement, placed by Blue Cross on the op-ed page of *The New York Times,* which urges you to take advantage of science by changing your life habits, with the suggestion that if you do so, by adopting seven easy-to-follow items of life-style, you can achieve eleven added years beyond what you'll get if you don't. Since today's average figure is around seventy-two for all parties in both sexes, this might mean going on until at least the age of eighty-three. You can do this formidable thing, it is claimed, by simply eating breakfast, exercising regularly, maintaining normal weight, not smoking cigarettes, not drinking excessively, sleeping eight hours each night, and not eating between meals.

The science which produced this illumination was a careful study by California epidemiologists, based on a questionnaire given to about seven thousand people. Five years after the questionnaire, a body count was made by sorting through the county death certificates, and the 371 people who had died were matched up with their answers to the questions. To be sure, there were more deaths among the heavy smokers and drinkers, as you might expect from the known incidence of lung cancer in smokers and cirrhosis and auto accidents among drinkers. But there was also a higher mortality among those who said they didn't eat breakfast, and even higher in those who took no exercise, no exercise at all, not even going off in the family car for weekend picnics. Being up to 20 percent overweight was not so bad, surprisingly, but being *underweight* was clearly associated with a higher death rate.

The paper describing these observations has been widely quoted, and not just by Blue Cross. References to the Seven Healthy Life Habits keep turning up in popular magazines and in the health columns of newspapers, always with that promise of eleven more years.

The findings fit nicely with what is becoming folk doctrine about disease. You become ill because of not living right. If you get cancer it is, somehow or other, your own fault. If you didn't cause it by smoking or drinking or eating the wrong things, it came from allowing yourself to persist with the wrong kind of personality, in the wrong environment. If you have a coronary occlusion, you didn't run enough. Or you were too tense, or you *wished* too much, and didn't get a good enough sleep. Or you got fat. Your fault.

But eating breakfast? It is a kind of enchantment, pure magic.

You have to read the report carefully to discover that there is another, more banal way of explaining the findings. Leave aside the higher deaths in heavy smokers and drinkers, for there is no puzzle in either case; these are dangerous things to do. But it is hard to imagine any good reason for dying within five years from not eating a good breakfast, or any sort of breakfast.

The other explanation turns cause and effect around. Among the people in that group of seven thousand who answered that they don't eat breakfast, don't go off on picnics, are underweight, and can't sleep properly, there were surely some who were already ill when the questionnaire arrived. They didn't eat breakfast because they couldn't stand the sight of food. They had lost their appetites, were losing weight, didn't feel up to moving around much, and had trouble sleeping. They didn't play tennis or go off on family picnics because they didn't *feel* good. Some of these people probably had an undetected cancer, perhaps of the pancreas; others may have had hypertension or early kidney failure or some other organic disease which the questionnaire had no way of picking up. The study did not ascertain the causes of death in the 371, but just a few deaths from such undiscerned disorders would have made a significant statistical impact. The author of the paper was careful to note these possible interpretations, although the point was not made strongly, and the general sense you have in reading it is that you can live on and on if only you will eat breakfast and play tennis.

The popular acceptance of the notion of Seven Healthy Life Habits, as a way of staying alive, says something important about today's public attitudes, or at least the attitudes in the public mind, about disease and dying. People have always wanted causes that are simple and easy to comprehend, and about which the individual can *do* something. If you believe that you can ward off the common causes of premature death — cancer, heart disease, and stroke, diseases whose pathogenesis we really do not understand — by jogging, hoping, and eating and sleeping regularly, these are good things to believe even if not necessarily true. Medicine has survived other periods of unifying theory, constructed to explain all of human disease, not always as benign in their effects as this one is likely to be. After all, if people can be induced to give up smoking, stop overdrinking and overeating, and take some sort of regular exercise, most of them are bound to feel the better for leading more orderly, regular lives, and many of them are surely going to look better.

Nobody can say an unfriendly word against the sheer goodness of keeping fit, but we should go carefully with the promises.

There is also a bifurcated ideological appeal contained in the seven-life-habits doctrine, quite apart from the subliminal notion of good luck in the numbers involved (7 come 11). Both ends of the political spectrum can find congenial items. At the further right, it is attractive to hear that the individual, the good old freestanding, free-enterprising American citizen, is responsible for his own health and when things go wrong it is his own damn fault for smoking and drinking and living wrong (and he can jolly well pay for it). On the other hand, at the left, it is nice to be told that all our health problems, including dying, are caused by failure of the community to bring up its members to live properly, and if you really want to improve the health of the people, research is not the answer; you should upheave the present society and invent a better one. At either end, you can't lose.

In between, the skeptics in medicine have a hard time of it. It is much more difficult to be convincing about ignorance concerning disease mechanisms than it is to make claims for full comprehension, especially when the comprehension leads, logically or not, to some sort of action. When it comes to serious illness, the public tends, understandably, to be more skeptical about the skeptics, more willing to believe the true believers. It is medicine's oldest dilemma, not to be settled by candor or by any kind of rhetoric; what it needs is a lot of time and patience, waiting for science to come in, as it has in the past, with the solid facts.

CHAPTER THIRTY-FOUR

The Wonderful

Mistake

THE GREATEST SINGLE ACHIEVEMENT OF NATURE TO DATE WAS SURELY the invention of the molecule of DNA. We have had it from the very beginning, built into the first cell to emerge, membranes and all, somewhere in the soupy water of the cooling planet three thousand million years or so ago. All of today's DNA, strung through all the cells of the earth, is simply an extension and elaboration of that first molecule. In a fundamental sense we cannot claim to have made progress, since the method used for growth and replication is essentially unchanged.

But we have made progress in all kinds of other ways. Although it is out of fashion today to talk of progress in evolution if you use that word to mean anything like improvement, implying some sort of value judgment beyond the reach of science, I cannot think of a better term to describe what has happened. After all, to have come all the way from a system of life possessing only one kind of primitive microbial cell, living out colorless lives in hummocks of algal mats, to what we see around us today—the City of Paris, the State of Iowa, Cambridge University, Woods Hole, the succession of travertine-lined waterfalls and lakes like flights of great stairs in Yugoslavia's Plitvice, the horse-chestnut tree in my backyard, and the columns of neurons arranged in modules in the cerebral cortex of vertebrates—*has* to represent improvement. We have come a long way on that old molecule.

We could never have done it with human intelligence, even if molecular biologists had been flown in by satellite at the beginning, laboratories and all, from some other solar system. We have evolved scientists, to be sure, and so we know a lot about DNA, but if our kind of mind had been confronted with the problem of designing a similar replicating molecule, starting from scratch, we'd never have succeeded. We would have made one fatal mistake: our molecule would have been perfect. Given enough time, we would have figured out how to do this, nucleotides, enzymes, and all, to make flawless, exact copies, but it would never have occurred to us, thinking as we do, that the thing had to be able to make errors.

The capacity to blunder slightly is the real marvel of DNA. Without this special attribute, we would still be anaerobic bacteria and there would be no music. Viewed individually, one by one, each of the mutations that have brought us along represents a random, totally spontaneous accident, but it is no accident at all that mutations occur; the molecule of DNA was ordained from the beginning to make small mistakes.

If we had been doing it, we would have found some way to correct this, and evolution would have been stopped in its tracks. Imagine the consternation of human scientists, successfully engaged in the letter-perfect replication of prokaryotes, nonnucleated cells like bacteria, when nucleated cells suddenly turned up. Think of the agitated commissions assembled to explain the scandalous proliferation of trilobites all over the place, the mass firings, the withdrawal of tenure.

To err is human, we say, but we don't like the idea much, and it is harder still to accept the fact that erring is biological as well. We prefer sticking to the point, and insuring ourselves against change. But there it is: we are here by the purest chance, and by mistake at that. Somewhere along the line, nucleotides were edged apart to let new ones in; maybe viruses moved in, carrying along bits of other, foreign genomes; radiation from the sun or from outer space caused tiny cracks in the molecule, and humanity was conceived.

And maybe, given the fundamental instability of the molecule, it had to turn out this way. After all, if you have a mechanism designed to keep changing the ways of living, and if all the new forms have to fit together as they plainly do, and if every improvised new gene representing an embellishment in an individual is likely to be selected for the species, and if you have enough time, maybe the system is simply bound to develop brains sooner or later, and awareness.

Biology needs a better word than "error" for the driving force in evolution. Or maybe "error" will do after all, when you remember that it came from an old root meaning to wander about, looking for something.

CHAPTER THIRTY-FIVE

Ponds

LARGE AREAS OF MANHATTAN ARE AFLOAT. I REMEMBER WHEN THE new Bellevue Hospital was being built, fifteen years ago; the first stage was the most spectacular and satisfying, an enormous square lake. It was there for the two years, named Lake Bellevue, while the disconsolate Budget Bureau went looking for cash to build the next stage. It was fenced about and visible only from the upper windows of the old hospital, but pretty to look at, cool and blue in midsummer, frozen gleaming as Vermont in January. The fence, like all city fences, was always broken, and we could have gone down to the lake and used it, but it was known to be an upwelling of the East River. At Bellevue there were printed rules about the East River: if anyone fell in, it was an emergency for the Infectious-Disease Service, and the first measures, after resuscitation, were massive doses of whatever antibiotics the hospital pharmacy could provide.

But if you cleaned the East River you could have ponds all over town, up and down the East Side of Manhattan anyway. If you lifted out the Empire State Building and the high structures nearby, you would have, instantly, an inland sea. A few holes bored in the right places would let water into the subways, and you'd have lovely underground canals all across to the Hudson, uptown to the Harlem River, downtown to the Battery, a Venice underground, without pigeons.

It wouldn't work, though, unless you could find a way to keep out the fish. New Yorkers cannot put up with live fish out in the open. I cannot explain this, but it is so.

There is a new pond, much smaller than Lake Bellevue, on First Avenue between Seventieth and Seventy-first, on the east side of the street. It emerged sometime last year, soon after a row of old flats had been torn down and the hole dug for a new apartment building. By now it is about average size for Manhattan, a city block long and about forty feet across, maybe eight feet deep at the center, more or less kidney-shaped, rather like an outsized suburban swimming pool except for the things floating, and now the goldfish.

With the goldfish, it is almost detestable. There are, clearly visible from the sidewalk, hundreds of them. The neighborhood people do not walk by and stare into it through the broken fence, as would be normal for any other Manhattan pond. They tend to cross the street, looking away.

Now there are complaints against the pond, really against the goldfish. How could people do such a thing? Bad enough for pet dogs and cats to be abandoned, but who could be so unfeeling as to abandon goldfish? They must have come down late at night, carrying their bowls, and simply dumped them in. How could they?

The ASPCA was called, and came one afternoon with a rowboat. Nets were used, and fish taken away in new custodial bowls, some to Central Park, others to ASPCA headquarters, to the fish pound. But the goldfish have multiplied, or maybe those people with their bowls keep coming down late at night for their furtive, unfeeling dumping. Anyway, there are too many fish for the ASPCA, for which this seems to be a new kind of problem. An official stated for the press that the owners of the property would be asked to drain the pond by pumping, and then the ASPCA would come back with nets to catch them all.

You'd think they were rats or roaches, the way people began to talk. Get those goldfish out of that pond, I don't care how you do it. Dynamite, if necessary. But get rid of them. Winter is coming, someone said, and it is deep enough so that they'll be swimming around underneath the ice. Get them out.

It is this knowledge of the East River, deep in the minds of all Manhattan residents, more than the goldfish themselves, I think. Goldfish in a glass bowl are harmless to the human mind, maybe even helpful to minds casting about for something, anything, to think about. But goldfish let loose, propagating themselves, worst of all *surviving* in what has to be a sessile eddy of the East River, somehow threaten us all. We do not like to think that life is possible under some conditions, especially the conditions of a Manhattan pond. There are four abandoned tires, any number of broken beer bottles, fourteen shoes and a single sneaker, and a visible layer, all over the surface, of that grayish-green film that settles on all New York surfaces. The mud at the banks of the pond is not proper country mud but reconstituted Manhattan landfill, ancient garbage, fossilized coffee grounds and grapefruit rind, the defecation of a city. For goldfish to be swimming in such water, streaking back and forth mysteriously in small schools, feeding, obviously feeding, looking as healthy and well-off as goldfish in the costliest kind of window-box aquarium, means something is wrong with our standards. It is, in some deep sense beyond words, insulting.

I thought I noticed a peculiar sort of fin on the undersurface of two of the fish. Perhaps, it occurs to me now in a rush of exultation, in such a pond as this, with all its chemical possibilities, there are contained some mutagens, and soon there will be schools of mutant goldfish. Give them just a little more time, I thought. And then, with the most typically Manhattan thought I've ever thought, I thought: The ASPCA will come again, next month, with their rowboat and their nets. The proprietor will begin pumping out the pond. The nets will flail, the rowboat will settle, and then the ASPCA officials will give a sudden shout of great dismay. And with a certain amount of splashing and grayish-greenish spray, at all the edges of the pond, up all the banks of ancient New York landfill mud, crawling on their new little feet, out onto the sidewalks, up and down and across the street, into doorways and up the fire escapes, some of them with little suckers on their little feet, up the sides of buildings and into open windows, looking for something, will come the goldfish.

It won't last, of course. Nothing like this ever does. The mayor will come and condemn it in person. The Health Department will come and recommend the purchase of cats from out of town because of the constitutional boredom of city cats. The NIH will send up teams of professionals from Washington with a new kind of antifish spray, which will be recalled four days later because of toxicity to cats.

After a few weeks it will be finished anyway, like a lot of New York events. The goldfish will dive deep and vanish, the pond will fill up with sneakers, workmen will come and pour concrete over everything, and by next year the new building will be up and occupied by people all unaware of their special environmental impact. But what a time it was.

CHAPTER THIRTY-SIX

To Err Is Human

EVERYONE MUST HAVE HAD AT LEAST ONE PERSONAL EXPERIENCE WITH a computer error by this time. Bank balances are suddenly reported to have jumped from $379 into the millions, appeals for charitable contributions are mailed over and over to people with crazy-sounding names at your address, department stores send the wrong bills, utility companies write that they're turning everything off, that sort of thing. If you manage to get in touch with someone and complain, you then get instantaneously typed, guilty letters from the same computer, saying, "Our computer was in error, and an adjustment is being made in your account."

These are supposed to be the sheerest, blindest accidents. Mistakes are not believed to be part of the normal behavior of a good machine. If things go wrong, it must be a personal, human error, the result of fingering, tampering, a button getting stuck, someone hitting the wrong key. The computer, at its normal best, is infallible.

I wonder whether this can be true. After all, the whole point of computers is that they represent an extension of the human brain, vastly improved upon but nonetheless human, superhuman maybe. A good computer can think clearly and quickly enough to beat you at chess, and some of them have even been programmed to write obscure verse. They can do anything we can do, and more besides.

It is not yet known whether a computer has its own consciousness, and it would be hard to find out about this. When you walk into one of those great halls now built for the huge machines, and stand listening, it is easy to imagine that the faint, distant noises are the sound of thinking, and the turning of the spools gives them the look of wild creatures rolling their eyes in the effort to concentrate, choking with information. But real thinking, and dreaming, are other matters.

On the other hand, the evidences of something like an *unconscious,* equivalent to ours, are all around, in every mail. As extensions of the human brain, they have been constructed with the same property of error, spontaneous, uncontrolled, and rich in possibilities.

Mistakes are at the very base of human thought, embedded there, feeding the structure like root nodules. If we were not provided with the knack of being wrong, we could never get anything useful done. We think our way along by choosing between right and wrong alternatives, and the wrong choices have to be made as frequently as the right ones. We get along in life this way. We are built to make mistakes, coded for error.

We learn, as we say, by "trial and error." Why do we always say that? Why not "trial and rightness" or "trial and triumph"? The old phrase puts it that way because that is, in real life, the way it is done.

A good laboratory, like a good bank or a corporation or government, has to run like a computer. Almost everything is done flawlessly, by the book, and all the numbers add up to the predicted sums. The days go by. And then, if it is a lucky day, and a lucky laboratory, somebody makes a mistake: the wrong buffer, something in one of the blanks, a decimal misplaced in reading counts, the warm room off by a degree and a half, a mouse out of his box, or just a misreading of the day's protocol. Whatever, when the results come in, something is obviously screwed up, and then the action can begin.

The misreading is not the important error; it opens the way. The next step is the crucial one. If the investigator can bring himself to say, "But even so, look at that!" then the new finding, whatever it is, is ready for snatching. What is needed, for progress to be made, is the move based on the error.

Whenever new kinds of thinking are about to be accomplished, or new varieties of music, there has to be an argument beforehand. With two sides debating in the same mind, haranguing, there is an amiable understanding that one is right and the other wrong. Sooner or later the thing is settled, but there can be no action at all if there are not the two sides, and the argument. The hope is in the faculty of wrongness, the tendency toward error. The capacity to leap across mountains of information to land lightly on the wrong side represents the highest of human endowments.

It may be that this is a uniquely human gift, perhaps even stipulated in our genetic instructions. Other creatures do not seem to have DNA sequences for making mistakes as a routine part of daily living, certainly not for programmed error as a guide for action.

We are at our human finest, dancing with our minds, when there are more choices than two. Sometimes there are ten, even twenty different ways to go, all but one bound to be wrong, and the richness of selection in such situations can lift us onto totally new ground. This process is called exploration and is based on human fallibility. If we had only a single center in our brains, capable of responding only when a correct decision was to be made, instead of the jumble of different, credulous, easily conned clusters of neurons that provide for being flung off into blind alleys, up trees, down dead ends, out into blue sky, along wrong turnings, around bends, we could only stay the way we are today, stuck fast.

The lower animals do not have this splendid freedom. They are limited, most of them, to absolute infallibility. Cats, for all their good side, never make mistakes. I have never seen a maladroit, clumsy, or blundering cat. Dogs are sometimes fallible, occasionally able to make charming minor mistakes, but they get this way by trying to mimic their masters. Fish are flawless in everything they do. Individual cells in a tissue are mindless machines, perfect in their performance, as absolutely inhuman as bees.

We should have this in mind as we become dependent on more complex computers for the arrangement of our affairs. Give the computers their heads, I say; let them go their way. If we can learn to do this, turning our heads to one side and wincing while the work proceeds, the possibilities for the future of mankind, and computerkind, are limitless. Your average good computer can make calculations in an instant which would take a lifetime of slide rules for any of us. Think of what we could gain from the near infinity of precise, machine-made miscomputation which is now so easily within our grasp. We would begin the solving of some of our hardest problems. How, for instance, should we go about organizing ourselves for social living on a planetary scale, now that we have become, as a plain fact of life, a single community? We can assume, as a working hypothesis, that all the right ways of doing this are unworkable. What we need, then, for moving ahead, is a set of wrong alternatives much longer and more interesting than the short list of mistaken courses that any of us can think up right now. We need, in fact, an infinite list, and when it is printed out we need the computer to turn on itself and select, at random, the next way to go. If it is a big enough mistake, we could find ourselves on a new level, stunned, out in the clear, ready to move again.

CHAPTER THIRTY-SEVEN

The Selves

THERE ARE PSYCHIATRIC PATIENTS WHO ARE SAID TO BE INCAPACI-
tated by having more than one self. One of these, an attractive intelligent young woman in distress, turned up on a television talk show a
while back, sponsored to reveal her selves and their disputes. She
possessed, she said, or was possessed by, no fewer than eight other
separate women, all different, with different names, arguing and
elbowing their way into control of the enterprise, causing unending
confusion and embarrassment. She (they) wished to be rid of all of them
(her), except of course herself (themselves).

People like this are called hysterics by the professionals, or maybe
schizophrenics, and there is, I am told, nothing much that can be done.
Having more than one self is supposed to be deeply pathological in
itself, and there is no known way to evict trespassers.

I am not sure that the number of different selves is in itself all that
pathological; I hope not. Eight strikes me personally as a reasonably
small and easily manageable number. It is the simultaneity of their
appearance that is the real problem, and I should think psychiatry would
do better by simply persuading them to queue up and wait their turn, as
happens in the normal rest of us. Couldn't they be conditioned some
way, by offering rewards or holding out gently threatening sanctions?
"How *do* you do, I'm absolutely delighted to see you here and I have
exactly fifty-five minutes, after which I very much regret to say someone else will be dropping in, but could I see you again tomorrow at this
same time, do have a chocolate mint and let's just talk, just the two of
us." That sort of thing might help at least to get them lined up in some
kind of order.

Actually, it would embarrass me to be told that more than a single self
is a kind of disease. I've had, in my time, more than I could possibly
count or keep track of. The great difference, which keeps me feeling

normal, is that mine (ours) have turned up one after the other, on an orderly schedule. Five years ago I was another person, juvenile, doing and saying things I couldn't possibly agree with now. Ten years ago I was a stranger. Twenty—forty years ago . . . I've forgotten. The only thing close to what you might call illness, in my experience, was in the gaps in the queue when one had finished and left the place before the next one was ready to start, and there was nobody around at all. Luckily, that has happened only three or four times that I can recall, once when I'd become a very old child and my adolescent hadn't appeared, and a couple of times later on when there seemed to be some confusion about who was next up. The rest of the time they have waited turns and emerged on cue ready to take over, sometimes breathless and needing last-minute briefing but nonetheless steady enough to go on. The surprising thing has always been how little background information they seemed to need, considering how the times changed. I cannot remember who it was five years ago. He was reading linguistics and had just discovered philology, as I recall, but he left before getting anything much done.

To be truthful there have been a few times when they were all there at once, like those girls on television, clamoring for attention, whole committees of them, a House Committee, a Budget Committee, a Grievance Committee, even a Committee on Membership, although I don't know how any of them ever got in. No chairman, ever, certainly not me. At the most I'm a sort of administrative assistant. There's never an agenda. At the end I bring in the refreshments.

What do we meet about? It is hard to say. The door bangs open and in they come, calling for the meeting to start, and then they all talk at once. Odd to say, it is not just a jumble of talk; they tend to space what they're saying so that words and phrases from one will fit into short spaces left in silence by the others. At good times it has the feel of an intensely complicated conversation, but at others the sounds are more like something overheard in a crowded station. At worse times the silences get out of synchrony, interrupting each other; it is as though all the papers had suddenly blown off the table.

We never get anything settled. In recent years I've sensed an increase in their impatience with me, whoever they think I am, and with the fix they're in. They don't come right out and say so, but what they are beginning to want more than anything else is a chairman.

The worst times of all have been when I've wanted to be just one. Try walking out on the ocean beach at night, looking at stars, thinking, Be one, be one. Doesn't work, ever. Just when you feel ascension, turning, wheeling, and that whirring sound like a mantel clock getting ready to strike, the other selves begin talking. Whatever you're thinking, they say, it's not like that at all.

The only way to quiet them down, get them to stop, is to play music. That does it. Bach stops them every time, in their tracks, almost as though that's what they've been waiting for.

CHAPTER THIRTY-EIGHT

The Health-Care System

THE HEALTH-CARE SYSTEM OF THIS COUNTRY IS A STAGGERING ENTER-
prise, in any sense of the adjective. Whatever the failures of distribution
and lack of coordination, it is the gigantic scale and scope of the total
collective effort that first catches the breath, and its cost. The dollar
figures are almost beyond grasping. They vary from year to year,
always upward, ranging from something like $10 billion in 1950 to an
estimated $140 billion in 1978, with much more to come in the years
just ahead, whenever a national health-insurance program is installed.
The official guess is that we are now investing a round 8 percent of the
GNP in Health; it could soon rise to 10 or 12 percent.

Those are the official numbers, and only for the dollars that flow in an
authorized way—for hospital charges, physician's fees, prescribed
drugs, insurance premiums, the construction of facilities, research, and
the like.

But these dollars are only part of it. Why limit the estimates to the
strictly professional costs? There is another huge marketplace, in which
vast sums are exchanged for items designed for the improvement of
Health.

The television and radio industry, no small part of the national
economy, feeds on Health, or, more precisely, on disease, for a large part
of its sustenance. Not just the primarily medical dramas and the illness
or surgical episodes threaded through many of the nonmedical stories,
in which the central human dilemma is illness; almost all the commercial announcements, in an average evening, are pitches for items to
restore failed health: things for stomach gas, constipation, headaches,

nervousness, sleeplessness or sleepiness, arthritis, anemia, disquiet, and the despair of malodorousness, sweat, yellowed teeth, dandruff, furuncles, piles. The food industry plays the role of surrogate physician, advertising breakfast cereals as though they were tonics, vitamins, restoratives; they are now out-hawked by the specialized Health-food industry itself, with its nonpolluted, organic, "naturally" vitalizing products. Chewing gum is sold as a tooth cleanser. Vitamins have taken the place of prayer.

The publishing industry, hardcover, paperbacks, magazines, and all, seems to be kept alive by Health, new techniques for achieving mental health, cures for arthritis, and diets mostly for the improvement of everything.

The transformation of our environment has itself become an immense industry, costing rather more than the moon, in aid of Health. Pollution is supposed to be primarily a medical problem; when the television weatherman tells whether New York's air is "acceptable" or not that day, he is talking about human lungs, he believes. Pollutants which may be impairing photosynthesis by algae in the world's oceans, or destroying all the life in topsoil, or killing all the birds are being worried about lest they cause cancer in us, for heaven's sake.

Tennis has become more than the national sport; it is a rigorous discipline, a form of collective physiotherapy. Jogging is done by swarms of people, out onto the streets each day in underpants, moving in a stolid sort of rapid trudge, hoping by this to stay alive. Bicycles are cures. Meditation may be good for the soul but it is even better for the blood pressure.

As a people, we have become obsessed with Health.

There is something fundamentally, radically unhealthy about all this. We do not seem to be seeking more exuberance in living as much as staving off failure, putting off dying. We have lost all confidence in the human body.

The new consensus is that we are badly designed, intrinsically fallible, vulnerable to a host of hostile influences inside and around us, and only precariously alive. We live in danger of falling apart at any moment, and are therefore always in need of surveillance and propping up. Without the professional attention of a health-care system, we would fall in our tracks.

This is a new way of looking at things, and perhaps it can only be accounted for as a manifestation of spontaneous, undirected, societal *propaganda*. We keep telling each other this sort of thing, and back it comes on television or in the weekly newsmagazines, confirming all the fears, instructing us, as in the usual final paragraph of the personal-advice columns in the daily paper, to "seek professional help." Get a checkup. Go on a diet. Meditate. Jog. Have some surgery. Take two tablets, with water. *Spring* water. If pain persists, if anomie persists, if boredom persists, see your doctor.

It is extraordinary that we have just now become convinced of our bad health, our constant jeopardy of disease and death, at the very time when the facts should be telling us the opposite. In a more rational world, you'd think we would be staging bicentennial ceremonies for the celebration of our general good shape. In the year 1976, out of a population of around 220 million, only 1.9 million died, or just under 1 percent, not at all a discouraging record once you accept the fact of mortality itself. The life expectancy for the whole population rose to seventy-two years, the longest stretch ever achieved in this country. Despite the persisting roster of still-unsolved major diseases—cancer, heart disease, stroke, arthritis, and the rest—most of us have a clear, unimpeded run at a longer and healthier lifetime than could have been foreseen by any earlier generation. The illnesses that plague us the most, when you count up the numbers in the U.S. Vital Statistics reports, are respiratory and gastrointestinal infections, which are, by and large, transient, reversible affairs needing not much more than Grandmother's advice for getting through safely. Thanks in great part to the improved sanitary engineering, nutrition, and housing of the past century, and in real but less part to contemporary immunization and antibiotics, we are free of the great infectious diseases, especially tuberculosis and lobar pneumonia, which used to cut us down long before our time. We are even beginning to make progress in our understanding of the mechanisms underlying the chronic illnesses still with us, and sooner or later, depending on the quality and energy of biomedical research, we will learn to cope effectively with most of these, maybe all. We will still age away and die, but the aging, and even the dying, can become a healthy process. On balance, we ought to be more pleased with ourselves than we are, and more optimistic for the future.

The trouble is, we are being taken in by the propaganda, and it is bad not only for the spirit of society; it will make any health-care system, no matter how large and efficient, unworkable. If people are educated to believe that they are fundamentally fragile, always on the verge of mortal disease, perpetually in need of support by health-care professionals at every side, always dependent on an imagined discipline of "preventive" medicine, there can be no limit to the numbers of doctors' offices, clinics, and hospitals required to meet the demand. In the end, we would all become doctors, spending our days screening each other for disease.

We are, in real life, a reasonably healthy people. Far from being ineptly put together, we are amazingly tough, durable organisms, full of health, ready for most contingencies. The new danger to our well-being, if we continue to listen to all the talk, is in becoming a nation of healthy hypochondriacs, living gingerly, worrying ourselves half to death.

And we do not have time for this sort of thing anymore, nor can we afford such a distraction from our other, considerably more urgent problems. Indeed, we should be worrying that our preoccupation with personal health may be a symptom of copping out, an excuse for running upstairs to recline on a couch, sniffing the air for contaminants, spraying the room with deodorants, while just outside, the whole of society is coming undone.

CHAPTER THIRTY-NINE

On Cloning a

Human Being

IT IS NOW THEORETICALLY POSSIBLE TO RECREATE AN IDENTICAL creature from any animal or plant, from the DNA contained in the nucleus of any somatic cell. A single plant root-tip cell can be teased and seduced into conceiving a perfect copy of the whole plant; a frog's intestinal epithelial cell possesses the complete instructions needed for a new, same frog. If the technology were further advanced, you could do this with a human being, and there are now startled predictions all over the place that this will in fact be done, someday, in order to provide a version of immortality for carefully selected, especially valuable people.

The cloning of humans is on most of the lists of things to worry about from Science, along with behavior control, genetic engineering, transplanted heads, computer poetry, and the unrestrained growth of plastic flowers.

Cloning is the most dismaying of prospects, mandating as it does the elimination of sex with only a metaphoric elimination of death as compensation. It is almost no comfort to know that one's cloned, identical surrogate lives on, especially when the living will very likely involve edging one's real, now aging self off to the side, sooner or later. It is hard to imagine anything like filial affection or respect for a single, unmated nucleus; harder still to think of one's new, self-generated self as anything but an absolute, desolate orphan. Not to mention the complex interpersonal relationship involved in raising one's self from infancy, teaching the language, enforcing discipline, instilling good manners, and the like. How would you feel if you became an incorrigible juvenile delinquent by proxy, at the age of fifty-five?

The public questions are obvious. Who is to be selected, and on what qualifications? How to handle the risks of misused technology, such as self-determined cloning by the rich and powerful but socially objectionable, or the cloning by governments of dumb, docile masses for the world's work? What will be the effect on all the uncloned rest of us of human sameness? After all, we've accustomed ourselves through hundreds of millennia to the continual exhilaration of uniqueness; each of us is totally different, in a fundamental sense, from all the other four billion. Selfness is an essential fact of life. The thought of human nonselfness, precise sameness, is terrifying, when you think about it.

Well, don't think about it, because it isn't a probable possibility, not even as a long shot for the distant future, in my opinion. I agree that you might clone some people who would look amazingly like their parental cell donors, but the odds are that they'd be almost as different as you or me, and certainly more different than any of today's identical twins.

The time required for the experiment is only one of the problems, but a formidable one. Suppose you wanted to clone a prominent, spectacularly successful diplomat, to look after the Middle East problems of the distant future. You'd have to catch him and persuade him, probably not very hard to do, and extirpate a cell. But then you'd have to wait for him to grow up through embryonic life and then for at least forty years more, and you'd have to be sure all observers remained patient and unmeddlesome through his unpromising, ambiguous childhood and adolescence.

Moreover, you'd have to be sure of recreating his environment, perhaps down to the last detail. "Environment" is a word which really means people, so you'd have to do a lot more cloning than just the diplomat himself.

This is a very important part of the cloning problem, largely overlooked in our excitement about the cloned individual himself. You don't have to agree all the way with B. F. Skinner to acknowledge that the environment does make a difference, and when you examine what we really mean by the word "environment" it comes down to other human beings. We use euphemisms and jargon for this, like "social forces," "cultural influences," even Skinner's "verbal community," but what is meant is the dense crowd of nearby people who talk to, listen to, smile or frown at, give to, withhold from, nudge, push, caress, or flail out at the individual. No matter what the genome says, these people have a lot to do with shaping a character. Indeed, if all you had was the genome, and no people around, you'd grow a sort of vertebrate plant, nothing more.

So, to start with, you will undoubtedly need to clone the parents. No question about this. This means the diplomat is out, even in theory,

since you couldn't have gotten cells from both his parents at the time
when he was himself just recognizable as an early social treasure. You'd
have to limit the list of clones to people already certified as sufficiently
valuable for the effort, with both parents still alive. The parents would
need cloning and, for consistency, their parents as well. I suppose you'd
also need the usual informed-consent forms, filled out and signed, not
easy to get if I know parents, even harder for grandparents.

But this is only the beginning. It is the whole family that really
influences the way a person turns out, not just the parents, according to
current psychiatric thinking. Clone the family.

Then what? The way each member of the family develops has already
been determined by the environment set around him, and this environment is more people, people outside the family, schoolmates,
acquaintances, lovers, enemies, car-pool partners, even, in special circumstances, peculiar strangers across the aisle on the subway. Find
them, and clone them.

But there is no end to the protocol. Each of the outer contacts has his
own surrounding family, and his and their outer contacts. Clone them
all.

To do the thing properly, with any hope of ending up with a genuine
duplicate of a single person, you really have no choice. You must clone
the world, no less.

We are not ready for an experiment of this size, nor, I should think,
are we willing. For one thing, it would mean replacing today's world by
an entirely identical world to follow immediately, and this means no
new, natural, spontaneous, random, chancy children. No children at
all, except for the manufactured doubles of those now on the scene. Plus
all those identical adults, including all of today's politicians, all seen
double. It is too much to contemplate.

Moreover, when the whole experiment is finally finished, fifty years
or so from now, how could you get a responsible scientific reading on
the outcome? Somewhere in there would be the original clonee, probably lost and overlooked, now well into middle age, but everyone around
him would be precise duplicates of today's everyone. It would be today's
same world, filled to overflowing with duplicates of today's people and
their same, duplicated problems, probably all resentful at having had to
go through our whole thing all over, sore enough at the clonee to make
endless trouble for him, if they found him.

And obviously, if the whole thing were done precisely right, they
would still be casting about for ways to solve the problem of universal
dissatisfaction, and sooner or later they'd surely begin to look around at
each other, wondering who should be cloned for his special value to

society, to get us out of all this. And so it would go, in regular cycles, perhaps forever.

I once lived through a period when I wondered what Hell could be like, and I stretched my imagination to try to think of a perpetual sort of damnation. I have to confess, I never thought of anything like this.

I have an alternative suggestion, if you're looking for a way out. Set cloning aside, and don't try it. Instead, go in the other direction. Look for ways to get mutations more quickly, new variety, different songs. Fiddle around, if you must fiddle, but never with ways to keep things the same, no matter who, not even yourself. Heaven, somewhere ahead, has got to be a change.

CHAPTER FORTY

On Etymons and Hybrids

AN ETYMON IS SUPPOSED TO BE A PURE ORE OF A WORD, CRYSTALLINE, absolutely original, signifying just what it was always intended to signify. They are very rare these days. Most of the words we use are hybrids, pieced together out of old, used speech by a process rather like the recycling of waste. We keep stores of discarded words around, out beyond the suburbs of our minds, stacked like scrap metal.

When you do run across a primary, original word, the experience is both disturbing and vaguely pleasurable, like coming across a friend's picture in an old high-school annual. They are all very old, and the most meaningful ones date all the way back to Indo-European roots which became the parents of cognate words in Sanskrit, Persian, Greek, Latin, and, much later, most of the English language. *Sen* meant old, *spreg* meant speak, *swem* was swim, *nomen* was name, a *porko* was a young pig, *dent* was a tooth. *Eg* was I and my ego, *tu* was thou, *yu* were you, and *me* was me. *Nek* was death. A *mormor* was a murmur. *Mater, pater, bhrater,* and *swesor* were the immediate family, and *nepots* were the nephews and nieces. A *yero* was a year. A *wopsa* was a wasp and an *aspa* was an aspen. A *deru* was a tree, and also something durable and true. To *gno* was to know. *Akwa* was water, and to *bhreu* was to boil. Using basic Indo-European and waving your hands, you could get around the world almost as well as with New York English.

Some of the first words have changed their meaning drastically, of course. *Bhedh* was the source of our "bead," but it originally meant to ask or bid; "bead" started out as a word for prayer. *Dheye* meant to look and see, and moved from *dhyana* in Sanskrit, meaning to meditate, to *jhana* in Pali, to *ch'an* in Chinese, to *zen* in Japanese.

You'd think modern science would be inventing lots of brand-new etymons to meet its needs, but it is not so. Most of our terms for new things are reconditioned words. "Thermodynamics," first spoken a century ago, is an antique shop: the Indo-European *gwher,* meaning warm, was turned into *thermos* in Greek, while *deu,* to do, became *dunesthai* in Greek, meaning capable of, and hence dynamic (the same *deu* is the source of "dynamite," "bonus," and "bonbon"). A "bit," in computer jargon, although designed as the least ambiguous of terms by combining parts of "binary" and "digit," has a tangle of meanings in its origin: "binary" came from *dwo,* meaning two, which led also to "twig," "double," and "doubt"; "digit" began as *deik,* to show or teach, and moved into English in company with "token," "paradigm," and "ditto," also "toe."

A nucleic acid (from *ken,* later *knu,* plus *ak*) is a sort of nut coupled to something sharp.

"Cholera toxin" could be translated by an outsider new to our language as a bright and shiny bow and arrow. *Ghel* was at first the word for shining, later yellow; it turned to *ghola,* then *khole* in Greek, meaning bile, then into "choler" and "cholera" in English. "Toxin" was originally *tekw,* a word meaning to run or flee, later becoming *toxsa* in Persian and *toxon* in Greek, meaning bow and arrow; the toxin meaning may have come from the poison used to tip the arrows, or, as Robert Graves suggested, from the yew tree *taxus,* from which arrows were best made and whose berries were long thought to be poisonous.

The word for poison came by a devious route, like a long-delayed afterthought. It derives from *poi,* to drink, becoming *potare* in Latin, whence "potion" (and also "symposium," from *sun,* together, plus *posis,* to drink). The venomous meaning did not come until the notion of love potions evolved, and then the idea of poison came to consciousness.

There is the same strange history behind the word "venom." This began as the simple word *wen,* meaning to wish or will, leading more or less directly to "win." Along the way, a fork led to "venus," "venery," and "venerate," all indicating varieties of love. The love potion was called *venin,* and somehow this gradually acquired today's sense of venom.

Nobody can explain why "poison" and "venom" come from love potions. Perhaps it was because the pharmacology of the day was primitive and chancy, a very thin line away from toxicology. Or maybe there was a commonsense consensus that any sort of chemical additive intended to induce false love is, by its nature, a fundamental poison. It tells something important about the good taste of earlier human beings that venom and poison were taken resentfully out of the hands of artificial lovers and transferred to the stings of insects and the fangs of serpents.

A "virus" is a very ancient word, despite the newness of its meaning for us. The root was *weis,* meaning to flow, in the sense of oozing, and it went first from *wase* in Old English to *wose* in Middle English and thence to "ooze" itself. The meaning of something twisty and slippery derived, and the weasel was named. The associations became more unpleasant, indicating something noxious, and "virulence" of "viruses" were the resulting words. "Noxious," incidentally, came from *nek,* meaning death, by way of *necare* and *nocere* in Latin, providing "necropsy" and cognate words for us; nectar was the drink of the gods because it prevented death (*tar,* meaning to overcome).

All of this has the sound of a series of accidents. It may be that the evolution of language was largely a matter of luck, like the evolution of creatures. Even though the facts of the matter have been firmly nailed down by two centuries of meticulous philological scholarship, there is a general, unavoidable sense of high improbability in the whole business. If this is the way words evolved, it seems to have depended upon a lot of pure chance, or, as the French say, hazard.

Chance. Now, there's a word. Partridge gives it almost two columns of the finest print, but not under itself. If you want to look up "chance" you must find "cadence," the nearest thing to an etymon but a long way off at that. "Cadence" comes from *kad,* meaning to fall. *Kad* led to *cadere* in Latin and *cad* in Sanskrit, also meaning to fall, sometimes to die, and from this came a cascade of words with the sense of risk and transiency: "cadaver," "decay," "casualty," "deciduous," and "casuistry."

The notion of falling gave rise to words like "cadence" and "cadenza" and "cascade." The idea of chance came, as you may have guessed, from the falling of dice.

Incidentally, "hazard" also came from dice, by way of Old French *hasard* and Spanish *azar,* from the Arabic *yasara,* to play at dice. The game of dice is named for the die used for playing, and this comes from Indo-European *do,* which originally meant to give, later changing to "donation," "dowry," "endow," "dose," and "antidote." In Vulgar Latin the verb *dare* came to mean play, leading to *datum* as a playing piece, then *dee* in Old English, then "die" and "dice."

It is obvious that this sort of thing could not have been worked out by any intentional human intelligence. Today's language is the result of an interminable series of small blunders, one after another, leading us back through a near infinity of time. The words are simply let loose by all of us, allowed to fly around out there in the dark, bumping into each other, mating in crazy ways, producing wild, random hybrids, beyond the control of reason.

Just think how much better we could manage if we put our minds to it. All it needs is better, clearheaded organization, with a more efficient administrative control of human speech. Management is what has been lacking. If, as seems to be the case, sometimes deplorably, today's most necessary words have been created by this improbable process of hybridization, then hybridization is the business we should now begin to take in hand. All we have to learn is how to pair one word with another so that mating can occur, and then sort out the progeny to our thinking. Governments will need to become involved in this, for we shall be requiring whole new institutions all around the earth, occupying huge tracts of land in national capitals, devoted to the breeding of words, like the Agricultural Experimental Stations of the past century. The breeding of words can become the bureaucratic preoccupation for the future, as in the past, but better organized, with more committees. Given a stockpile of innovative in-house creativity for the generation of novel words, substituting numbers for the input of letters wherever feasible, and fiscally optimized by computer capacitization for targeting in on core issues relating to aims, goals and priorities, and learned skills, we might at last be freed from our dependence on the past. New hybrids, synthesized in agencies of our local institutions, could then take the place of those Indo-European words, with all their primitive, pre-civilized, embarrassing resonances.

To start with, we ought to get another word to take the place of "hybrid." Not that it doesn't describe itself satisfactorily, but there is something not sufficiently straightforward about it for the scientific needs it is intended to serve. "Hybrid" is itself a relatively new word, easily disposed of without sentiment, but standing blank-faced behind it is the Latin *hybrida,* which was the name of the unsuitable offspring of a wild boar and a domestic sow. The word had no use in English until around the seventeenth century, when a casual mention of hybrids was made, referring to the boar-sow mismatch. It was not until the mid-nineteenth century that it really entered the language. At that time it was needed for botany, zoology, and the rapidly developing discipline of philology, and there were even usages in politics (hybrid bills in Parliament).

The real trouble with "hybrid" is in its more distant origins. It is a word that carries its own disapproval inside. Before being "hybrid" it was *hubris,* an earlier Greek word indicating arrogance, isolence against the gods. *Hubris* itself came from two Indo-European roots, *ud,* meaning up or out, and *gwer,* with the meaning of violence and strength. Outrage was the general sense. *Hubris* became a naturalized English word in the late nineteenth century, exhumed by classical scholars at Oxford and Cambridge, and promptly employed as slang to describe the deliberate use of high intellectual capacity to get oneself into trouble. Hubris was the risk of losing in an academic equivalent of jujitsu; if you used your full mental powers you could be hurled, by your own efforts, out into limbo.

The latest hybrids to join the products of botanists and zoologists are the combinations between the nucleic acids of mammalian and bacterial cells which can be brought about, easy as stringing beads, by the new recombinant-DNA technology. There are people who wish to stop the manufacture of these hybrids, on grounds that the biological properties of such new beings might be harmful.

Make up our own language? With committees in institutes? What a way to talk.

CHAPTER FORTY-ONE

The Hazards of

Science

THE CODE WORD FOR CRITICISM OF SCIENCE AND SCIENTISTS THESE days is "hubris." Once you've said that word, you've said it all; it sums up, in a word, all of today's apprehensions and misgivings in the public mind—not just about what is perceived as the insufferable attitude of the scientists themselves but, enclosed in the same word, what science and technology are perceived to be doing to make this century, this near to its ending, turn out so wrong.

"Hubris" is a powerful word, containing layers of powerful meaning, derived from a very old word, but with a new life of its own, growing way beyond the limits of its original meaning. Today, it is strong enough to carry the full weight of disapproval for the cast of mind that thought up atomic fusion and fission as ways of first blowing up and later heating cities as well as the attitudes which led to strip-mining, offshore oil wells, Kepone, food additives, SSTs, and the tiny spherical particles of plastic recently discovered clogging the waters of the Sargasso Sea.

The biomedical sciences are now caught up with physical science and technology in the same kind of critical judgment, with the same pejorative word. Hubris is responsible, it is said, for the whole biological revolution. It is hubris that has given us the prospects of behavior control, psychosurgery, fetal research, heart transplants, the cloning of prominent politicians from bits of their own eminent tissue, iatrogenic disease, overpopulation, and recombinant DNA. This last, the new technology that permits the stitching of one creature's genes into the DNA of another, to make hybrids, is currently cited as the ultimate example of hubris. It is hubris for man to manufacture a hybrid on his own.

So now we are back to the first word again, from "hybrid" to "hubris," and the hidden meaning of two beings joined unnaturally together by man is somehow retained. Today's joining is straight out of Greek mythology: it is the combining of man's capacity with the special prerogative of the gods, and it is really in this sense of outrage that the word "hubris" is being used today. That is what the word has grown into, a warning, a code word, a shorthand signal from the language itself: if man starts doing things reserved for the gods, deifying himself, the outcome will be something worse for him, symbolically, than the litters of wild boars and domestic sows were for the ancient Romans.

To be charged with hubris is therefore an extremely serious matter, and not to be dealt with by murmuring things about antiscience and antiintellectualism, which is what many of us engaged in science tend to do these days. The doubts about our enterprise have their origin in the most profound kind of human anxiety. If we are right and the critics are wrong, then it has to be that the word "hubris" is being mistakenly employed, that this is not what we are up to, that there is, for the time being anyway, a fundamental misunderstanding of science.

I suppose there is one central question to be dealt with, and I am not at all sure how to deal with it, although I am quite certain about my own answer to it. It is this: are there some kinds of information leading to some sorts of knowledge that human beings are really better off not having? Is there a limit to scientific inquiry not set by what is knowable but by what we *ought* to be knowing? Should we stop short of learning about some things, for fear of what we, or someone, will do with the knowledge? My own answer is a flat no, but I must confess that this is an intuitive response and I am neither inclined nor trained to reason my way through it.

There has been some effort, in and out of scientific quarters, to make recombinant DNA into the issue on which to settle this argument. Proponents of this line of research are accused of pure hubris, of assuming the rights of gods, of arrogance and outrage; what is more, they confess themselves to be in the business of making live hybrids with their own hands. The mayor of Cambridge and the attorney general of New York have both been advised to put a stop to it, forthwith.

It is not quite the same sort of argument, however, as the one about limiting knowledge, although this is surely part of it. The knowledge is already here, and the rage of the argument is about its application in technology. Should DNA for making certain useful or interesting proteins be incorporated into *E. coli* plasmids or not? Is there a risk of inserting the wrong sort of toxins or hazardous viruses, and then having the new hybrid organisms spread beyond the laboratory? Is this a technology for creating new varieties of pathogens, and should it be stopped because of this?

If the argument is held to this level, I can see no reason why it cannot be settled, by reasonable people. We have learned a great deal about the handling of dangerous microbes in the last century, although I must say that the opponents of recombinant-DNA research tend to downgrade this huge body of information. At one time or another, agents as hazardous as those of rabies, psittacosis, plague, and typhus have been dealt with by investigators in secure laboratories, with only rare instances of self-infection of the investigators themselves, and no instances at all of epidemics. It takes some high imagining to postulate the creation of brand-new pathogens so wild and voracious as to spread from equally secure laboratories to endanger human life at large, as some of the arguers are now maintaining.

But this is precisely the trouble with the recombinant-DNA problem: it has become an emotional issue, with too many irretrievably lost tempers on both sides. It has lost the sound of a discussion of technological safety, and begins now to sound like something else, almost like a religious controversy, and here it is moving toward the central issue: are there some things in science we should not be learning about?

There is an inevitably long list of hard questions to follow this one, beginning with the one which asks whether the mayor of Cambridge should be the one to decide, first off.

Maybe we'd be wiser, all of us, to back off before the recombinant-DNA issue becomes too large to cope with. If we're going to have a fight about it, let it be confined to the immediate issue of safety and security, of the recombinants now under consideration, and let us by all means have regulations and guidelines to assure the public safety wherever these are indicated or even suggested. But if it is possible let us stay off that question about limiting human knowledge. It is too loaded, and we'll simply not be able to cope with it.

By this time it will have become clear that I have already taken sides in the matter, and my point of view is entirely prejudiced. This is true, but with a qualification. I am not so much in favor of recombinant-DNA research as I am opposed to the opposition to this line of inquiry. As a longtime student of infectious-disease agents I do not take kindly the declarations that we do not know how to keep from catching things in laboratories, much less how to keep them from spreading beyond the laboratory walls. I believe we learned a lot about this sort of thing, long ago. Moreover, I regard it as a form of hubris-in-reverse to claim that man can make deadly pathogenic microorganisms so easily. In my view, it takes a long time and a great deal of interliving before a microbe can become a successful pathogen. Pathogenicity is, in a sense, a highly skilled trade, and only a tiny minority of all the numberless tons of microbes on the earth has ever been involved itself in it; most bacteria are busy with their own business, browsing and recycling the rest of life. Indeed, pathogenicity often seems to me a sort of biological accident in which signals are misdirected by the microbe or misinterpreted by the host, as in the case of endotoxin, or in which the intimacy between host and microbe is of such long standing that a form of molecular mimicry becomes possible, as in the case of diphtheria toxin. I do not believe that by simply putting together new combinations of genes one can create creatures as highly skilled and adapted for dependence as a pathogen must be, any more than I have ever believed that microbial life from the moon or Mars could possibly make a living on this planet.

But, as I said, I'm not at all sure this is what the argument is really about. Behind it is that other discussion, which I wish we would not have to become enmeshed in.

I cannot speak for the physical sciences, which have moved an immense distance in this century by any standard, but it does seem to me that in the biological and medical sciences we are still far too ignorant to begin making judgments about what sorts of things we should be learning or not learning. To the contrary, we ought to be grateful for whatever snatches we can get hold of, and we ought to be out there on a much larger scale than today's, looking for more.

We should be very careful with that word "hubris," and make sure it is not used when not warranted. There is a great danger in applying it to the search for knowledge. The application of knowledge is another matter, and there is hubris in plenty in our technology, but I do not believe that looking for new information about nature, at whatever level, can possibly be called unnatural. Indeed, if there is any single attribute of human beings, apart from language, which distinguishes them from all other creatures on earth, it is their insatiable, uncontrollable drive to learn things and then to exchange the information with others of the species. Learning is what we do, when you think about it. I cannot think of a human impulse more difficult to govern.

But I can imagine lots of reasons for trying to govern it. New information about nature is very likely, at the outset, to be upsetting to someone or other. The recombinant-DNA line of research is already upsetting, not because of the dangers now being argued about but because it is disturbing, in a fundamental way, to face the fact that the genetic machinery in control of the planet's life can be fooled around with so easily. We do not like the idea that anything so fixed and stable as a species line can be changed. The notion that genes can be taken out of one genome and inserted in another is unnerving. Classical mythology is peopled with mixed beings—part man, part animal or plant—and most of them are associated with tragic stories. Recombinant DNA is a reminder of bad dreams.

The easiest decision for society to make in matters of this kind is to appoint an agency, or a commission, or a subcommittee within an agency to look into the problem and provide advice. And the easiest course for a committee to take, when confronted by any process that appears to be disturbing people or making them uncomfortable, is to recommend that it be stopped, at least for the time being.

I can easily imagine such a committee, composed of unimpeachable public figures, arriving at the decision that the time is not quite ripe for further exploration of the transplantation of genes, that we should put this off for a while, maybe until next century, and get on with other affairs that make us less discomfited. Why not do science on something more popular, say, how to get solar energy more cheaply? Or mental health?

The trouble is, it would be very hard to stop once this line was begun. There are, after all, all sorts of scientific inquiry that are not much liked by one constituency or another, and we might soon find ourselves with crowded rosters, panels, standing committees, set up in Washington for the appraisal, and then the regulation, of research. Not on grounds of the possible value and usefulness of the new knowledge, mind you, but for guarding society against scientific hubris, against the kinds of knowledge we're better off without.

It would be absolutely irresistible as a way of spending time, and people would form long queues for membership. Almost anything would be fair game, certainly anything to do with genetics, anything relating to population control, or, on the other side, research on aging. Very few fields would get by, except perhaps for some, like mental health, in which nobody really expects anything much to happen, surely nothing new or disturbing.

The research areas in the greatest trouble would be those already containing a sense of bewilderment and surprise, with discernible prospects of upheaving present dogmas.

It is hard to predict how science is going to turn out, and if it is really good science it is impossible to predict. This is in the nature of the enterprise. If the things to be found are actually new, they are by definition unknown in advance, and there is no way of telling in advance where a really new line of inquiry will lead. You cannot make choices in this matter, selecting things you think you're going to like and shutting off the lines that make for discomfort. You either have science or you don't, and if you have it you are obliged to accept the surprising and disturbing pieces of information, even the overwhelming and upheaving ones, along with the neat and promptly useful bits. It is like that.

The only solid piece of scientific truth about which I feel totally confident is that we are profoundly ignorant about nature. Indeed, I regard this as the major discovery of the past hundred years of biology. It is, in its way, an illuminating piece of news. It would have amazed the brightest minds of the eighteenth-century Enlightenment to be told by any of us how little we know, and how bewildering seems the way ahead. It is this sudden confrontation with the depth and scope of ignorance that represents the most significant contribution of twentieth-century science to the human intellect. We are, at last, facing up to it. In earlier times, we either pretended to understand how things worked or ignored the problem, or simply made up stories to fill the gaps. Now that we have begun exploring in earnest, doing serious science, we are getting glimpses of how huge the questions are, and how far from being answered. Because of this, these are hard times for the human intellect, and it is no wonder that we are depressed. It is not so bad being ignorant if you are totally ignorant; the hard thing is knowing in some detail the reality of ignorance, the worst spots and here and there the not-so-bad spots, but no true light at the end of any tunnel nor even any tunnels that can yet be trusted. Hard times, indeed.

But we are making a beginning, and there ought to be some satisfaction, even exhilaration, in that. The method works. There are probably no questions we can think up that can't be answered, sooner or later, including even the matter of consciousness. To be sure, there may well be questions we can't think up, ever, and therefore limits to the reach of human intellect which we will never know about, but that is another matter. Within our limits, we should be able to work our way through to all our answers, if we keep at it long enough, and pay attention.

I am putting it this way, with all the presumption and confidence that I can summon, in order to raise another, last question. Is this hubris? Is there something fundamentally unnatural, or intrinsically wrong, or hazardous for the species in the ambition that drives us all to reach a comprehensive understanding of nature, including ourselves? I cannot believe it. It would seem to me a more unnatural thing, and more of an offense against nature, for us to come on the same scene endowed as we are with curiosity, filled to overbrimming as we are with questions, and naturally talented as we are for the asking of clear questions, and then for us to do nothing about it or, worse, to try to suppress the questions. This is the greater danger for our species, to try to pretend that we are another kind of animal, that we do not need to satisfy our

curiosity, that we can get along somehow without inquiry and exploration and experimentation, and that the human mind can rise above its
ignorance by simply asserting that there are things it has no need to
know. This, to my way of thinking, is the real hubris, and it carries
danger for us all.

CHAPTER FORTY-TWO

On Warts

WARTS ARE WONDERFUL STRUCTURES. THEY CAN APPEAR OVERNIGHT on any part of the skin, like mushrooms on a damp lawn, full grown and splendid in the complexity of their architecture. Viewed in stained sections under a microscope, they are the most specialized of cellular arrangements, constructed as though for a purpose. They sit there like turreted mounds of dense, impenetrable horn, impregnable, designed for defense against the world outside.

In a certain sense, warts are both useful and essential, but not for us. As it turns out, the exuberant cells of a wart are the elaborate reproductive apparatus of a virus.

You might have thought from the looks of it that the cells infected by the wart virus were using this response as a ponderous way of defending themselves against the virus, maybe even a way of becoming more distasteful, but it is not so. The wart is what the virus truly wants; it can flourish only in cells undergoing precisely this kind of overgrowth. It is not a defense at all; it is an overwhelming welcome, an enthusiastic accommodation meeting the needs of more and more virus.

The strangest thing about warts is that they tend to go away. Fully grown, nothing in the body has so much the look of toughness and permanence as a wart, and yet, inexplicably and often very abruptly, they come to the end of their lives and vanish without a trace.

And they can be made to go away by something that can only be called thinking, or something like thinking. This is a special property of warts which is absolutely astonishing, more of a surprise than cloning or recombinant DNA or endorphin or acupuncture or anything else currently attracting attention in the press. It is one of the great mystifications of science: warts can be ordered off by the skin by hypnotic suggestion.

Not everyone believes this, but the evidence goes back a long way and is persuasive. Generations of internists and dermatologists, and their grandmothers for that matter, have been convinced of the phenomenon. I was once told by a distinguished old professor of medicine, one of Sir William Osler's original bright young men, that it was his practice to paint gentian violet over a wart and then assure the patient firmly that it would be gone in a week, and he never saw it fail. There have been several meticulous studies by good clinical investigators, with proper controls. In one of these, fourteen patients with seemingly intractable generalized warts on both sides of the body were hypnotized, and the suggestion was made that all the warts on one side of the body would begin to go away. Within several weeks the results were indisputably positive; in nine patients, all or nearly all of the warts on the suggested side had vanished, while the control side had just as many as ever.

It is interesting that most of the warts vanished precisely as they were instructed, but it is even more fascinating that mistakes were made. Just as you might expect in other affairs requiring a clear understanding of which is the right and which the left side, one of the subjects got mixed up and destroyed the warts on the wrong side. In a later study by a group at the Massachusetts General Hospital, the warts on both sides were rejected even though the instructions were to pay attention to just one side.

I have been trying to figure out the nature of the instructions issued by the unconscious mind, whatever that is, under hypnosis. It seems to me hardly enough for the mind to say, simply, get off, eliminate yourselves, without providing something in the way of specifications as to how to go about it.

I used to believe, thinking about this experiment when it was just published, that the instructions might be quite simple. Perhaps nothing more detailed than a command to shut down the flow through all the precapillary arterioles in and around the warts to the point of strangulation. Exactly how the mind would accomplish this with precision, cutting off the blood supply to one wart while leaving others intact, I couldn't figure out, but I was satisfied to leave it there anyhow. And I was glad to think that my unconscious mind would have to take the responsibility for this, for if I had been one of the subjects I would never have been able to do it myself.

But now the problem seems much more complicated by the information concerning the viral etiology of warts, and even more so by the currently plausible notion that immunologic mechanisms are very likely implicated in the rejection of warts.

If my unconscious can figure out how to manipulate the mechanisms needed for getting around that virus, and for deploying all the various cells in the correct order for tissue rejection, then all I have to say is that my unconscious is a lot further along than I am. I wish I had a wart right now, just to see if I am that talented.

There ought to be a better word than "Unconscious," even capitalized, for what I have, so to speak, in mind. I was brought up to regard this aspect of thinking as a sort of private sanitarium, walled off somewhere in a suburb of my brain, capable only of producing such garbled information as to keep my mind, my proper Mind, always a little off balance.

But any mental apparatus that can reject a wart is something else again. This is not the sort of confused, disordered process you'd expect at the hands of the kind of Unconscious you read about in books, out at the edge of things making up dreams or getting mixed up on words or having hysterics. Whatever, or whoever, is responsible for this has the accuracy and precision of a surgeon. There almost has to be a Person in charge, running matters of meticulous detail beyond anyone's comprehension, a skilled engineer and manager, a chief executive officer, the head of the whole place. I never thought before that I possessed such a tenant. Or perhaps more accurately, such a landlord, since I would be, if this is in fact the situation, nothing more than a lodger.

Among other accomplishments, he must be a cell biologist of world class, capable of sorting through the various classes of one's lymphocytes, all with quite different functions which I do not understand, in order to mobilize the right ones and exclude the wrong ones for the task of tissue rejection. If it were left to me, and I were somehow empowered to call up lymphocytes and direct them to the vicinity of my wart (assuming that I could learn to do such a thing), mine would come tumbling in all unsorted, B cells and T cells, suppressor cells and killer cells, and no doubt other cells whose names I have not learned, incapable of getting anything useful done.

Even if immunology is not involved, and all that needs doing is to shut off the blood supply locally, I haven't the faintest notion how to set that up. I assume that the selective turning off of arterioles can be done by one or another chemical mediator, and I know the names of some of them, but I wouldn't dare let things like these loose even if I knew how to do it.

Well, then, who does supervise this kind of operation? Someone's got to, you know. You can't sit there under hypnosis, taking suggestions in and having them acted on with such accuracy and precision, without assuming the existence of something very like a controller. It wouldn't do to fob off the whole intricate business on lower centers without sending along a quite detailed set of specifications, way over my head.

Some intelligence or other knows how to get rid of warts, and this is a disquieting thought.

It is also a wonderful problem, in need of solving. Just think what we would know, if we had anything like a clear understanding of what goes on when a wart is hypnotized away. We would know the identity of the cellular and chemical participants in tissue rejection, conceivably with some added information about the ways that viruses create foreignness in cells. We would know how the traffic of these reactants is directed, and perhaps then be able to understand the nature of certain diseases in which the traffic is being conducted in wrong directions, aimed at the wrong cells. Best of all, we would be finding out about a kind of superintelligence that exists in each of us, infinitely smarter and possessed of technical know-how far beyond our present understanding. It would be worth a War on Warts, a Conquest of Warts, a National Institute of Warts and All.

CHAPTER FORTY-THREE

On Transcendental Metaworry (TMW)

IT IS SAID THAT MODERN, INDUSTRIALIZED, CIVILIZED HUMAN BEINGS are uniquely nervous and jumpy, unprecedentedly disturbed by the future, despaired by the present, sleepless at memories of the recent past, all because of the technological complexity and noisiness of the machinery by which we are surrounded, and the rigidified apparatus of cold steel and plastic which we have constructed between ourselves and the earth. Incessant worry, according to this view, is a modern invention. To turn it off, all we need to do is turn off the engines and climb down into the countryside. Primitive man, rose-garlanded, slept well.

I doubt this. Man has always been a specifically anxious creature with an almost untapped capacity for worry; it is a gift that distinguishes him from other forms of life. There is undoubtedly a neural center deep in the human brain for mediating this function, like the centers for hunger or sleep.

Prehistoric man, without tools or fire to be thinking about, must have been the most anxious of us all. Fumbling about in dimly lit caves, trying to figure out what he ought really to be doing, sensing the awesome responsibilities for toolmaking just ahead, he must have spent a lot of time contemplating his thumbs and fretting about them. I can imagine him staring at his hands, apposing thumbtips to each fingertip in amazement, thinking, By God, that's something to set us apart from the animals—and then the grinding thought, What on earth are they for? There must have been many long, sleepless nights, his mind all thumbs.

It would not surprise me to learn that there were ancient prefire committees, convened to argue that thumbs might be taking us too far, that we'd have been better off with simply another finger of the usual sort.

Worrying is the most natural and spontaneous of all human functions. It is time to acknowledge this, perhaps even to learn to do it better. Man is the Worrying Animal. It is a trait needing further development, awaiting perfection. Most of us tend to neglect the activity, living precariously out on the thin edge of anxiety but never plunging in.

For total immersion in the experience of pure, illuminating harassment, I can recommend a modification of the technique of Transcendental Meditation, which I stumbled across after reading an article on the practice in a scholarly magazine and then trying it on myself, sitting on an overturned, stove-in canoe under a beech tree in my backyard. Following closely the instructions, I relaxed, eyes closed, breathing regularly, repeating a recommended mantra, in this instance the word "oom," over and over. The conditions were suitable for withdrawal and detachment; my consciousness, which normally spends its time clutching for any possible handhold, was prepared to cut adrift. Then, suddenly, the telephone began to ring inside the house, rang several times between breathed "oom"s, and stopped. In the instant, I discovered Transcendental Worry.

Transcendental Worry can be engaged in at any time, by anyone, regardless of age, sex, or occupation, and in almost any circumstance. For beginners, I advise twenty-minute sessions, in the morning before work and late in the evening just before insomnia.

What you do is sit down someplace, preferably by yourself, and tense all muscles. If you make yourself reasonably uncomfortable at the outset, by sitting on a canoe bottom, say, the tension will come naturally. Now close the eyes, concentrate on this until the effort causes a slight tremor of the eyelids. Now breathe, thinking analytically about the muscular effort involved; it is useful to attempt breathing through one nostril at a time, alternating sides.

Now, the mantra. The word "worry," repeated quite rapidly, is itself effective, because of the allusive cognates in its history. Thus, intruding into the recitation of the mantra comes the recollection that it derives from the Indo-European root *wer,* meaning to turn or bend in the sense of evading, which became *wyrgan* in Old English, meaning to kill by strangling, with close relatives "weird," "writhe," "wriggle," "wrestle," and "wrong." "Wrong" is an equally useful mantra, for symmetrical reasons.

Next, try to float your consciousness free. You will feel something like this happening after about three minutes, and, almost simultaneously with the floating, yawing and sinking will begin. This complex of conjoined sensations becomes an awareness of concentrated, irreversible trouble.

Finally you will begin to hear the *zing,* if you are successful. This is a distant, rhythmic sound, not timed with either the breathing or the mantra. After several minutes, you will discover by taking your pulse that the *zing* is synchronous, and originates somewhere in the lower part of the head or perhaps high up in the neck, presumably due to turbulence at the bend of an artery, maybe even the vibration of a small plaque. Now you are In Touch.

Nothing remains but to allow the intensification of Transcendental Worry to proceed spontaneously to the next stage, termed the Primal Wince. En route, you pass through an almost confluent series of pictures, random and transient, jerky and running at overspeed like an old movie, many of them seemingly trivial but each associated with a sense of dropping abruptly through space (it is useful, here, to recall that "vertigo" also derives from *wer*). You may suddenly see, darting across the mind like a shrieking plumed bird, a current electric-light bill, or the vision of numbers whirring too fast to read on a gasoline pump, or the last surviving humpback whale, singing a final song into empty underseas, or simply the television newscast announcing that détente now signifies a Soviet-American Artificial-Heart Project. Or late bulletins from science concerning the pulsing showers of neutrino particles, aimed personally by collapsing stars, which cannot be escaped from even at the bottom of salt mines in South Dakota. Watergate, of course. The music of John Cage. The ascending slopes of chalked curves on academic blackboards, interchangeably predicting the future population of pet dogs in America, rats in Harlem, nuclear explosions overhead and down in salt mines, suicides in Norway, crop failures in India, the number of people at large. The thought of moon gravity as a cause of baldness. The unpreventability of continental drift. The electronic guitar. The slipping away of things, the feel of rugs sliding out from under everywhere. These images become confluent and then amorphous, melting together into a solid, gelatinous thought of skewness. When this happens, you will be entering the last stage, which is pure worry about pure worry. This is the essence of the Wisdom of the West, and I shall call it Transcendental Metaworry (TMW).

Now, as to the usefulness of TMW. First of all, it tends to fill the mind completely at times when it could otherwise be empty. Instead of worrying at random, continually and subliminally, wondering always what it is that you've forgotten and ought to be worrying about, you get the full experience, all in a rush, on a schedule which you arrange for yourself.

Secondly, it makes the times of the day when there is really nothing to worry about intensely pleasurable, because of the contrast.

Thirdly, I have forgotten the third advantage, which is itself one less thing to worry about.

There are, of course, certain disadvantages, which must be faced up to. TMW is, admittedly, a surrogate experience, a substitute for the real thing, and in this sense there is always the danger of overdoing it. Another obvious danger is the likely entry of technology into the field. I have no doubt that there will soon be advertisements in the back pages of small literary magazines, offering for sale, money back if dissatisfied (or satisfied), electronic devices encased in black plastic boxes with dials, cathode screens, earphones with simulated sonic booms, and terminals to be affixed at various areas of the scalp so that brain waves associated with pure TMW can be identified and volitionally selected. These will be marketed under attractive trade names, like the Angst Amplifier or the Artificial Heartsink. The thought of such things is something else to worry about, but perhaps not much more than the average car radio.

CHAPTER FORTY-FOUR

An Apology

THE ROLE PLAYED BY THE OBSERVER IN BIOLOGICAL RESEARCH IS complicated but not bizarre: he or she simply observes, describes, interprets, maybe once in a while emits a hoarse shout, but that is that; the act of observing does not alter fundamental aspects of the things observed, or anyway isn't supposed to.

It is very different in modern physics. The uncertainty principle doesn't mean that the observer necessarily destroys the precise momentum, or shifts the particle, in the act of observing, although these things happen. It is a more profound effect. The observer, and his apparatus, *create* the reality to be observed. Without him, there are all sorts of possibilities for single particles, in all sorts of wave patterns. The reality to be studied by his instruments is not simply there; it is brought into existence by the laboratory.

I got to thinking about this, but couldn't hold my mind still long enough. Words kept getting in the way. The glossary of physics is an enchantment in itself: "charm," "strangeness," "strong" and "weak" forces, "quarks." "Matter" is rather a dreamy word in itself, growing out of an Indo-European root based on baby talk: *ma,* which became *mater,* later differentiating into words like "maternal," "material," and "matrix." Demeter's name came from this root, when she was the goddess of the whole earth.

Then, while I was thinking about this, I suddenly remembered that I've been doing some physical observing on my own, without formal training and with only a pencil point as instrument, and perhaps I've caused trouble without intending to. I did not mean to change things, and I would like to say that I am sorry for the disturbance, if there was a disturbance.

Several times, in the past year or so, I have sat at my desk in an upper-floor room facing north on East Sixty-ninth Street, looking straight at the reflections of the sun in one or another windowpane of a tall apartment building on Seventy-second and Third Avenue. The panes where the sun appears, around early afternoon, vary slowly with the season, as you might expect, and much more quickly with the time of day. If I look long enough, I can carry as many as eight yellow-green afterimages of the sun, place them wherever I want to on my wall, and move them up or down, all eight suns, at will.

Now, I have to say what I've been doing.

On occasion, I place my pencil point (this is best done with a well-sharpened pencil) in the middle of my paper (I write on a yellow lined pad) in the center of my desk, keeping an eye on the Seventy-second and Third apartment, and then I hold the point there.

What I do, at these times, is to change the way the system works. Instead of having the earth rotate around itself every twenty-four hours, I hold the pencil point firmly and make the sun revolve slowly around East Sixty-ninth Street. Anyone can do this. It takes a bit of heaving to get it started, but after a few minutes of hard thought you can hold East Sixty-ninth as the still, central point, and then you can feel the sun rolling up behind you from the right side, making the great circle around. Once you've got the sun started, it is not too difficult to organize the rest of the solar system, so that the whole apparatus is circling around an immobile, still earth and, more specifically, spinning around a central point on the Upper East Side of Manhattan. There are some eccentricities and asymmetries to cope with, to be sure, and it is not a tidy event, but it works nonetheless.

What I did not realize when I began to do this was that it entailed, necessarily, more than just the solar system.

You have to get the galaxy swinging around, all the way round, in just twenty-four hours, and then there are all the other galaxies, which cannot be left dangling out there. They must be swung at the same time, in exact pace with the local sun, and at the same time, while they are being heaved around, whistling through the turbulence of solar wind, they have to be permitted their own frictionless, rhythmic dance around each other, with their own components dancing within their interiors. It is an immense task, and you must hold the pencil point firmly to get it done right. You have to do the whole thing, completely, or you will shake the structure to pieces.

If you want the sun to revolve around the earth in a complete turn every twenty-four hours, you must bring along the whole universe, all the galaxies, all the items in space, clear out to the curved edge.

The hardest part of it is the speed you need to swing around the outermost galaxies, so that everything goes round within the twenty-four hours. What it means is that you need enormous rates of travel, far beyond the speed of light, or you'll have parts dawdling, hanging behind at the outer edges, and it won't work. The universe will swing around the fixed, motionless earth every twenty-four hours, but you must be willing to put the time in on it and keep a firm hold on the pencil.

What bothers me now is the effect this may have had on the cosmologists, who may be looking at things in Pasadena, or Puerto Rico, or Palomar, or Pittsburgh, or wherever. It is probably all right during the times when I have been swinging the universe around, assuming that I'm doing it all of a piece, and that there are, in fact, no membranes of attachment at the edges which I may, unwittingly, be tearing loose. But what happens when I become tired of it, which I do, and let the pencil go, and go off to think about something else? I should think there must be some sort of lurch, some tremor all the way out to the edge, while the readjustment is made to the old way, with the earth turning over and over every twenty-four hours all by itself, and swinging around the sun.

I thought I should say something about this, in case some corrections in the observations are needed for the times when I've done it. But also, it occurs to me that my manipulations may not be the only ones going on. It is entirely possible, now that I think about it, that there is someone over on Central Park West, in his apartment, swinging the universe around a still point in the upper Eighties. Or even someone in Teaneck. Or, skewing everything beyond my comprehension, farther west, even out to San Francisco. This may, in fact, be going on all the time, heaving the universe this way and that, around one still point after another, sometimes even pulling against each other, and the astronomers should certainly be told of this before it is too late to make sense of the mess of numbers.

I am sorry to have done this, myself, but this does not mean that I can be sure of stopping. Once you have held the pencil point with all that precision, on a single fine point, and swung the whole whistling universe around that point, shrinking celestial masses of matter to nothing at all in the necessary speed, feeling the whole thing yaw and heave and almost spin off beyond control, but still holding it there, spinning, it is hard to stop.

CHAPTER FORTY-FIVE

On Disease

THE MENINGOCOCCUS, VIEWED FROM A DISTANCE, SEEMS TO HAVE THE characteristics of an implacable, dangerous enemy of the whole human race. Epidemics sweep through military barracks, across schoolyards, sometimes over the populations of whole cities. The organism invades the bloodstream, then the meningeal space; the outcome is meningitis, a formidable and highly fatal affliction in the days before chemotherapy. The engagement has the look of specificity, in the sense that the meningococcus appears to be particularly adapted for life in the meninges of human beings. You might even say it makes its living this way, a predator with us as prey.

But it is not so. When you count up the total number of people infected by the meningococcus, and then compare this with the number coming down with meningitis, the arrangement has a quite different look. The cases of actual meningitis are always a very small minority. There is an infection of the majority, to be sure, but it is confined to the rhinopharynx and usually goes unnoticed by the infected people; they produce antimeningococcal antibodies in their blood a few days after the infection, and the organisms may or may not persist in the pharyngeal mucosa, but that is the end of the affair; there is no invasion of the central nervous system.

The cases of meningitis are the exception. The rule for meningococcal infection is a benign, transient infection of the upper respiratory tract, hardly an infection at all, more like an equable association. It is still a mystery that meningitis develops in some patients, but it is unlikely that this represents a special predilection of the bacteria; it may be that the defense mechanisms of affected patients are flawed in some special way, so that the meningococci are granted access, invited in, so to say. Whatever, the disease is a sort of abnormal event in nature, rather like an accident.

The virus of lymphocytic choriomeningitis is ubiquitous among mice. The classical disease is a lethal form of meningitis, in which the exudate over the surface of the brain is composed entirely of lymphocytes. At first glance, the disease seems to represent invasion of, and damage to, the central nervous system by a virus specifically adapted for such behavior. In actual fact, however, the disease is caused by invasion of the brain surface by the host's own lymphocytes, rather than by any neurotoxic property of the virus. If the lymphocyte response is prevented—as, for example, by inducing infection during fetal life so that "tolerance" to the virus occurs—the outcome is a persistent virus infection everywhere, including the central nervous system, but without any evidence of brain disease. If the immunological response is now restored, by implanting lymphoid tissue from normal, nontolerant mice, meningitis then occurs within a few days. The new lymphocytes swarm over the surface of the brain, looking for the virus, and this is fatal. The disease is, essentially, the result of the host's response to the virus.

Cortisone, which has among its numerous properties the capacity to turn off various defense reactions against bacteria, also seems to turn off the most conspicuous clinical manifestations of infectious disease. Finland, in the early 1950s, shortly after cortisone became available for clinical research, treated several patients with pneumococcal lobar pneumonia and primary atypical pneumonia with cortisone, and observed what seemed at first a miraculous clinical cure. Within a few hours the fever, malaise, prostration, chest pain, and cough vanished, and the patients felt themselves to be restored to abundant good health, asking for dinner and claiming to be able to get up and around. At the same time, however, the X-ray evidence of pneumonia showed an alarming extension of the process, and the experiment was promptly terminated. Subsequently, others observed a similar dramatic elimination of disease manifestations in typhoid fever and rickettsial infection, also associated with the unacceptable trade-off of enhanced spread of infection.

The most spectacular examples of host governance of disease mechanisms are the array of responses elicited in various animals by the lipopolysaccharide endotoxins of gram-negative bacteria. Here the microbial toxin does not even seem to be, in itself, toxic. Although the material has powerful effects on various cells and tissues, including polymorphonuclear leukocytes, platelets, lymphocytes, macrophages, arteriolar smooth muscle, and on complement and the coagulation mechanism, all of these effects represent perfectly normal responses, things done every day in the normal course of living. What makes it a disaster is that they are all turned on at once by the host, as though in response to an alarm signal, and the outcome is widespread tissue destruction, as in the generalized Shwartzman reaction, or outright failure of the circulation of blood, as in endotoxin shock.

The Shwartzman reaction can be prevented by simply lifting out one of the participants in the response. This is done by removing the polymorphonuclear leukocytes temporarily, by treatment with nitrogen mustard, or by preventing blood coagulation with heparin. Animals so treated are unable to develop either the local or generalized Shwartzman reaction. The phenomena of lethal shock can be totally prevented by prior treatment with cortisone.

It is not known how endotoxin acts to produce its signal, but the mechanism seems to be a very old one in nature. One of the most sensitive of all experimental animals is the horseshoe crab, *Limulus polyhemus,* in which an injection into the bloodstream of 1 microgram of lipopolysaccharide will cause a violent response. The circulating hemocytes become enmeshed in dense aggregates, bound up in a coagulated protein which is secreted by these cells, with the result that the flow of blood comes to a standstill and the animal dies. What this seems to represent is an enormously exaggerated defense reaction, aimed at protecting *Limulus* against invasion by gram-negative pathogens. Frederick Bang has demonstrated that the hemocyte granules contain a coagulable protein, which is extruded when gram-negative bacteria enter the tissues; normally, one assumes, individual microorganisms are entrapped in this way and subsequently phagocytosed. When the purified endotoxin is injected into the blood, this becomes propaganda, information that bacteria are everywhere, needing entrapment, and all the hemocytes extrude the protein, forthwith. Indeed, there is now evidence that the signal of endotoxin is received, directly, by a receptor contained in extracts of the hemocytes; hence the exquisitely sensitive method for assaying endotoxin in the presence of *Limulus* hemocyte extract, in which coagulation is produced by lipopolysaccharide in concentrations as low as 1 nanogram per milliliter.

From the horseshoe crab's point of view, this is no doubt a valuable and efficient mechanism for the purpose of keeping out pathogens. When it works well, against single microorganisms or small clusters, it carries no hazard. But when barriers are breached and bacteria appear in large numbers, or when purified endotoxin is injected in the laboratory, it becomes an expensive kind of defense. Thus, the defense mechanism becomes itself the disease and the cause of death, while the bacteria play the role of bystanders, innocent from their viewpoint.

Even when bacteria are frontally toxic and destructive for the cells of the host, as in the case of organisms which elaborate exotoxins, there is some question as to the directness of the encounter. The diphtheria bacillus would not be in any sense a pathogen were it not for its toxin, but the toxin-cell reaction must be a two-way relationship of great intimacy, involving the recognition and fitting precisely into the molecular machinery of the cell, as though the toxin were being mistaken for a normal participant in protein synthesis. Moreover, the toxin is not, properly speaking, the diphtheria bacillus' own idea; it is made by the bacterium under instructions from a virus, the bacteriophage. Only the organisms that have become lysogenic for the virus are toxigenic. Diphtheria is not simply an infection by the diphtheria bacillus; it is an infection by a bacteriophage, whose real business in life is infecting the bacillus. It is even conceivable that the genetic information that enables the phage to induce the bacterium to produce a toxin was picked up elsewhere in the course of long intimacy with the animal host, and this may explain why the toxin is itself so closely similar to the host cell's own constituents.

It is certainly a strange relationship, without any of the straightforward predator-prey aspects that we used to assume for infectious disease. It is hard to see what the diphtheria bacillus has to gain in life from the capacity to produce such a toxin. Corynebacteria live well enough in the surface of human respiratory membranes, and the production of a necrotic pseudomembrane carries the risk of killing off the host and ending the relationship. It does not, in short, make much sense, and appears more like a biological mix-up than an evolutionary advantage.

The most malevolent of all microbial exotoxins for human beings is botulinus, and here there is no question as to the irrelevancy of the toxin. Tetanus and its toxin represent accidents in the same sense. It is interesting, though, that these organisms, like the diphtheria bacillus, and also the group A streptococcus and its erythrogenic toxin, are toxigenic because of having been infected by a phage. If it is a generality that bacteria will make exotoxins only when they are supplied with specifications by a virus, this is an extraordinary puzzle.

We were all reassured, when the first moon landing was ready to be made, that the greatest precautions would be taken to protect the life of the earth, especially human life, against infection by whatever there might be alive on the moon. And, in fact, the elaborate ceremony of lunar asepsis was performed after each of the early landings; the voyagers were masked and kept behind plate glass, quarantined away from contact with the earth until it was a certainty that we wouldn't catch something from them. The idea that germs are all around us, trying to get at us, to devour and destroy us, is so firmly rooted in modern consciousness that it made sense to think that strange germs, from the moon, would be even scarier and harder to handle.

It is true, of course, that germs are all around us; they comprise a fair proportion of the sheer bulk of the soil, and they abound in the air. But it is certainly not true that they are our natural enemies. Indeed, it comes as a surprise to realize that such a tiny minority of the bacterial populations of the earth has any interest at all in us. The commonest of encounters between bacteria and the higher forms of life take place after the death of the latter, in the course of recycling the elements of life. This is obviously the main business of the microbial world in general, and it has nothing to do with disease.

It is probably true that symbiotic relationships between bacteria and their metazoan hosts are much more common in nature than infectious disease, although I cannot prove this. But if you count up all the indispensable microbes that live in various intestinal tracts, supplying essential nutrients or providing enzymes for the breakdown of otherwise indigestible food, and add all the peculiar bacterial aggregates that live like necessary organs in the tissues of many insects, plus all the bacterial symbionts engaged in nitrogen fixation in collaboration with legumes, the total mass of symbiotic life is overwhelming. Alongside, the list of important bacterial infections of human beings is short indeed.

It might be different, I suppose, if we had learned less about sanitation, nutrition, and crowding, and it is in fact different for the newborn children in places where these things are not done well. The greatest cause of infant mortality, far and away, is enteric infection spread by a contaminated environment. But, by and large, infection has become a relatively minor threat to life as we have civilized ourselves and installed plumbing, and even less a threat now that we have antibiotics.

But even before all this, when times were uniformly awful everywhere, in the centuries of the great plagues, the war between microbes and men was never really an event of great scale, and more often than not, the violence of those diseases was due primarily to the violence of the host's defense mechanism. Leprosy, like tuberculosis, is a highly destructive disease, but the destruction is in large part immunological, under governance of the host. The major lesions of syphilis, including those of arteritis and perhaps also tabes, are based, at least in part, on immunological reactions in response to the spirochete.

Today, with so much of infectious disease under control, we are left with a roster of important illnesses which it has become fashionable to call "degenerative." They include chronic diseases of the brain and cord, chronic nephritis, arthritic arteriosclerosis, and various disorders caused by impedance to blood circulation. Although the underlying mechanisms governing such diseases are still largely mysterious, it is becoming the popular view that many of them may be the result of environmental influences — the things we eat or breathe or touch. As in so much of the thinking about cancer, we are in search of outside causes for the things that go wrong.

It may turn out, however, when we have learned more about pathogenesis in general, that most of the events that underlie the tissue damage in these diseases are host mechanisms, under host control. We are vulnerable because of our very intricacy and complexity. We are systems of mechanisms, subject to all the small disturbances, tiny monkey wrenches, that can, in the end, produce the wracking and unhinging of interminable chains of coordinated, meticulously timed interaction.

CHAPTER FORTY-SIX

On Natural Death

THERE ARE SO MANY NEW BOOKS ABOUT DYING THAT THERE ARE NOW special shelves set aside for them in bookshops, along with the health-diet and home-repair paperbacks and the sex manuals. Some of them are so packed with detailed information and step-by-step instructions for performing the function that you'd think this was a new sort of skill which all of us are now required to learn. The strongest impression the casual reader gets, leafing through, is that proper dying has become extraordinary, even an exotic experience, something only the specially trained get to do.

Also, you could be led to believe that we are the only creatures capable of the awareness of death, that when all the rest of nature is being cycled through dying, one generation after another, it is a different kind of process, done automatically and trivially, more "natural," as we say.

An elm in our backyard caught the blight this summer and dropped stone dead, leafless, almost overnight. One weekend it was a normal-looking elm, maybe a little bare in spots but nothing alarming, and the next weekend it was gone, passed over, departed, taken. Taken is right, for the tree surgeon came by yesterday with his crew of young helpers and their cherry picker, and took it down branch by branch and carted it off in the back of a red truck, everyone singing.

The dying of a field mouse, at the jaws of an amiable household cat, is a spectacle I have beheld many times. It used to make me wince. Early in life I gave up throwing sticks at the cat to make him drop the mouse, because the dropped mouse regularly went ahead and died anyway, but I always shouted unaffections at the cat to let him know the sort of animal he had become. Nature, I thought, was an abomination.

Recently I've done some thinking about that mouse, and I wonder if his dying is necessarily all that different from the passing of our elm. The main difference, if there is one, would be in the matter of pain. I do not believe that an elm tree has pain receptors, and even so, the blight seems to me a relatively painless way to go even if there were nerve endings in a tree, which there are not. But the mouse dangling tail-down from the teeth of a gray cat is something else again, with pain beyond bearing, you'd think, all over his small body.

There are now some plausible reasons for thinking it is not like that at all, and you can make up an entirely different story about the mouse and his dying if you like. At the instant of being trapped and penetrated by teeth, peptide hormones are released by cells in the hypothalamus and the pituitary gland; instantly these substances, called endorphins, are attached to the surfaces of other cells responsible for pain perception; the hormones have the pharmacologic properties of opium; there is no pain. Thus it is that the mouse seems always to dangle so languidly from the jaws, lies there so quietly when dropped, dies of his injuries without a struggle. If a mouse could shrug, he'd shrug.

I do not know if this is true or not, nor do I know how to prove it if it is true. Maybe if you could get in there quickly enough and administer naloxone, a specific morphine antagonist, you could turn off the endorphins and observe the restoration of pain, but this is not something I would care to do or see. I think I will leave it there, as a good guess about the dying of a cat-chewed mouse, perhaps about dying in general.

Montaigne had a hunch about dying, based on his own close call in a riding accident. He was so badly injured as to be believed dead by his companions, and was carried home with lamentations, "all bloody, stained all over with the blood I had thrown up." He remembers the entire episode, despite having been "dead, for two full hours," with wonderment:

> It seemed to me that my life was hanging only by the tip of my lips. I closed my eyes in order, it seemed to me, to help push it out, and took pleasure in growing languid and letting myself go. It was an idea that was only floating on the surface of my soul, as delicate and feeble as all the rest, but in truth not only free from distress but mingled with that sweet feeling that people have who have let themselves slide into sleep. I believe that this is the same state in which people find themselves whom we see fainting in the agony of death, and I maintain that we pity them without cause. . . . In order to get used to the idea of death, I find there is nothing like coming close to it.

Later, in another essay, Montaigne returns to it:

If you know not how to die, never trouble yourself; Nature will in a moment fully and sufficiently instruct you; she will exactly do that business for you; take you no care for it.

The worst accident I've ever seen was on Okinawa, in the early days of the invasion, when a jeep ran into a troop carrier and was crushed nearly flat. Inside were two young MPs, trapped in bent steel, both mortally hurt, with only their heads and shoulders visible. We had a conversation while people with the right tools were prying them free. Sorry about the accident, they said. No, they said, they felt fine. Is everyone else okay, one of them said. Well, the other one said, no hurry now. And then they died.

Pain is useful for avoidance, for getting away when there's time to get away, but when it is end game, and no way back, pain is likely to be turned off, and the mechanisms for this are wonderfully precise and quick. If I had to design an ecosystem in which creatures had to live off each other and in which dying was an indispensable part of living, I could not think of a better way to manage.

CHAPTER FORTY-SEVEN

A Trip Abroad

I DO NOT BELIEVE FOR A MINUTE THAT WE ARE NEARING THE END OF human surprise, despite resonantly put arguments by wonderfully informed scientists who tell us that after molecular biology and astrophysics there is really very little more to learn of substance. Except, they always add, for the nature of human consciousness, and that, they always add, is placed beyond our reach by the principle of indeterminacy; that is, our thought is so much at the center of life that it cannot sit still while we examine it.

But there may be a way out of this; it may turn out that consciousness is a much more generalized mechanism, shared round not only among ourselves but with all the other conjoined things of the biosphere. Thus, since we are not, perhaps, so absolutely central, we may be able to get a look at it, but we will need a new technology for this kind of neurobiology; in which case we will likely find that we have a whole eternity of astonishment stretching out ahead of us. Always assuming, of course, that we're still here.

We must rely on our scientists to help us find the way through the near distance, but for the longer stretch of the future we are dependent on the poets. We should learn to question them more closely, and listen more carefully. A poet is, after all, a sort of scientist, but engaged in a qualitative science in which nothing is measurable. He lives with data that cannot be numbered, and his experiments can be done only once. The information in a poem is, by definition, not reproducible. His pilot runs involve a recognition of things that pop into his head. The skill consists in his capacity to decide quickly which things to retain, which to eject. He becomes an equivalent of scientist, in the act of examining and sorting the things popping in, finding the marks of remote similarity, points of distant relationship, tiny irregularities that indicate that this one is really the same as that one over there only more important. Gauging the fit, he can meticulously place pieces of the universe together, in geometric configurations that are as beautiful and balanced as crystals. Musicians and painters listen, and copy down what they hear.

I wish that poets were able to give straight answers to straight questions, but that is like asking astrophysicists to make their calculations on their fingers, where we can watch the process. What I would like to know is: how should I feel about the earth, these days? Where has all the old nature gone? What became of the wild, writhing, unapproachable mass of the life of the world, and what happened to our old, panicky excitement about it? Just in fifty years, since I was a small boy in a suburban town, the world has become a structure of steel and plastic, intelligible and diminished. Mine was a puzzling maple grove of a village on the outskirts of New York City, and it vanished entirely, trees and all. It is now a syncytium of apartment houses, sprouting out of a matrix of cement flooded and jelled over an area that once contained 25,000 people who walked on grass. Now I live in another, more distant town, on a street with trees and lawns, and at night I can hear the soft sound of cement, moving like incoming tide, down the Sunrise Highway from New York.

If you fly around the earth and keep looking down, you will see that we have inserted ourselves everywhere. All fields are tilled. All mountains have been climbed and are being covered with concrete and plastic; some mountains, like the Appalachians, are simply cut down like trees. The fish are all trapped and domesticated, farmed in zoned undersea pastures. As for the animals, we will never have enough plastic bags for the bodies; soon the only survivors will be the cattle and sheep for the feeding of us, and the dogs and cats in our houses, fed while it lasts on the flesh of whales. And the rats and roaches, and a few reptiles.

The winged insects are vanishing, the calcium in the shells of eggs, and the birds.

We have dominated and overruled nature, and from now on the earth is ours, a kitchen garden until we learn to make our own chlorophyll and float it out in the sun inside plastic membranes. We will build Scarsdale on Mount Everest.

We will have everything under control, managed. Then what do we do? On long Sunday afternoons, what do we do, when there is nobody to talk to but ourselves?

It is because of these problems that we are now engaged in scrutinizing with such intensity the dark, bare flanks of Mars, hideous with lifelessness as it seems to be. We are like a family looking through travel brochures.

There is such a thing as too much of this. Because of our vast numbers and the rapidity with which we have developed prosthetic devices enabling us to hear and see each other, in person, all around the earth, we have become obsessed with ourselves. You'd think, to hear us think, that there was nothing else of significance on the earth except us.

Perhaps we should try to get away, for a while anyway. A change of scene might do us a world of good.

The trouble is, the barrenness of all the local planets. Perhaps we will be unlucky with our green thumbs, unable to create or maintain the faintest gasp of life on Mars or Titan. What's to stop us from looking elsewhere, farther on? If we can learn to navigate before the solar wind, we could, out there, hoist sail and tack our way out to where the wind fades off, practicing free-falls all the while, probing for gravity, trusting to luck, taking our chances. It would be like old times.

CHAPTER FORTY-EIGHT

On Meddling

WHEN YOU ARE CONFRONTED BY ANY COMPLEX SOCIAL SYSTEM, SUCH as an urban center or a hamster, with things about it that you're dissatisfied with and anxious to fix, you cannot just step in and set about fixing with much hope of helping. This realization is one of the sore discouragements of our century. Jay Forrester has demonstrated it mathematically, with his computer models of cities in which he makes clear that whatever you propose to do, based on common sense, will almost inevitably make matters worse rather than better. You cannot meddle with one part of a complex system from the outside without the almost certain risk of setting off disastrous events that you hadn't counted on in other, remote parts. If you want to fix something you are first obliged to understand, in detail, the whole system, and for very large systems you can't do this without a very large computer. Even then, the safest course seems to be to stand by and wring hands, but not to touch.

Intervening is a way of causing trouble.

If this is true, it suggests a new approach to the problems of cities, from the point of view of experimental pathology: maybe some of the things that have gone wrong are the result of someone's efforts to be helpful.

It makes a much simpler kind of puzzle. Instead of trying to move in and change things around, try to reach in gingerly and simply extract the intervener.

The identification and extraction of isolated meddlers is the business of modern medicine, at least for the fixing of diseases caused by identifiable microorganisms. The analogy between a city undergoing disintegration and a diseased organism does not stretch the imagination too far. Take syphilis, for instance. In the old days of medicine, before the recognition of microbial disease mechanisms, a patient with advanced syphilis was a complex system gone wrong without any single, isolatable cause, and medicine's approach was, essentially, to meddle. The analogy becomes more spectacular if you begin imagining what would happen if we knew everything else about modern medicine with the single exception of microbial infection and the spirochete. We would be doing all sorts of things to intervene: new modifications of group psychotherapy to correct the flawed thinking of general paresis, transplanting hearts with aortas attached for cardiovascular lues, administering immunosuppressant drugs to reverse the autoimmune reactions in tabes, enucleating gummas from the liver, that sort of effort. We might even be wondering about the role of stress in this peculiar, "multifactorial," chronic disease, and there would be all kinds of suggestions for "holistic" approaches, ranging from changes in the home environment to White House commissions on the role of air pollution. At an earlier time we would have been busy with bleeding, cupping, and purging, as indeed we once were. Or incantations, or shamanist fits of public ecstasy. Anything, in the hope of bringing about a change for the better in the whole body.

These were the classical examples of medical intervention in the prescientific days, and there can be no doubt that most of them did more harm than good, excepting perhaps the incantations.

With syphilis, of course, the problem now turns out to be simple. All you have to do, armed with the sure knowledge that the spirochete is the intervener, is to reach in carefully and eliminate this microorganism. If you do this quickly enough, before the whole system has been shaken to pieces, it will put itself right and the problem solves itself.

Things are undoubtedly more complicated in pathological social systems. There may be more than one meddler involved, maybe a whole host of them, maybe even a *system* of meddlers infiltrating all parts of the system you're trying to fix. If this is so, then the problem is that much harder, but it is still approachable, and soluble, once you've identified the fact of intervention.

It will be protested that I am setting up a new sort of straw demonology, postulating external causes for pathological events that are intrinsic. Is it not in the nature of complex social systems to go wrong, all by themselves, without external cause? Look at overpopulation. Look at Calhoun's famous model, those crowded colonies of rats and their malignant social pathology, all due to their own skewed behavior. Not at all, is my answer. All you have to do is find the meddler, in this case Professor Calhoun himself, and the system will put itself right. The trouble with those rats is not the innate tendency of crowded rats to go wrong, but the scientists who took them out of the world at large and put them into too small a box.

I do not know who the Calhouns of New York City may be, but it seems to me a modest enough proposal that they be looked for, identified, and then neatly lifted out. Without them and their intervening, the system will work nicely. Not perfectly, perhaps, but livably enough.

We have a roster of diseases which medicine calls "idiopathic," meaning that we do not know what causes them. The list is much shorter than it used to be; a century ago, common infections like typhus fever and tuberculous meningitis were classed as idiopathic illnesses. Originally, when it first came into the language of medicine, the term had a different, highly theoretical meaning. It was assumed that most human diseases were intrinsic, due to inbuilt failures of one sort or another, things gone wrong with various internal humors. The word "idiopathic" was intended to mean, literally, a disease having its own origin, a primary disease without any external cause. The list of such disorders has become progressively shorter as medical science has advanced, especially within this century, and the meaning of the term has lost its doctrinal flavor; we use "idiopathic" now to indicate simply that the cause of a particular disease is unknown. Very likely, before we are finished with medical science, and with luck, we will have found that all varieties of disease are the result of one or another sort of meddling, and there will be no more idiopathic illness.

With time, and a lot more luck, things could turn out this way for the social sciences as well.

CHAPTER FORTY-NINE

On Committees

THE MARKS OF SELFNESS ARE LAID OUT IN OUR BEHAVIOR IRREVERSIBLY, unequivocally, whether we are assembled in groups or off on a stroll alone. Nobody can be aware of the unique immunologic labels of anyone else, outside a laboratory, nor can we smell with any reliability the pheromonal differences among ourselves. So, all we have to go by is how we walk, sound, write letters, turn our heads. We are infallible at this. Nobody is really quite like anyone else; there are reminders here and there, but no exact duplicates; we are four billion unique individuals.

Thus when committees gather, each member is necessarily an actor, uncontrollably acting out the part of himself, reading the lines that identify him, asserting his identity. This takes quite a lot of time and energy, and while it is going on there is little chance of anything else getting done. Many committees have been appointed in one year and gone on working well into the next decade, with nothing much happening beyond these extended, uninterruptible displays by each member of his special behavioral marks.

If it were not for such compulsive behavior by the individuals, committees would be a marvelous invention for getting collective thinking done. But there it is. We are designed, coded, it seems, to place the highest priority on being individuals, and we must do this first, at whatever cost, even if it means disability for the group.

This is surely the driving idea behind democracy, and it is astonishing that the system works at all, let alone well. The individual is the real human treasure, and only when he has been cultivated to full expression of his selfness can he become of full value to society. Like many attractive social ideas, it is authentic, ancient Chinese. Integrity is the most personal of qualities; groups and societies cannot possess it until single mortals have it in hand. It is hard work for civilization.

But individuality can be carried too far, and you can see it happening almost all the time in committees. There are some very old words for criticizing the display of too much individuality. When someone becomes too separate, too removed, out of communication, his behavior is called egregious. This was once a nice word, meaning "out of the herd," signifying distinction and accomplishment, but by the linguistic process of pejoration the word took on an antisocial significance. Overindividuals are called peculiar, strange, eccentric. The worst sort are idiots, from *idios,* originally meaning personal and private.

These days, with the increasing complexity of the organizations in which we live and the great numbers of us becoming more densely packed together, the work of committees can be a deadly serious business. This is especially so when there is need to forecast the future. By instinct, each of us knows that this is a responsibility not to be trusted to any single person; we have to do it together.

Because of the urgency of the problems ahead, various modifications of the old standard committee have been divised in recent years, in efforts to achieve better grades of collective thought. There are the think tanks, hybrids between committee and factory, little corporations for thinking. There are governmental commissions and panels, made up of people brought to Washington and told to sit down together and think out collective thoughts. Industries have organized their own encounter groups, in which executives stride around crowded rooms bumping and shouting at each other in hopes of prodding out new ideas. But the old trouble persists: people assembled for group thought are still, first of all, individuals in need of expressing selfness.

The latest invention for getting round this is the Delphi technique. This was an invention of the 1960s, worked out by some RAND Corporation people dissatisfied with the way committees laid plans for the future. The method has a simple, almost silly sound. Instead of having meetings, questionnaires are circulated to the members of a group, and each person writes his answers out and sends them back in silence. Then the answers are circulated to all members and they are asked to reconsider and fill out the questionnaires again, after paying attention to the other views. And so forth. Three cycles are usually enough. By that time as much of a consensus has been reached as can be reached, and the final answers are said to be substantially more reliable, and often more interesting, than first time around. In some versions, new questions can be introduced by the participants at the same time that they are providing answers.

It is almost humiliating to be told that Delphi works, sometimes wonderfully well. One's first reaction is resentment at still another example of social manipulation, social-science trickery, behavior control.

But, then, confronted by the considerable evidence that the technique really does work—at least for future-forecasting in industry and government—one is bound to look for the possibly good things about it.

Maybe, after all, this is a way of preserving the individual and all his selfness, and at the same time linking minds together so that a group can do collective figuring. The best of both worlds, in short.

What Delphi is, is a really quiet, thoughtful conversation, in which everyone gets a chance to *listen*. The background noise of small talk, and the recurrent sonic booms of vanity, are eliminated at the outset, and there is time to think. There are no voices, and therefore no rising voices. It is, when you look at it this way, a great discovery. Before Delphi, real listening in a committee meeting has always been a near impossibility. Each member's function was to talk, and while other people were talking the individual member was busy figuring out what he ought to say next in order to shore up his own original position. Debating is what committees really do, not thinking. Take away the need for winning points, leading the discussion, protecting one's face, gaining applause, shouting down opposition, scaring opponents, all that kind of noisy activity, and a group of bright people can get down to quiet thought. It is a nice idea, and I'm glad it works.

It is interesting that Delphi is the name chosen, obviously to suggest the oracular prophetic function served. The original Delphi was Apollo's place, and Apollo was the god of prophecy, but more than that. He was also the source of some of the best Greek values: moderation, sanity, care, attention to the rules, deliberation. Etymologically, in fact, Apollo may have had his start as a committee. The word *apollo* (and perhaps the related word *apello*) originally meant a political gathering. The importance of public meetings for figuring out what to do next must have been perceived very early as fundamental to human society, therefore needing incorporation into myth and the creation of an administrative deity; hence Apollo, the Dorian god of prophecy.

The Pythian prophetess of Delphi was not really supposed to enunciate clear answers to questions about the future. On the contrary, her pronouncements often contained as much vagueness as the *I Ching,* and were similarly designed to provide options among which choice was possible. She symbolized something more like the committee's agenda. When she collapsed in ecstasy on the tripod, murmuring ambiguities, she became today's questionnaire. The working out of the details involved a meticulous exegesis of the oracle's statements, and this was the task of the *exegetai,* a committee of citizens, partly elected by the citizens of Athens and partly appointed by the Delphi oracle. The system seems to have worked well enough for a long time, constructing the statutory and legal basis for Greek religion.

Today's Delphi thus represents a refinement of an ancient social device, with a novel modification of committee procedure constraining groups of people to think more quietly, and to listen. The method seems new, as a formal procedure, but it is really very old, perhaps as old as human society itself. For in real life, this is the way we've always arrived at decisions, even though it has always been done in a disorganized way. We pass the word around; we ponder how the case is put by different people; we read the poetry; we meditate over the literature; we play the music; we change our minds; we reach an understanding. Society evolves this way, not by shouting each other down, but by the unique capacity of unique, individual human beings to comprehend each other.

CHAPTER FIFTY

The Scrambler in the Mind

LINGUISTIC SCHOLARS DO A LOT OF ARGUING WITH EACH OTHER OVER matters of theory, as they should. You would expect learned men who must spend their lives trying to figure out language, which is to say how to understand humanity all at once, to disagree often, even to become testy and impatient with each other, which, having more to worry about, they seem in fact to do rather more than their colleagues in other fields of academic science.

There is a hard technical problem which confronts linguists, and especially the savants who are today's version of philosophers. They are compelled to use as their sole research instrument the very apparatus that they wish to study, and this makes them especially vulnerable to the sort of hazard that physicists have had on their minds since Heisenberg. The closer linguists come to the center of their problem, the more they must manipulate the mechanism they are examining with precisely the same mechanism; no wonder that just at the moment when it seems within reach there is a twitch and a tremor and it shifts away in a blur.

You can see this happening in some of the books written about language, especially in books by writers who are not themselves professional and therefore cautious linguists. Brought in from outside to explain matters to the public at large, such writers always reach a point where suddenly the prose itself becomes wildly incomprehensible, disintegrating into nonsense. Usually this happens after the elements of linguistic logic have been nicely laid out, the fundamental notions of transformational grammar explained, the question whether some languages are more "complex" than others dealt with, and the mathematic techniques for deep analysis of sentences fully described. Equipped with so much powerfully usable information, the nonprofessional moves straight ahead, unaware that he is now stepping across the frontier into an unknown and maybe unknowable land, and he vanishes from sight.

I'm not sure what happens, exactly, at this stage of communication. I would like to believe that something goes wrong with the transmitter of information, and that what the reader is given is nonsense in the act of transmission, but I could be wrong about this. Perhaps it is plain, lucid prose after all, and the trouble is at my end, in my brain; maybe I do not possess receptors for this kind of talk.

Or maybe I alter it as it comes in, without realizing that I'm doing this.

I've had the same uncomfortable misgiving on other occasions, in matters not involving linguistics. Gödel's Theorem was once explained to me by a patient, gentle mathematician, and just as I was taking it all in, nodding appreciatively at the beauty of the whole idea, I suddenly felt something like the silent flicking of a mercury wall switch and it all turned to nonsense inside my head. I have had similar experiences listening to electronic music, and even worse ones reading poetry criticism. It is not like blanking out or losing interest or drifting off, not at all. My mind is, if anything, more alert, grasping avidly at every phrase, but then the switch is thrown and what comes in is transformed into an unfathomable code.

This brings me to my theory about the brain, my brain anyway. I believe there is a center someplace, maybe in the right hemisphere, which has a scrambling function similar to those electronic devices attached to the telephones of important statesmen which instantly convert all confidential sentences to gibberish.

Maybe there is a need for secrecy where language is involved. It is conceivable that if we had anything like full, conscious comprehension of what we are doing, our speech would be degraded to a permanent stammer or even into dead silence. It would be an impossible intellectual feat to turn out the simplest of sentences, the lovely Wallace Stevens sentence, for example: *"The man replied, Things as they are, are changed upon the blue guitar."* Doing that sort of thing, monitoring all the muscles, keeping an eye on the syntax, watching out for the semantic catastrophes risked by the slightest change in word order, taking care of the tone of voice and expression around the eyes and mouth, and worrying most of all about the danger of saying something meaningless, would be much harder to accomplish than if you were put in charge of your breathing and told to look after that function, breath by breath forever, with your conscious mind.

A scrambler in the brain would be a protective device, preserving the delicate center of the mechanism of language against tinkering and meddling, shielding the mind against information with which it has no intention of getting involved.

You might think that if there were a neuronal scrambler in one part of the brain, there ought to be a symmetrically placed descrambling center, somewhere in another lobule, capable of putting distintegrated information back into something like its original order. I doubt this. I concede that the brain is unlikely to risk filling itself up with totally meaningless noise, but I think it more likely that such really deep and dangerous scrambled notions as the true nature of speech are reassembled into unrecognizably pleasant experiences, like small talk or music or sleep. Some people, very quick on their feet, can catch a fleeting glimpse of a thought just at the moment of its disappearance into the scrambler, and poems by people like Stevens are made in this way. But for most of us the business is done automatically, out of sight, and I suppose this is just as well.

CHAPTER FIFTY-ONE

Notes on

Punctuation

THERE ARE NO PRECISE RULES ABOUT PUNCTUATION (FOWLER LAYS out some general advice (as best he can under the complex circumstances of English prose (he points out, for example, that we possess only four stops (the comma, the semicolon, the colon and the period (the question mark and exclamation point are not, strictly speaking, stops; they are indicators of tone (oddly enough, the Greeks employed the semicolon for their question mark (it produces a strange sensation to read a Greek sentence which is a straightforward question: Why weepest thou; (instead of Why weepest thou? (and, of course, there are parentheses (which are surely a kind of punctuation making this whole matter much more complicated by having to count up the left-handed parentheses in order to be sure of closing with the right number (but if the parentheses were left out, with nothing to work with but the stops, we would have considerably more flexibility in the deploying of layers of meaning than if we tried to separate all the clauses by physical barriers (and in the latter case, while we might have more precision and exactitude for our meaning, we would lose the essential flavor of language, which is its wonderful ambiguity)))))))))))).

The commas are the most useful and usable of all the stops. It is highly important to put them in place as you go along. If you try to come back after doing a paragraph and stick them in the various spots that tempt you you will discover that they tend to swarm like minnows into all sorts of crevices whose existence you hadn't realized and before you know it the whole long sentence becomes immobilized and lashed up squirming in commas. Better to use them sparingly, and with affection, precisely when the need for each one arises, nicely, by itself.

I have grown fond of semicolons in recent years. The semicolon tells you that there is still some question about the preceding full sentence; something needs to be added; it reminds you sometimes of the Greek usage. It is almost always a greater pleasure to come across a semicolon than a period. The period tells you that that is that; if you didn't get all the meaning you wanted or expected, anyway you got all the writer intended to parcel out and now you have to move along. But with a semicolon there you get a pleasant little feeling of expectancy; there is more to come; to read on; it will get clearer.

Colons are a lot less attractive, for several reasons: firstly, they give you the feeling of being rather ordered around, or at least having your nose pointed in a direction you might not be inclined to take if left to yourself, and, secondly, you suspect you're in for one of those sentences that will be labeling the points to be made: firstly, secondly and so forth, with the implication that you haven't sense enough to keep track of a sequence of notions without having them numbered. Also, many writers use this system loosely and incompletely, starting out with number one and number two as though counting off on their fingers but then going on and on without the succession of labels you've been led to expect, leaving you floundering about searching for the ninthly or seventeenthly that ought to be there but isn't.

Exclamation points are the most irritating of all. Look! they say, look at what I just said! How amazing is my thought! It is like being forced to watch someone else's small child jumping up and down crazily in the center of the living room shouting to attract attention. If a sentence really has something of importance to say, something quite remarkable, it doesn't need a mark to point it out. And if it is really, after all, a banal sentence needing more zing, the exclamation point simply emphasizes its banality!

Quotation marks should be used honestly and sparingly, when there is a genuine quotation at hand, and it is necessary to be very rigorous about the words enclosed by the marks. If something is to be quoted, the *exact* words must be used. If part of it must be left out because of space limitations, it is good manners to insert three dots to indicate the omission, but it is unethical to do this if it means connecting two thoughts which the original author did not intend to have tied together. Above all, quotation marks should not be used for ideas that you'd like to disown, things in the air so to speak. Nor should they be put in place around clichés; if you want to use a cliché you must take full responsibility for it yourself and not try to fob it off on anon., or on society. The most objectionable misuse of quotation marks, but one which illustrates the dangers of misuse in ordinary prose, is seen in advertising, especially in advertisements for small restaurants, for example "just around the corner," or "a good place to eat." No single, identifiable, citable person ever really said, for the record, "just around the corner," much less "a good place to eat," least likely of all for restaurants of the type that use this type of prose.

The dash is a handy device, informal and essentially playful, telling you that you're about to take off on a different tack but still in some way connected with the present course — only you have to remember that the dash is there, and either put a second dash at the end of the notion to let the reader know that he's back on course, or else end the sentence, as here, with a period.

The greatest danger in punctuation is for poetry. Here it is necessary to be as economical and parsimonious with commas and periods as with the words themselves, and any marks that seem to carry their own subtle meanings, like dashes and little rows of periods, even semicolons and question marks, should be left out altogether rather than inserted to clog up the thing with ambiguity. A single exclamation point in a poem, no matter what else the poem has to say, is enough to destroy the whole work.

The things I like best in T. S. Eliot's poetry, especially in the *Four Quartets,* are the semicolons. You cannot hear them, but they are there, laying out the connections between the images and the ideas. Sometimes you get a glimpse of a semicolon coming, a few lines farther on, and it is like climbing a steep path through woods and seeing a wooden bench just at a bend in the road ahead, a place where you can expect to sit for a moment, catching your breath.

Commas can't do this sort of thing; they can only tell you how the different parts of a complicated thought are to be fitted together, but you can't sit, not even take a breath, just because of a comma,

CHAPTER FIFTY-TWO

The Deacon's Masterpiece

THE BRIGHTEST AND MOST OPTIMISTIC OF MY PRESENTIMENTS ABOUT the future of human health always seem to arouse a curious mixture of resentment and dismay among some very intelligent listeners. It is as though I'd said something bad about the future. Actually, all I claim, partly on faith and partly from spotty but unmistakable bits of evidence out of the past century of biomedical science, is that mankind will someday be able to think his way around the finite list of major diseases that now close off life prematurely or cause prolonged incapacitation and pain. In short, we will someday be a disease-free species.

Except for gaining a precise insight into the nature of human consciousness (which may elude us for a very long time, perhaps forever), I cannot imagine any other limits to the profundity of our understanding of living things. It may happen within the next few centuries, maybe longer, but when it does it will bring along, inevitably, the most detailed sorts of explanations for human disease mechanisms. It is an article of faith with me that we will then know how to intervene directly, to turn them around or prevent them.

Something like this has already happened for most of the major infections. Even though we are still in a primitive, earliest stage in the emergence of biology, as compared, say, to physics, we have accomplished enough basic science to permit the development of specific antimicrobial antiserums and an impressive list of safe, rational viral vaccines. Within fifty years after the recognition of bacteria as pathogens we had classified them and learned enough of their metabolic intricacies so that the field was ready for antibiotics. In the years since the late 1940s the first great revolution in technology in all the long history of medicine has occurred, and infectious diseases that used to devastate whole families have now been almost forgotten.

Events moved rapidly in the field of infection, and this may have represented abnormally good luck. For some of the others—heart disease, cancer, stroke, the senile psychoses, diabetes, schizophrenia, emphysema, hypertension, arthritis, tropical parasitism, and the like—we may be in for a longer, more difficult pull, but maybe not. With the pace of research having increased so rapidly in the last two decades, and the remarkable new young brains enlisted for the work of biology, we could be in for surprises at almost any time. Anyway, sooner or later, they will all become nonmysteries, accountable and controllable.

These prospects seem to me exciting and heartening, and it is hard to face the mute, sidelong glances of disapproval that remarks along these lines usually generate. You'd think I'd announced an ultimate calamity.

The trouble comes from the automatic question, "Then what?" It is the general belief that we need our diseases—that they are natural parts of the human condition. It goes against nature to tamper and manipulate them out of existence, as I propose. "Then what?" What on earth will we die of? Are we to go on forever, disease-free, with nothing to occupy our minds but the passage of time? What are the biologists doing to us? How can you finish life honorably, and die honestly, without a disease?

This last is a very hard question, almost too hard to face, and therefore just the sort of question you should look around for a poem to answer, and there is one. It is "The Deacon's Masterpiece, or, the Wonderful 'One-Hoss Shay,'" by Oliver Wendell Holmes. On the surface, this piece of rather dreadful nineteenth-century doggerel seems to concern the disintegration of a well-made carriage, but inside the verse, giving it the staying power to hold on to our minds for over a full century, is a myth about human death.

Moreover, it is a myth for the modern mind. It used to be the common wisdom that the living body was a vulnerable, essentially ramshackle affair, always at a risk of giving way at one point or another, too complicated to stay in one piece. These days, with what is being learned about cellular biology, especially the form and function of subcellular structures and their macromolecular components, and the absolutely flawless arrangements for drawing on solar energy for the needs of all kinds of cells, the most impressive aspect of life is its sheer, tough power. With this near view, it becomes a kind of horrifying surprise to realize that things can go wrong—that a disorder of one part can bring down the whole amazing system. Looked at this way, disease seems a violation of nature, an appalling mistake. There must be a better way to go.

Thus, a detailed anatomy of Holmes's carriage can be read as a metaphor for a live organism — or, for that matter, a cell:

> Now in building of chaises, I tell you what,
> There is always *somewhere* a weakest spot —
> In hub, tire, felloe, in spring or thill,
> In panel, or crossbar, or floor, or sill,
> In screw, bolt, thoroughbrace — lurking
>   still. . . .
> And that's the reason, beyond a doubt,
> That a chaise *breaks down,* but doesn't *wear out.*

This was the nineteenth-century view of disease, and the source of our trouble today. It assumes that there is always, somewhere, a weakest part, as though foreordained. Without fundamental, localized flaws in the system, it might simply age away. As it is, it is doomed to break down prematurely, unless you can figure out how to find and fix the flawed item. Dr. Holmes, in the science of his day, saw little likelihood of this, but he did see, in his imagination, the possibility of sustained perfection. The Deacon is his central, Olympian Creator, symbolizing Nature, incapable of fumbling. What he designs is the perfect organism.

> . . . so built that it *couldn'* break dawn . . .
> . . . "the weakes' place mus' stan' the strain;
> 'N' the way t' fix it, uz I maintain,
> Is only jest
> T' make that place uz strong uz the rest."

Then, the successive acts of creation, collectively miraculous, scriptural in tone:

> . . . the strongest oak,
> That couldn't be split nor bent nor broke . . .
> He sent for lancewood to make the thills;
> The crossbars were ash, from the straightest trees,
> The panels of white-wood, that cuts like cheese,
> But lasts like iron for things like these. . . .

> Step and prop-iron, bolt and screw,
> Spring, tire, axle, and linchpin too,
> Steel of the finest, bright and blue;
> Thoroughbrace bison-skin, thick and wide;
> Boot, top, dasher, from tough old hide . . .
> That was the way he "put her through."
> "There!" said the Deacon, "naow she'll dew!"

And dew she did. The chaise lived, in fact, for a full, unblemished hundred years of undiseased life, each perfect part supported by all the rest. It was born from the Deacon's hands in 1755, the year of the great Lisbon earthquake, and it died on the earthquake centenary, to the hour, in 1855.

The death was the greatest marvel of all. Up to the last minute, the final turn of the splendid wheels, the thing worked perfectly. There was aging, of course, and Holmes concedes this in his myth, but it was a respectable, decent, proper sort of aging:

> A general flavor of mild decay,
> But nothing local, as one may say.
> There couldn't be—for the Deacon's art
> Had made it so like in every part
> That there wasn't a chance for one to start.

And then, the hour of death:

> . . . the wheels were just as strong as the thills,
> And the floor was just as strong as the sills,
> And the panels just as strong as the
> floor. . . .
> And the back crossbar as strong as the
> fore . . .
> And yet, *as a whole,* it is past a doubt
> In another hour it will be *worn out!*

What a way to go!

> First of November, 'Fifty-five!
> This morning the parson takes a drive.
> Now, small boys, get out of the way!
> Here comes the wonderful one-hoss shay,
> Drawn by a rat-tailed, ewe-necked bay.
> "Huddup!" said the parson. Off went they.

And the death scene itself. No tears, no complaints, no listening closely for last words. No grief. Just, in the way of the world, total fulfillment. Listen:

> All at once the horse stood still,
> Close by the meet'n'-house on the hill.
> First a shiver, and then a thrill,
> Then something decidedly like a spill —
> And the parson was sitting upon a rock,
> At half past nine by the meet'n'-house clock —

And, finally, the view of the remains:

> What do you think the parson found,
> When he got up and stared around?
> The poor old chaise in a heap or mound,
> As if it had been to the mill and ground! . . .
> . . . it went to pieces all at once —
> All at once, and nothing first —
> Just as bubbles do when they burst.

My favorite line in all this is one packed with the most abundant meaning, promising aging as an orderly, drying-up process, terminated by the most natural of events: "As if it had been to the mill and ground!"

This is, in high metaphor, what happens when a healthy old creature, old man or old mayfly, dies. There is no outside evil force, nor any central flaw. The dying is built into the system so that it can occur at once, at the end of a preclocked, genetically determined allotment of living. Centralization ceases, the forces that used to hold cells together are disrupted, the cells lose recognition of each other, chemical signaling between cells comes to an end, vessels become plugged by thrombi and disrupt their walls, bacteria are allowed free access to tissues normally forbidden, organelles inside cells begin to break apart; nothing holds together; it is the bursting of billions of bubbles, all at once.

What a way to go!

CHAPTER FIFTY-THREE

How to Fix the Premedical Curriculum

THE INFLUENCE OF THE MODERN MEDICAL SCHOOL ON LIBERAL-ARTS education in this country over the last decade has been baleful and malign, nothing less. The admission policies of the medical schools are at the root of the trouble. If something is not done quickly to change these, all the joy of going to college will have been destroyed, not just for that growing majority of undergraduate students who draw breath only to become doctors, but for everyone else, all the students, and all the faculty as well.

The medical schools used to say they wanted applicants as broadly educated as possible, and they used to mean it. The first two years of medical school were given over entirely to the basic biomedical sciences, and almost all entering students got their first close glimpse of science in those years. Three chemistry courses, physics, and some sort of biology were all that were required from the colleges. Students were encouraged by the rhetoric of medical-school catalogues to major in such nonscience disciplines as history, English, philosophy. Not many did so; almost all premedical students in recent generations have had their majors in chemistry or biology. But anyway, they were authorized to spread around in other fields if they wished.

There is still some talk in medical deans' offices about the need for general culture, but nobody really means it, and certainly the premedical students don't believe it. They concentrate on science.

They concentrate on science with a fury, and they live for grades. If there are courses in the humanities that can be taken without risk to class standing they will line up for these, but they will not get into anything tough except science. The so-called social sciences have become extremely popular as stand-ins for traditional learning.

The atmosphere of the liberal-arts college is being poisoned by premedical students. It is not the fault of the students, who do not start out as a necessarily bad lot. They behave as they do in the firm belief that if they behave any otherwise they won't get into medical school.

I have a suggestion, requiring for its implementation the following announcement from the deans of all the medical schools: henceforth, any applicant who is self-labeled as a "premed," distinguishable by his course selection from his classmates, will have his dossier placed in the third stack of three. Membership in a "premedical society" will, by itself, be grounds for rejection. Any college possessing something called a "premedical curriculum," or maintaining offices for people called "premedical advisers," will be excluded from recognition by the medical schools.

Now as to grades and class standing. There is obviously no way of ignoring these as criteria for acceptance, but it is the grades *in general* that should be weighed. And, since so much of the medical-school curriculum is, or ought to be, narrowly concerned with biomedical science, more attention should be paid to the success of students in other, nonscience disciplines before they are admitted, in order to assure the scope of intellect needed for a physician's work.

Hence, if there are to be MCAT tests, the science part ought to be made the briefest, and weigh the least. A knowledge of literature and languages ought to be the major test, and the scariest. History should be tested, with rigor.

The best thing would be to get rid of the MCATs, once and for all, and rely instead, wholly, on the judgment of the college faculties.

You could do this if there were some central, core discipline, universal within the curricula of all the colleges, which could be used for evaluating the free range of a student's mind, his tenacity and resolve, his innate capacity for the understanding of human beings, and his affection for the human condition. For this purpose, I propose that classical Greek be restored as the centerpiece of undergraduate education. The loss of Homeric and Attic Greek from American college life was one of this century's disasters. Putting it back where it once was would quickly make up for the dispiriting impact which generations of spotty Greek in translation have inflicted on modern thought. The capacity to read Homer's language closely enough to sense the terrifying poetry in some of the lines could serve as a shrewd test for the qualities of mind and character needed in a physician.

If everyone had to master Greek, the college students aspiring to medical school would be placed on the same footing as everyone else, and their identifiability as a separate group would be blurred, to everyone's advantage. Moreover, the currently depressing drift on some campuses toward special courses for prelaw students, and even prebusiness students, might be inhibited before more damage is done.

Latin should be put back as well, but not if it is handled, as it ought to be, by the secondary schools. If Horace has been absorbed prior to college, so much for Latin. But Greek is a proper discipline for the college mind.

English, history, the literature of at least two foreign languages, and philosophy should come near the top of the list, just below Classics, as basic requirements, and applicants for medical school should be told that their grades in these courses will count more than anything else.

Students should know that if they take summer work as volunteers in the local community hospital, as ward aides or laboratory assistants, this will not necessarily be held against them, but neither will it help.

Finally, the colleges should have much more of a say about who goes on to medical school. If they know, as they should, the students who are typically bright and also respected, this judgment should carry the heaviest weight for admission. If they elect to use criteria other than numerical class standing for recommending applicants, this evaluation should hold.

The first and most obvious beneficiaries of this new policy would be the college students themselves. There would no longer be, anywhere where they could be recognized as a coherent group, the "premeds," that most detestable of all cliques eating away at the heart of the college. Next to benefit would be the college faculties, once again in possession of the destiny of their own curriculum, for better or worse. And next in line, but perhaps benefiting the most of all, are the basic-science faculties of the medical schools, who would once again be facing classrooms of students who are ready to be startled and excited by a totally new and unfamiliar body of knowledge, eager to learn, unpreoccupied by the notions of relevance that are paralyzing the minds of today's first-year medical students already so surfeited by science that they want to start practicing psychiatry in the first trimester of the first year.

Society would be the ultimate beneficiary. We could look forward to a generation of doctors who have learned as much as anyone can learn, in our colleges and universities, about how human beings have always lived out their lives. Over the bedrock of knowledge about our civilization, the medical schools could then construct as solid a structure of medical science as can be built, but the bedrock would always be there, holding everything else upright.

CHAPTER FIFTY-FOUR

A Brief Historical Note on Medical Economics

I HAD FORGOTTEN WHAT THINGS WERE LIKE IN THE GOOD OLD DAYS of medicine, and how different. I knew, of course, that the science and technology have undergone changes of great magnitude, and doctors now can accomplish such cures and relief of disability as were beyond the imagination when I was young. But there is another difference, and I'd forgotten about this.

I found it the other day while glancing through the yearbook of my class at Harvard Medical School at the time of graduation, in 1937. Albert Coons was the editor of the book, which contains the usual photographs of faculty eminences and administrators, and a smaller picture of each member of my class with a brief biographical sketch, including a line for the graduate's career plans. Coons, incidentally, who spent his life in immunologic research, beginning with the discovery of the method for labeling antibodies with fluorescent dyes, known ever since as the Coons Technique, stated in the note under his picture that he intended to practice internal medicine, in the East. Matter of fact, almost all my classmates who subsequently went into careers of research and teaching were quite sure at the time of graduation that they would become practitioners.

I digress. What I wanted to say is that Coons, as editor, decided to do something more ambitious for the yearbook than simply record the class statistics, and prepared a long questionnaire which was sent to all the alumni of the medical school from the classes which had graduated ten, twenty, and thirty years earlier. I remember the discussion at the time of sending the questionnaire, and particularly the feeling we all had that we were sampling the very extremes of seniority: graduates of the classes of 1927 and 1917 seemed to us figures from a very remote past, and those of 1907 were as far away as Galen.

To everyone's surprise, 60 percent of the 265 alumni filled out the questionnaire and returned it, pretty good for amateur social scientists of that time.

The findings of greatest interest, presented in some detail in the yearbook, concerned the net incomes of the alumni, which were, by the standards of the day, significantly higher than the AMA's figures for American physicians in general. This was reassuring to my class. We knew that interns and residents got room and board but no salary to speak of. We were glad to hear that Harvard graduates did better financially once out in practice. We were of course quick to say to ourselves that it wasn't the money that mattered, just that it seemed fair to conclude that if they made all that much more money they were most likely finer physicians.

Now for the difference, and the surprise. The median net income of the group of 165 Harvard Medical School graduates, ten to thirty years out of School, was between $5,000 and $10,000 a year. In the ten-year class, 43 percent made less than $5,000. Only five men earned over $20,000, and a single surgeon, twenty years out, made $50,000. Seven graduates of the class of 1927 had incomes below $2,500.

The alumni were invited to send in comments along with the questionnaire, in a space marked "Remarks," with the understanding that since so much of the form was directed at finding out how much money they were making they might like to say something about life in general. As it turned out, most of the "Remarks" were also about money, a typical comment being the following: "I am satisfied with medicine as a life's work. However, I should recommend it only for the man who has plenty of money in back of him. Many men never make much in medicine."

Forty-one years ago, that was the way it was.

CHAPTER FIFTY-FIVE

Why Montaigne Is Not a Bore

FOR THE WEEKEND TIMES WHEN THERE IS NOTHING NEW IN THE HOUSE to read, and it is raining, and nothing much to think about or write about, and the afternoon stretches ahead all bleak and empty, there is nothing like Montaigne to make things better.

He liked to scratch his ears: "Scratching is one of Nature's sweetest gratifications."

Writing skeptically about the accounts of miracles which were commonplace news items in his time, he remarks, "I have seen no more evident monstrosity and miracle in the world than myself. . . . The more I frequent myself and know myself, the more my deformity astonishes me, and the less I understand myself."

It is one of the encouraging aspects of our civilization that Montaigne has never gone out of print. Even in the first decades after his death, when he was politically disliked for having taken a middle-of-the-road stand between the two extremes then arguing over power, the essays went through four editions and had already been translated into English and Spanish. He has since been made available to all the written languages of the earth, and scholars of all nations have built prosperous careers on his three books.

I used to stumble my way through the Florio translation, hard going because of the antique language but worth all the trouble nonetheless, until the Donald Frame version in American English came out, and I was off and running. It became my habit to turn the top corner of any page on which something so remarkable was written that I knew I would want to find it again. I have a poor memory and need to do this sort of thing. Now, eight years or so later, more than half the corners are turned, so that the book looks twice as thick sitting on the table, and I have discovered a new interest in Montaigne: what is there on all those unturned pages that I have read but forgotten, still there to be discovered?

He is resolved from the first page to tell you absolutely everything about himself, and so he does. At the greatest length, throughout all 876 pages of the Frame translation, he tells you and tells you about himself.

This ought to be, almost be definition, the achievement of a great bore. How does it happen that Montaigne is not ever, not on any of all those pages, even a bit of a bore? Not even in the interminable "Apology for Raymond Sebond," which I passed over as a dull essay for several years. I knew that he had translated a theological tract by Sebond to please his father, and the essay contained his thoughts following the tedious experience. So I passed it by at each reading, or leafed it through quickly, absorbing nothing, turning no corners. Then, one day, I got into it, and never got out again. Raymond Sebond is the least of concerns; having given a dutiful nod to his father and Sebond in the first paragraphs, and an obligatory homily on the usefulness of reason for arriving at truth, Montaigne simply turns his mind loose and writes whatever he feels like writing. Mostly, he wants to say that reason is not a special, unique gift of human beings, marking us off from the rest of Nature. Bees are better at organizing societies. Elephants are more concerned for the welfare of other elephants, and clever at figuring things out; they will fill up the man-dug elephant trap with timber and earth in order to bring the trapped elephant to the surface. He is not even sure that language is any more complex or subtle than the exchanges of gestures and fragrances among the beasts. He catalogues a long list of creatures, magpies, jackals, foxes, songbirds, horses, dogs, oxen, turtles, fish, lions, whatnot, in anecdotes drawn mostly from the ancient classics to show how reasonable and essentially amiable they are, demonstrating to his own satisfaction "how much superiority the animals have over us, and how feeble is our skill to imitate them." It is the greatest fun.

Montaigne makes friends in the first few pages of the book, and he becomes the best and closest of all your friends as the essays move along. To be sure, he does go on and on about himself, but that self turns out to be the reader's self as well. Moreover, he does not pose, ever. He likes himself, to be sure, but is never swept off his feet after the fashion of bores. He is fond of his mind, and affectionately entertained by everything in his head.

He is, of course, a moralist and, like all the greatest moralists, also a humorist. I cannot imagine anyone reading Montaigne carefully, paying attention, concentrating on what he has to say, without smiling most of the time.

It is the easiest of conversations with a very old friend. Long silences are permitted, encouraged. The text is interrupted on every page by quotations from classical writers, in the custom of the day, but these often serve as mere resting places needing little focusing.

You can move through the essays casually, if you like, glancing at the pages as though at the view of the lawn through the window, waiting for something of interest to turn up. And then, "By the way," he says, and now you lean forward in your chair, and he begins to tell you what it is like to be a human being.

Self-appraisal is Montaigne's occupation in life. Not self-preoccupation or self-obsession, almost never self-approval. At best, a sort of qualified self-satisfaction, a puzzled resolve to put up with the man inside. For Montaigne, the nearest and most engrossing item in all of Nature is Montaigne; not the dearest but the nearest and therefore the easiest to get to know.

He was fascinated by his own inconstancy, and came to believe that inconsistency is an identifying biological characteristic of human beings in general. "We are all patchwork," he says, "so shapeless and diverse in composition that each bit, each moment, plays its own game."

There were no psychiatrists around in his day, but if there had been Montaigne would have had cautionary advice for them: "It has often seemed to me that even good authors are wrong to insist on fashioning a consistent and solid fabric out of us. They choose one general characteristic, and go and arrange and interpret all of man's actions to fit their picture; and if they cannot twist them enough, they go and set them down to dissimulation. . . . Nothing is harder for me than to believe in men's consistency, nothing easier than to believe in their inconsistency." We become so many different people in ourselves, at so many different times, he declares, "There is as much difference between us and ourselves as between us and others." The matter is too complicated for analysis; he concedes that the effort can be made "to probe the inside and discover what springs set men in motion," but, he warns, "Since this is an arduous and hazardous undertaking, I wish fewer people would meddle with it." This, mind you, four hundred years ago.

He despairs of making any sense of himself. He writes, "All contradictions may be found in me . . . bashful, insolent; chaste, lascivious; talkative, taciturn; tough, delicate; clever, stupid; surly, affable; lying, truthful; learned, ignorant; liberal, miserly and prodigal: all this I see in myself to some extent according to how I turn. . . . I have nothing to say about myself absolutely, simply and solidly, without confusion and without mixture, or in one word."

Having discovered and faced all this, he is not in the least troubled by it. He accepts the limitations and infirmities of himself, and of humanity, with equanimity, even exuberance. "There is nothing so beautiful and legitimate as to play the man well and duly; nor any science so arduous as to know how to live this life of ours well and naturally. And of our maladies the most wild and barbarous is to despise our being. . . . For my part, I love life and cultivate it."

And so, on he goes, page after page, giving away his thoughts without allowing himself to be constrained by any discipline of consistency. "The greatest thing of the world," he writes, "is for a man to know how to be his own." As it turns out, contrary to his own predictions, what emerges is all his own, all of a piece, intact and solid as any rock. He is, as he says everywhere, an ordinary man. He persuades you of his ordinariness on every page. You cannot help but believe him in this; he is, above all else, an honest and candid man. And here is the marvel of his book: if Montaigne is an ordinary man, then what an encouragement, what a piece of work is, after all, an ordinary man! You cannot help but hope.

CHAPTER FIFTY-SIX

On Thinking About Thinking

AT ANY WAKING MOMENT THE HUMAN HEAD IS FILLED ALIVE WITH molecules of thought called notions. The mind is made up of dense clouds of these structures, flowing at random from place to place, bumping against each other and caroming away to bump again, leaving random, two-step tracks like the paths of Brownian movement. They are small round structures, featureless except for tiny projections that are made to fit and then lock onto certain other particles of thought possessing similar receptors. Much of the time nothing comes of the activity. The probability that one notion will encounter a matched one, fitting closely enough for docking, is at the outset vanishingly small.

But when the mind is heated a little, the movement speeds up and there are more encounters. The probability is raised.

The receptors are branched and complex, with configurations that are wildly variable. For one notion to fit with another it is not required that the inner structure of either member be the same; it is only the outside signal that counts for docking. But when any two are locked together they become a very small memory. Their motion changes. Now, instead of drifting at random through the corridors of the mind, they move in straight lines, turning over and over, searching for other pairs. Docking and locking continue, pairs are coupled to pairs, and aggregates are formed. These have the look of live, purposeful organisms, hunting for new things to fit with, sniffing for matched receptors, turning things over, catching at everything. As they grow in size, anything that seems to fit, even loosely, is tried on, stuck on, hung from the surface wherever there is room. They become like sea creatures, decorated all over with other creatures living as symbionts.

At this stage of its development, each mass of conjoined, separate notions, remembering and searching at the same time, shifts into its own fixed orbit, swinging in long elliptical loops around the center of the mind, rotating slowly as it goes. Now it is an idea.

Sometimes a mass of particles is packed so solidly that it begins, by something like gravitational force, to attract to itself everything else in the mind. The center then fails to hold, everything becomes skewed, other aggregates yaw and wobble into new orbits around the new dense mass, and nothing can escape the attraction. It is then a black hole, the mind seems to vanish from sight, and sleep occurs.

This is not the normal course of events, however. Under proper circumstances, when all the orbiting structures are evenly balanced, there is harmony. New notions, formed by impulses arriving from the outside, drift through the atmosphere. They lock to each other, pair up, double and redouble, and then, when things are going well, are swept onto the surface of one or another of the great orbiting aggregates. When the force of attraction is not strong enough for attachment, the new notions may simply move into tiny orbits around the aggregated ideas. This is not yet thinking, but it is the last stage in preparation for a thought.

The process of sorting and selecting, when many aggregates are simultaneously in flight and the separate orbits are now arranged in shimmering membranes very close to each other, is like a complicated, meticulously ordered dance. New notions are flung from one elliptical path into the next, collide with unmatched surfaces and bound away, to be caught and held in place by masses at a distance.

Now the motion of all the structures, large and small, becomes patterned and ceaselessly motoric, like the *Brandenburgs*. The aggregates begin to send out streamers, plumes of thought, which touch and adhere. Sometimes, not often but sometimes, all the particles are organized in aggregates and all the aggregates are connected, and the mind becomes a single structure, motile now and capable of purposeful, directional movement. Now the hunt begins again, for something similar, with matching receptors, *outside*.

Counterpoint is but one aspect of the process of combination, separation, recall, and recombination. Dance is only one aspect of the movement. The darting forward to meet new pairs of notions, built into new aggregates, the orbiting and occasional soaring of massive aggregates out of orbit and off into other spaces, most of all the continual switching of solitary particles of thought from one orbit into the next, like electrons, up and down depending on the charges around and the masses involved, accomplished as though by accident but always adhering to laws—all these have the look of music. There is no other human experience they can remind one of.

I suggest, then, that we turn it around. Instead of using what we can guess at about the nature of thought to explain the nature of music, start over again. Begin with music and see what this can tell us about the sensation of thinking. Music is the effort we make to explain to ourselves how our brains work. We listen to Bach transfixed because this is listening to a human mind. *The Art of the Fugue* is not a special pattern of thinking, it is not thinking about any particular thing. The spelling out of Bach's name in the great, unfinished layers of fugue at the end is no more than a transient notion, something flashed across the mind. The whole piece is not about thinking about something, it is about thinking. If you want, as an experiment, to hear the whole mind working, all at once, put on *The St. Matthew Passion* and turn the volume up all the way. That is the sound of the whole central nervous system of human beings, all at once.

CHAPTER FIFTY-SEVEN

On Embryology

A SHORT WHILE AGO, IN MID-1978, THE NEWEST ASTONISHMENT IN medicine, covering all the front pages, was the birth of an English baby nine months after conception in a dish. The older surprise, which should still be fazing us all, is that a solitary sperm and a single egg can fuse and become a human being under any circumstance, and that, however implanted, a mere cluster of the progeny of this fused cell affixed to the uterine wall will grow and differentiate into eight pounds of baby; this has been going on under our eyes for so long a time that we've gotten used to it; hence the outcries of amazement at this really minor technical modification of the general procedure—nothing much, really, beyond relocating the beginning of the process from the fallopian tube to a plastic container and, perhaps worth mentioning, the exclusion of the father from any role likely to add, with any justification, to his vanity.

There is, of course, talk now about extending the technology beyond the act of conception itself, and predictions are being made that the whole process of embryonic development, all nine months of it, will ultimately be conducted in elaborate plastic flasks. When this happens, as perhaps it will someday, it will be another surprise, with more headlines. Everyone will say how marvelously terrifying is the new power of science, and arguments over whether science should be stopped in its tracks will preoccupy senatorial subcommittees, with more head-lines. Meanwhile, the sheer incredibility of the process itself, whether it occurs in the uterus or *in* some sort of *vitro,* will probably be overlooked as much as it is today.

For the real amazement, if you want to be amazed, is the process. You start out as a single cell derived from the coupling of a sperm and an egg, this divides into two, then four, then eight, and so on, and at a certain stage there emerges a single cell which will have as all its progeny the human brain. The mere existence of that cell should be one of the great astonishments of the earth. People ought to be walking around all day, all through their waking hours, calling to each other in endless wonderment, talking of nothing except that cell. It is an unbelievable thing, and yet there it is, popping neatly into its place amid the jumbled cells of every one of the several billion human embryos around the planet, just as if it were the easiest thing in the world to do.

If you like being surprised, there's the source. One cell is switched on to become the whole trillion-cell, massive apparatus for thinking and imagining and, for that matter, being surprised. All the information needed for learning to read and write, playing the piano, arguing before senatorial subcommittees, walking across a street through traffic, or the marvelous human act of putting out one hand and leaning against a tree, is contained in that first cell. All of grammar, all syntax, all arithmetic, all music.

It is not known how the switching on occurs. At the very beginning of an embryo, when it is still nothing more than a cluster of cells, all of this information and much more is latent inside every cell in the cluster. When the stem cell for the brain emerges, it could be that the special quality of brainness is simply switched on. But it could as well be that everything else, every other potential property, is switched off, so that this most specialized of all cells no longer has its precursors' option of being a thyroid or a liver or whatever, only a brain.

No one has the ghost of an idea how this works, and nothing else in life can ever be so puzzling. If anyone does succeed in explaining it, within my lifetime, I will charter a skywriting airplane, maybe a whole fleet of them, and send them aloft to write one great exclamation point after another, around the whole sky, until all my money runs out.

CHAPTER FIFTY-EIGHT

Medical Lessons from History

IT IS CUSTOMARY TO PLACE THE DATE FOR THE BEGINNINGS OF modern medicine somewhere in the mid-1930s, with the entry of sulfonamides and penicillin into the pharmacopoeia, and it is usual to ascribe to these events the force of a revolution in medical practice. This is what things seemed like at the time. Medicine was upheaved, revolutionized indeed. Therapy had been discovered for great numbers of patients whose illnesses had previously been untreatable. Cures were now available. As we saw it then, it seemed a totally new world. Doctors could now *cure* disease, and this was astonishing, most of all to the doctors themselves.

It was, no doubt about it, a major occurrence in medicine, and a triumph for biological science applied to medicine but perhaps not a revolution after all, looking back from this distance. For the real revolution in medicine, which set the stage for antibiotics and whatever else we have in the way of effective therapy today, had already occurred one hundred years before penicillin. It did not begin with the introduction of science into medicine. That came years later. Like a good many revolutions, this one began with the destruction of dogma. It was discovered, sometime in the 1830s, that the greater part of medicine was nonsense.

The history of medicine has never been a particularly attractive subject in medical education, and one reason for this is that it is so unrelievedly deplorable a story. For century after century, all the way into the remote millennia of its origins, medicine got along by sheer guesswork and the crudest sort of empiricism. It is hard to conceive of a less scientific enterprise among human endeavors. Virtually anything that could be thought up for the treatment of disease was tried out at one time or another, and, once tried, lasted decades or even centuries before being given up. It was, in retrospect, the most frivolous and irresponsible kind of human experimentation, based on nothing but trial and error, and usually resulting in precisely that sequence. Bleeding, purging, cupping, the administration of infusions of every known plant, solutions of every known metal, every conceivable diet including total fasting, most of these based on the weirdest imaginings about the cause of disease, concocted out of nothing but thin air—this was the heritage of medicine up until a little over a century ago. It is astounding that the profession survived so long, and got away with so much with so little outcry. Almost everyone seems to have been taken in. Evidently one had to be a born skeptic, like Montaigne, to see through the old nonsense; but even Montaigne, who wrote scathingly about the illnesses caused by doctoring centuries before Ivan Illich, had little effect. Most people were convinced of the magical powers of medicine and put up with it.

Then, sometime in the early nineteenth century, it was realized by a few of the leading figures in medicine that almost all of the complicated treatments then available for disease did not really work, and the suggestion was made by several courageous physicians, here and abroad, that most of them actually did more harm than good. Simultaneously, the surprising discovery was made that certain diseases were self-limited, got better by themselves, possessed, so to speak, a "natural history." It is hard for us now to imagine the magnitude of this discovery and its effect on the practice of medicine. The long habit of medicine, extending back into the distant past, had been to treat everything with something, and it was taken for granted that every disease demanded treatment and might in fact end fatally if not treated. In a sober essay written on this topic in 1876, Professor Edward H. Clarke of Harvard reviewed what he regarded as the major scientific accomplishment of medicine in the preceding fifty years, which consisted of studies proving that patients with typhoid and typhus fever could recover all by themselves, without medical intervention, and often did better for being untreated than when they received the bizarre herbs, heavy metals, and fomentations that were popular at that time. Delirium tremens, a disorder long believed to be fatal in all cases unless subjected to constant and aggressive medical intervention, was observed to subside by itself more readily in patients left untreated, with a substantially improved rate of survival.

Gradually, over the succeeding decades, the traditional therapeutic ritual of medicine was given up, and what came to be called the "art of medicine" emerged to take its place. In retrospect, this art was really the beginning of the science of medicine. It was based on meticulous, objective, even cool observations of sick people. From this endeavor we learned the details of the natural history of illness, so that, for example, it came to be understood that typhoid and typhus were really two entirely separate, unrelated disorders, with quite different causes. Accurate diagnosis became the central purpose and justification for medicine, and as the methods for diagnosis improved, accurate prognosis also became possible, so that patients and their families could be told not only the name of the illness but also, with some reliability, how it was most likely to turn out. By the time this century had begun, these were becoming generally accepted as the principal responsibilities of the physician. In addition, a new kind of much less ambitious and flamboyant therapy began to emerge, termed "supportive treatment" and consisting in large part of plain common sense: good nursing care, appropriate bed rest, a sensible diet, avoidance of traditional nostrums and patent medicine, and a measured degree of trust that nature, in taking its course, would very often bring things to a satisfactory conclusion.

The doctor became a considerably more useful and respected professional. For all his limitations, and despite his inability to do much in the way of preventing or terminating illness, he could be depended on to explain things, to relieve anxieties, and to be on hand. He was trusted as an adviser and guide in difficult times, including the time of dying.

Meanwhile, starting in the last decade of the nineteenth century, the basic science needed for a future science of medicine got under way. The role of bacteria and viruses in illness was discerned, and research on the details of this connection began in earnest. The major pathogenic organisms, most notably the tubercle bacillus and the syphilis spirochete, were recognized for what they were and did. By the late 1930s this research had already paid off; the techniques of active and passive immunization had been worked out for diphtheria, tetanus, lobar pneumonia, and a few other bacterial infections; the taxonomy of infectious disease had become an orderly discipline; and the time was ready for sulfanilamide, penicillin, streptomycin, and all the rest. But it needs emphasizing that it took about fifty years of concentrated effort in basic research to reach this level; if this research had not been done we could not have guessed that streptococci and pneumococci exist, and the search for antibiotics would have made no sense at all. Without the long, painstaking research on the tubercle bacillus, we would still be thinking that tuberculosis was due to night air and we would still be trying to cure it by sunlight.

At that time, after almost a century of modified skepticism about therapy amounting finally to near nihilism, we abruptly entered a new era in which, almost overnight, it became possible with antibiotics to cure outright some of the most common and lethal illnesses of human beings—lobar pneumonia, meningitis, typhoid, typhus, tuberculosis, septicemias of various types. Only the virus diseases lay beyond reach, and even some of these were shortly to come under control—as in poliomyelitis and measles—by new techniques for making vaccines.

These events were simply overwhelming when they occurred. I was a medical student at the time of sulfanilamide and penicillin, and I remember the earliest reaction of flat disbelief concerning such things. We had given up on therapy, a century earlier. With a few exceptions which we regarded as anomalies, such as vitamin B for pellagra, liver extract for pernicious anemia, and insulin for diabetes, we were educated to be skeptical about the treatment of disease. Miliary tuberculosis and subacute bacterial endocarditis were fatal in 100 percent of cases, and we were convinced that the course of master diseases like these could never be changed, not in our lifetime or in any other.

Overnight, we became optimists, enthusiasts. The realization that disease could be turned around by treatment, provided that one knew enough about the underlying mechanism, was a totally new idea just forty years ago.

Most people have forgotten about that time, or are too young to remember it, and tend now to take such things for granted. They were born knowing about antibiotics, or the drugs simply fell by luck into their laps. We need reminding, now more than ever, that the capacity of medicine to deal with infectious disease was not a lucky fluke, nor was it something that happened simply as the result of the passage of time. It was the direct outcome of many years of hard work, done by imaginative and skilled scientists, none of whom had the faintest idea that penicillin and streptomycin lay somewhere in the decades ahead. It was basic science of a very high order, storing up a great mass of interesting knowledge for its own sake, creating, so to speak, a bank of information, ready for drawing on when the time for intelligent use arrived.

For example, it took a great deal of time, and work, before it could be understood that there were such things as hemolytic streptococci, that there were more than forty different serological types of the principal streptococcal species responsible for human disease, and that some of these were responsible for rheumatic fever and valvular heart disease. The bacteriology and immunology had to be done first, over decades, and by the early 1930s the work had progressed just far enough so that the connection between streptococcal infection and rheumatic fever could be perceived.

Not until this information was at hand did it become a certainty that rheumatic fever could be prevented, and with it a large amount of the chief heart disease affecting young people, if only a way could be found to prevent streptococcal infection. Similarly, the identification of the role of pneumococci in lobar pneumonia, of brucellae in undulant fever, typhoid bacilli in typhoid fever, the meningococci in epidemic meningitis, required the sorting out and analysis of what seemed at the time an immensely complicated body of information. Most of the labor in infectious-disease laboratories went into work of this kind in the first third of this century. When it was finished, the scene was ready for antibiotics.

What was not realized then and is not fully realized even now was how difficult it would be to accomplish the same end for the other diseases of man. We still have heart disease, cancer, stroke, schizophrenia, arthritis, kidney failure, cirrhosis, and the degenerative diseases associated with aging. All told, there is a list of around twenty-five major afflictions of man in this country, and a still more formidable list of parasitic, viral, and nutritional diseases in the less developed countries of the world, which make up the unfinished agenda of modern biomedical science.

How does one make plans for science policy with such a list? The quick and easy way is to conclude that these diseases, not yet mastered, are simply beyond our grasp. The thing to do is to settle down with today's versions of science and technology, and make sure that our health-care system is equipped to do the best it can in an imperfect world. The trouble with this approach is that we cannot afford it. The costs are already too high, and they escalate higher each year. Moreover, the measures available are simply not good enough. We cannot go on indefinitely trying to cope with heart disease by open-heart surgery, carried out at formidable expense after the disease has run its destructive course. Nor can we postpone such issues by oversimplifying the problems, which is what we do, in my opinion, by attributing so much of today's chronic and disabling disease to the environment, or to wrong ways of living. The plain fact of the matter is that we do not know enough about the facts of the matter, and we should be more open about our ignorance.

At the same time, and this will have a paradoxical sound, there has never been a period in medicine when the future has looked so bright. There is within medicine, somewhere beneath the pessimism and discouragement resulting from the disarray of the health-care system and its stupendous cost, an undercurrent of almost outrageous optimism about what may lie ahead for the treatment of human disease if we can only keep learning. The scientists who do research on the cardiovascular system are entirely confident that they will soon be working close to the center of things, and they no longer regard the mechanisms of heart disease as impenetrable mysteries. The cancer scientists, for all their public disagreements about how best to organize their research, are in possession of insights into the intimate functioning of normal and neoplastic cells that were unimaginable a few years back. The eukaryotic cell, the cell with a true nucleus, has itself become a laboratory instrument almost as neat and handy as the bacterial cell became in the early 1950s, ready now to be used for elucidating the mechanisms by which genes are switched on or off as developing cells differentiate or, as in the case of cancer cells, dedifferentiate. The ways in which carcinogenic substances, or viruses, or other factors still unrecognized intervene in the regulation of cell behavior represent problems still unsolved, but the problems themselves now appear to be approachable; with what has been learned in the past decade, they can now be worked on.

The neurobiologists can do all sorts of things in their investigation, and the brain is an organ different from what it seemed twenty-five years ago. Far from being an intricate but ultimately simplifiable mass of electronic circuitry governed by wiring diagrams, it now has the aspect of a fundamentally endocrine tissue, in which the essential reactions, the internal traffic of nerve impulses, are determined by biochemical activators and their suppressors. The technologies available for quantitative study of individual nerve cells are powerful and precise, and the work is now turning toward the functioning of collections of cells, the centers for visual and auditory perception and the like, because work at this level can now be done. It is difficult to think of problems that cannot be studied, ever. The matter of consciousness is argued over, naturally, as a candidate for perpetual unapproachability, but this has more the sound of a philosophical discussion. Nobody has the feeling any longer, as we used to believe, that we can never find out how the brain works.

The immunologists, the molecular biochemists, and the new generation of investigators obsessed with the structure and function of cell membranes have all discovered that they are really working together, along with the geneticists, on a common set of problems: how do cells and tissues become labeled for what they are, what are the forces that govern the orderly development and differentiation of tissues and organs, and how are errors in the process controlled?

There has never been a time like it, and I find it difficult to imagine that this tremendous surge of new information will terminate with nothing more than an understanding of how normal cells and tissues, and organisms, function. I regard it as a certainty that there will be uncovered, at the same time, detailed information concerning the mechanisms of disease.

The record of the past half century has established, I think, two general principles about human disease. First, it is necessary to know a great deal about underlying mechanisms before one can really act effectively; one had to know that the pneumococcus causes lobar pneumonia before one could begin thinking about antibiotics. One did not have to know all the details, not even how the pneumococcus does its damage to the lungs, but one had to know that it was there, and in charge.

Second, for every disease there is a single key mechanism that dominates all others. If one can find it, and then think one's way around it, one can control the disorder. This generalization is harder to prove, and arguable—it is more like a strong hunch than a scientific assertion—but I believe that the record thus far tends to support it. The most complicated, multicell, multitissue, and multiorgan diseases I know of are tertiary syphilis, chronic tuberculosis, and pernicious anemia. In each, there are at least five major organs and tissues involved, and each appears to be affected by a variety of environmental influences. Before they came under scientific appraisal each was thought to be what we now call a "multifactorial" disease, far too complex to allow for any single causative mechanism. And yet, when all the necessary facts were in, it was clear that by simply switching off one thing—the spirochete, the tubercle bacillus, or a single vitamin deficiency—the whole array of disordered and seemingly unrelated pathologic mechanisms could be switched off, at once.

I believe that a prospect something like this is the likelihood for the future of medicine. I have no doubt that there will turn out to be dozens of separate influences that can launch cancer, including all sorts of environmental carcinogens and very likely many sorts of virus, but I think there will turn out to be a single switch at the center of things, there for the finding. I think that schizophrenia will turn out to be a neurochemical disorder, with some central, single chemical event gone wrong. I think there is a single causative agent responsible for rheumatoid arthritis, which has not yet been found. I think that the central vascular abnormalities that launch coronary occlusion and stroke have not yet been glimpsed, but they are there, waiting to be switched on or off.

In short, I believe that the major diseases of human beings have become approachable biological puzzles, ultimately solvable. It follows from this that it is now possible to begin thinking about a human society relatively free of disease. This would surely have been an unthinkable notion a half century ago, and oddly enough it has a rather apocalyptic sound today. What will we do about dying, and about all that population, if such things were to come about? What can we die of, if not disease?

My response is that it would not make all that much difference. We would still age away and wear out, on about the same schedule as today, with the terminal event being more like the sudden disintegration and collapse all at once of Oliver Wendell Holmes's well-known one-hoss shay. The main effect, almost pure benefit it seems to me, would be that we would not be beset and raddled by disease in the last decades of life, as most of us are today. We could become a healthy species, not all that different from the healthy stocks of domestic plants and animals that we already take for granted. Strokes, and senile dementia, and cancer, and arthritis are not natural aspects of the human condition, and we ought to rid ourselves of such impediments as quickly as we can.

There is another argument against this view of the future which needs comment. It is said that we are fundamentally fallible as organisms, prone to failure, and if we succeed in getting rid of one set of ailments there will always be other new diseases, now waiting out in the forest, ready to take their places. I do not know why this is said, for I can see no evidence that such a thing has ever happened. To be sure, we have a higher incidence of chronic illness among older people than we had in the early years of this century, but that is because more of us have survived to become older people. No new disease, so far as I know, has come in to take the place of diphtheria, or smallpox, or whooping cough, or poliomyelitis. Nature being inventive, we will probably always have the odd new illness turning up, but not in order to fill out some ordained, predestined quota of human maladies.

Indeed, the official public-health tables of morbidity and mortality seem to be telling us this sort of thing already, even though, in all our anxiety, we seem unwilling to accept the news. We have already become in the Western world, on the record, the healthiest society in the history of humankind. Compared with a century ago, when every family was obliged to count on losing members throughout the early years of life, we are in a new world. A death in a young family has become a rare and dreadful catastrophe, no longer a commonplace event. Our estimated life expectancy, collectively, is longer this year than ever before in history. Part of this general and gradual improvement in health and survival is thanks to sanitary engineering, better housing, and, probably, more affluence, but a substantial part is also attributable, in recent years, to biomedical science. We have not done badly at all, and having begun so well, I see no reason why we should not do even better in the future.

My argument about how to do this will come as no surprise. I say that we must continue doing biomedical research, on about the same scale and scope as in the past twenty years, with expansion and growth of the enterprise being dependent on where new leads seem to be taking us. It is an expensive undertaking, but still it is less than 3 percent of the total annual cost of today's health industry, which at last count was over $140 billion, and it is nothing like as expensive as trying to live with the halfway technologies we are obliged to depend on in medicine today; if we try to stay with these for the rest of the century the costs will go through the ionosphere.

But I should like to insert a qualification in this argument, which may be somewhat more of a surprise, coming from a doctor. I believe that the major research effort, and far and away the greatest investment for the future, must be in the broad area of basic biological science. Here and there, to be sure, there will be opportunities for productive applied science, comparable, say, to the making of polio vaccine or the devising of multidrug therapy for childhood leukemia, but these opportunities will not come often, nor can they be forced into existence before their time. The great need now, for the medicine of the future, is for more information at the most fundamental levels of the living process. We are nowhere near ready for large-scale programs of applied science in medicine, for we do not yet know enough.

Good applied science in medicine, as in physics, requires a high degree of certainty about the basic facts at hand, and especially about their meaning, and we have not yet reached this point for most of medicine. Nor can we predict at this stage, with much confidence, which particular items of new information, from which fields, are the likeliest to be relevant to particular disease problems. In this circumstance there has to be a certain amount of guessing, even gambling, and my own view is that the highest yield for the future will come from whatever fields are generating the most interesting, exciting, and surprising sorts of information, most of all, surprising.

It seems to me that the safest and most prudent of bets to lay money on is surprise. There is a very high probability that whatever astonishes us in biology today will turn out to be usable, and useful, tomorrow. This, I think, is the established record of science itself, over the past two hundred years, and we ought to have more confidence in the process. It worked this way for the beginnings of chemistry; we obtained electricity in this manner; using surprise as a guide, we progressed from Newtonian physics to electromagnetism, to quantum mechanics and contemporary geophysics and cosmology. In biology, evolution and genetics were the earliest big astonishments, but what has been going on in the past quarter century is simply flabbergasting. For medicine, the greatest surprises lie still ahead of us, but they are there, waiting to be discovered or stumbled over, sooner or later.

I am arguing this way from the most practical, down-to-earth, pragmatic point of view. This kind of science is most likely, in the real world, to lead to significant improvements in human health, and at low cost. This is a point worth further emphasis, by the way. When medicine has really succeeded brilliantly in technology, as in immunization, for example, or antibiotics, or nutrition, or endocrine-replacement therapy, so that the therapeutic measures can be directed straight at the underlying disease mechanism and are decisively effective, the cost is likely to be very low indeed. It is when our technologies have to be applied halfway along against the progress of disease, or must be brought in after the fact to shore up the loss of destroyed tissue, that health care becomes enormously expensive. The deeper our understanding of a disease mechanism, the greater are our chances of devising direct and decisive measures to prevent disease, or to turn it around before it is too late.

So much for the practical side of the argument. We need much more basic science for the future of human health, and I will leave the matter there.

But I have one last thing to say about biological science. Even if I should be wrong about some of these predictions, and it turns out that we can blunder our way into treating or preventing one disease or another without understanding the process (which I will not believe until it happens), and if we continue to invest in biological science anyway, we cannot lose. The Congress, in its wisdom, cannot lose. The public cannot lose.

Here is what I have in mind.

These ought to be the best of times for the human mind, but it is not so. All sorts of things seem to be turning out wrong, and the century seems to be slipping through our fingers here at the end, with almost all promises unfulfilled. I cannot begin to guess at all the causes of our cultural sadness, not even the most important ones, but I can think of one thing that is wrong with us and eats away at us: we do not know enough about ourselves. We are ignorant about how we work, about where we fit in, and most of all about the enormous, imponderable system of life in which we are embedded as working parts. We do not really understand nature, at all. We have come a long way indeed, but just enough to become conscious of our ignorance. It is not so bad a thing to be totally ignorant; the hard thing is to be partway along toward real knowledge, far enough to be aware of being ignorant. It is embarrassing and depressing, and it is one of our troubles today.

It is a new experience for all of us. Only two centuries ago we could explain everything about everything, out of pure reason, and now most of that elaborate and harmonious structure has come apart before our eyes. We are *dumb*.

This is, in a certain sense, a health problem after all. For as long as we are bewildered by the mystery of ourselves, and confused by the strangeness of our uncomfortable connection to all the rest of life, and dumbfounded by the inscrutability of our own minds, we cannot be said to be healthy animals in today's world.

We need to know more. To come to realize this is what this seemingly inconclusive century has been all about. We have discovered how to ask important questions, and now we really do need, as an urgent matter, for the sake of our civilization, to obtain some answers. We now know that we cannot do this any longer by searching our minds, for there is not enough there to search, nor can we find the truth by guessing at it or by making up stories for ourselves. We cannot stop where we are, stuck with today's level of understanding, nor can we go back. I do not see that we have a real choice in this, for I can see only the one way ahead. We need science, more and better science, not for its technology, not for leisure, not even for health or longevity, but for the hope of wisdom which our kind of culture must acquire for its survival.

CHAPTER FIFTY-NINE

Leech Leech, Et Cetera

A FEW YEARS AGO, I BLUNDERED INTO THE FRINGES OF A MARVELOUS field of scholarship, comparative philology. I wondered—I forget the occasion—why leech was the word for the doctor and at the same time for the worm used by the doctor for so many centuries. Which came first, leech the doctor or leech the worm?

The lovely *American Heritage Dictionary* has a fifty-page appendix of Indo-European roots, based in large part on *Pokorny's Dictionary of Indo-European Languages*. My wife searched New York's bookstores and found a copy of *Pokorny* in a rare-book store for my birthday, and I have never since looked back.

The evolution of language can be compared to the biological evolution of species, depending on how far you are willing to stretch analogies. The first and deepest question is open and unanswerable in both cases: how did life start up at its very beginning? What was the very first human speech like?

Fossils exist for both, making it possible to track back to somewhere near the beginning. The earliest forms of life were the prokaryotes, organisms of the same shape and size as bacteria; chains of cocci and bacilli left unmistakable imprints within rocks dating back as far as 3.5 billion years. Similar microorganisms comprised the total life of the planet for the next 2.5 billion years, living free or, more often, gathered together as immense colonies in "algal mats," which later on fossilized into the formidable geological structures known as stromatolites. It was only recently, perhaps a billion years ago, that the prokaryotic algae had pumped enough oxygen into the earth's atmosphere so that nucleated cells could be formed. The mitochondria, which provide oxidative energy for all nucleated cells, and the chloroplasts of plant cells, which engage the sun's energy for producing the planet's food and oxygen, are the lineal descendants of bacteria and blue-green algae, and have lived as symbionts with the rest of us for a billion years.

The fossils of human language are much more recent, of course, and can only be scrutinized by the indirect methods of comparative philology, but they are certainly there. The most familiar ones are the Indo-European roots, prokaryote equivalents, the ancestors of most of the Western and some of the Eastern languages: Sanskrit, Greek, Latin, all the Slavic and Germanic tongues, Hittite, Tocharian, Iranian, Indic, some others, all originating in a common speech more than 20,000 years ago at a very rough guess. The original words from which the languages evolved were probably, at the outset, expressions of simple, non-nucleated ideas, unambiguous etymons.

The two leeches are an example of biological mimicry at work in language. The root for leech the doctor goes back to the start of language: *leg* was a word meaning "to collect," with derivatives meaning "to speak" and carried somehow the implication of knowledge and wisdom. It became *laece* in Old English, *lake* in Middle Dutch, with the meaning of doctor. Along the way, in early Germanic, it yielded *lekjaz*, a word meaning "an enchanter, speaking magic words," which would fit well with the duties of early physicians. The doctor was called the leech in English for many centuries, and a Danish doctor is still known as *Laege*, a Swedish one as *Lakere*.

Leg gave spawn to other progeny, different from the doctor but with related meanings. Lecture, logic, and logos are examples to flatter medicine's heart.

Leech the worm is harder to trace. The *OED* has it in tenth-century records as *lyce*, later *laece*, and then the two leeches became, for all practical purposes, the same general idea. Leech the doctor made his living by the use of leech the worm; leech the worm was believed (wrongly, I think) to have had restorative, health-giving gifts and was therefore, in its way, a sort of doctor. The technical term "assimilation" is used for this fusion of words with two different meanings into a single word carrying both. The idea of collecting has perhaps sustained the fusion, persisting inside each usage: blood for the leech, fees (and blood as well) for the doctor. Tax collectors were once called leeches, for the worm meaning, of course.

The word doctor came from *dek*, meaning something proper and acceptable, useful. It became *docere* in Latin, to teach, also *discere*, to learn, hence disciple. In Greek it was understood to mean an acceptable kind of teaching, thus dogma and orthodox. Decorum and decency are cognate words.

Medicine itself emerged from the root *med,* which meant something like measuring out, or taking appropriate measures. Latin used *med* to make *mederi,* to look after, to heal. The English words moderate and modest are also descendants of *med,* carrying instructions for medicine long since forgotten; medical students ought to meditate (another cognate) from time to time about these etymological cousins.

The physician came from a wonderful word, one of the master roots in the old language, *bheu,* meaning nature itself, being, existence. *Phusis* was made from this root in Greek, on its way to the English word physic, used for medicine in general, and physics, meaning the study of nature.

Doctor, medicine, and physician, taken together with the cognate words that grew up around them, tell us a great deal about society's ancient expectations from the profession, hard to live up to. Of all the list, moderate and modest seem to me the ones most in need of remembering. The root *med* has tucked itself inside these words, living as a successful symbiont, and its similar existence all these years inside medicine should be a steady message for the teacher, the healer, the collector of science, the old leech.

Medicine was once the most respected of all the professions. Today, when it possesses an array of technologies for treating (or curing) diseases which were simply beyond comprehension a few years ago, medicine is under attack for all sorts of reasons. Doctors, the critics say, are applied scientists, concerned only with the disease at hand but never with the patient as an individual, whole person. They do not really listen. They are unwilling or incapable of explaining things to sick people or their families. They make mistakes in their risky technologies; hence the rapidly escalating cost of malpractice insurance. They are accessible only in their offices in huge, alarming clinics or within the walls of terrifying hospitals. The word "dehumanizing" is used as an epithet for the way they are trained, and for the way they practice. The old art of medicine has been lost, forgotten.

The American medical schools are under pressure from all sides to bring back the family doctor—the sagacious, avuncular physician who used to make house calls, look after the illnesses of every member of the family, was even able to call the family dog by name. Whole new academic departments have been installed—some of them, in the state-run medical schools, actually legislated into existence—called, in the official catalogues, *Family Practice, Primary Health Care, Preventive Medicine, Primary Medicine.* The avowed intention is to turn out more general practitioners of the type that everyone remembers from childhood or from one's parents' or grandparents' childhood, or from books, movies, and television.

What is it that people have always expected from the doctor? How, indeed, has the profession of medicine survived for so much of human history? Doctors as a class have always been criticized for their deficiencies. Montaigne in his time, Molière in his, and Shaw had less regard for doctors and their medicine than today's critics. What on earth were the patients of physicians in the nineteenth century and the centuries before, all the way back to my professional ancestors, the shamans of prehistory, hoping for when they called for the doctor? In the years of the great plagues, when carts came through the town streets each night to pick up the dead and carry them off for burial, what was the function of the doctor? Bubonic plague, typhus, tuberculosis, and syphilis were representative examples of a great number of rapidly progressive and usually lethal infections, killing off most of the victims no matter what was done by the doctor. What did the man do, when called out at night to visit the sick for whom he had nothing to offer for palliation, much less cure?

Well, one thing he did, early on in history, was plainly magic. The shaman learned his profession the hardest way: he was compelled to go through something like a version of death itself, personally, and when he emerged he was considered qualified to deal with patients. He had epileptic fits, saw visions, and heard voices, lost himself in the wilderness for weeks on end, fell into long stretches of coma, and when he came back to life he was licensed to practice, dancing around the bedside, making smoke, chanting incomprehensibilities, and *touching* the patient everywhere. The touching was the real professional secret, never acknowledged as the central, essential skill, always obscured by the dancing and the chanting, but always busily there, the laying on of hands.

There, I think, is the oldest and most effective act of doctors, the touching. Some people don't like being handled by others, but not, or almost never, sick people. They *need* being touched, and part of the dismay in being very sick is the lack of close human contact. Ordinary people, even close friends, even family members, tend to stay away from the very sick, touching them as infrequently as possible for fear of interfering, or catching the illness, or just for fear of bad luck. The doctor's oldest skill in trade was to place his hands on the patient.

Over the centuries, the skill became more specialized and refined, the hands learned other things to do beyond mere contact. They probed to feel the pulse at the wrist, the tip of the spleen, or the edge of the liver, thumped to elicit resonant or dull sounds over the lungs, spread ointments over the skin, nicked veins for bleeding, but at the same time touched, caressed, and at the end held on to the patient's fingers.

Most of the men who practiced this laying on of hands must have possessed, to begin with, the gift of affection. There are, certainly, some people who do not like other people much, and they would have been likely to stay away from an occupation requiring touching. If, by mistake, they found themselves apprenticed for medicine, they probably backed off or, if not, turned into unsuccessful doctors.

Touching with the naked ear was one of the great advances in the history of medicine. Once it was learned that the heart and lungs made sounds of their own, and that the sounds were sometimes useful for diagnosis, physicians placed an ear over the heart, and over areas on the front and back of the chest, and listened. It is hard to imagine a friendlier human gesture, a more intimate signal of personal concern and affection, than these close bowed heads affixed to the skin. The stethoscope was invented in the nineteenth century, vastly enhancing the acoustics of the thorax, but removing the physician a certain distance from his patient. It was the earliest device of many still to come, one new technology after another, designed to increase that distance.

Today, the doctor can perform a great many of his most essential tasks from his office in another building without ever seeing the patient. There are even computer programs for the taking of a history: a clerk can ask the questions and check the boxes on a printed form, and the computer will instantly provide a printout of the diagnostic possibilities to be considered and the laboratory procedures to be undertaken. Instead of spending forty-five minutes listening to the chest and palpating the abdomen, the doctor can sign a slip which sends the patient off to the X-ray department for a CT scan, with the expectation of seeing within the hour, in exquisite detail, all the body's internal organs which he formerly had to make guesses about with his fingers and ears. The biochemistry laboratory eliminates the need for pondering and waiting for the appearance of new signs and symptoms. Computerized devices reveal electronic intimacies of the flawed heart or malfunctioning brain with a precision far beyond the touch or reach, or even the imagining, of the physician at the bedside a few generations back.

The doctor can set himself, if he likes, at a distance, remote from the patient and the family, never touching anyone beyond a perfunctory handshake as the first and only contact. Medicine is no longer the laying on of hands, it is more like the reading of signals from machines.

The mechanization of scientific medicine is here to stay. The new medicine works. It is a vastly more complicated profession, with more things to be done on short notice on which issues of life or death depend. The physician has the same obligations that he carried, overworked and

often despairingly, fifty years ago, but now with any number of technological maneuvers to be undertaken quickly and with precision. It
looks to the patient like a different experience from what his parents told
him about, with something important left out. The doctor seems less
like the close friend and confidant, less interested in him as a person,
wholly concerned with treating the disease. And there is no changing
this, no going back; nor, when you think about it, is there really any
reason for wanting to go back. If I develop the signs and symptoms of
malignant hypertension, or cancer of the colon, or subacute bacterial
endocarditis, I want as much comfort and friendship as I can find at
hand, but mostly I want to be treated quickly and effectively so as to
survive, if that is possible. If I am in bed in a modern hospital, worrying
about the cost of that bed as well, I want to get out as fast as possible,
whole if possible.

In my father's time, talking with the patient was the biggest part of
medicine, for it was almost all there was to do. The doctor-patient
relationship was, for better or worse, a long conversation in which the
patient was at the epicenter of concern and knew it. When I was an
intern and scientific technology was in its earliest stage, the talk was still
there, but hurried, often on the run.

Today, with the advance of medicine's various and complicated new
technologies, the ward rounds now at the foot of the bed, the drawing of
blood samples for automated assessment of every known (or suggested)
biochemical abnormality, the rolling of wheelchairs and litters down
through the corridors to the X-ray department, there is less time for
talking. The longest and most personal conversations held with hospital
patients when they come to the hospital are discussions of finances and
insurance, engaged in by personnel trained in accountancy, whose
scientific instruments are the computers. The hospitalized patient feels,
for a time, like a working part of an immense, automated apparatus. He
is admitted and discharged by batteries of computers, sometimes without even learning the doctors' names. The difference can be strange and
vaguely dismaying for patients. But there is another difference, worth
emphasis. Many patients go home speedily, in good health, cured of
their diseases. In my father's day this happened much less often, and
when it did, it was a matter of good luck or a strong constitution. When
it happens today, it is more frequently due to technology.

There are costs to be faced. Not just money, the real and heavy dollar
costs. The close-up, reassuring, warm touch of the physician, the
comfort and concern, the long, leisurely discussions in which everything including the dog can be worked into the conversation, are
disappearing from the practice of medicine, and this may turn out to be
too great a loss for the doctor as well as for the patient. This uniquely

subtle, personal relationship has roots that go back into the beginnings of medicine's history, and needs preserving. To do it right has never been easy; it takes the best of doctors, the best of friends. Once lost, even for as short a time as one generation, it may be too difficult a task to bring it back again.

If I were a medical student or an intern, just getting ready to begin, I would be more worried about this aspect of my future than anything else. I would be apprehensive that my real job, caring for sick people, might soon be taken away, leaving me with the quite different occupation of looking after machines. I would be trying to figure out ways to keep this from happening.

CHAPTER SIXTY

Nurses

WHEN MY MOTHER BECAME A REGISTERED NURSE AT ROOSEVELT hospital, in 1903, there was no question in anyone's mind about what nurses did as professionals. They did what the doctors ordered. The attending physician would arrive for his ward rounds in the early morning, and when he arrived at the ward office the head nurse would be waiting for him, ready to take his hat and coat, and his cane, and she would stand while he had his cup of tea before starting. Entering the ward, she would hold the door for him to go first, then his entourage of interns and medical students, then she followed. At each bedside, after he had conducted his examination and reviewed the patient's progress, he would tell the nurse what needed doing that day, and she would write it down on the part of the chart reserved for nursing notes. An hour or two later he would be gone from the ward, and the work of the rest of the day and the night to follow was the nurse's frenetic occupation. In addition to the stipulated orders, she had an endless list of routine things to do, all learned in her two years of nursing school: the beds had to be changed and made up with fresh sheets by an exact geometric design of folding and tucking impossible for anyone but a trained nurse; the patients had to be washed head to foot; bedpans had to be brought, used, emptied, and washed; temperatures had to be taken every four hours and meticulously recorded on the chart; enemas were to be given; urine and stool samples collected, labeled, and sent off to the laboratory; throughout the day and night, medications of all sorts, usually pills and various vegetable extracts and tinctures, had to be carried on trays from bed to bed. At most times of the year about half of the forty or so patients on the ward had typhoid fever, which meant that the nurse couldn't simply move from bed to bed in the performance of her duties; each typhoid case was screened from the other patients, and the nurse was required to put on a new gown and wash her hands in disinfectant before approaching the bedside. Patients with high fevers were sponged with cold alcohol at frequent intervals. The late-evening back rub was the rite of passage into sleep.

In addition to the routine, workaday schedule, the nurse was responsible for responding to all calls from the patients, and it was expected that she would do so on the run. Her rounds, scheduled as methodical progressions around the ward, were continually interrupted by these calls. It was up to her to evaluate each situation quickly: a sudden abdominal pain in a typhoid patient might signify intestinal perforation; the abrupt onset of weakness, thirst, and pallor meant intestinal hemorrhage; the coughing up of gross blood by a tuberculous patient was an emergency. Some of the calls came from neighboring patients on the way to recovery; patients on open wards always kept a close eye on each other: the man in the next bed might slip into coma or seem to be dying, or be indeed dead. For such emergencies the nurse had to get word immediately to the doctor on call, usually the intern assigned to the ward, who might be off in the outpatient department or working in the diagnostic laboratory (interns of that day did all the laboratory work themselves; technicians had not yet been invented) or in his room. Nurses were not allowed to give injections or to do such emergency procedures as spinal punctures or chest taps, but they were expected to know when such maneuvers were indicated and to be ready with appropriate trays of instruments when the intern arrived on the ward.

It was an exhausting business, but by my mother's accounts it was the most satisfying and rewarding kind of work. As a nurse she was a low person in the professional hierarchy, always running from place to place on orders from the doctors, subject as well to strict discipline from her own administrative superiors on the nursing staff, but none of this came through in her recollections. What she remembered was her usefulness.

Whenever my father talked to me about nurses and their work, he spoke with high regard for them as professionals. Although it was clear in his view that the task of the nurses was to do what the doctor told them to, it was also clear that he admired them for being able to do a lot of things he couldn't possibly do, had never been trained to do. On his own rounds later on, when he became an attending physician himself, he consulted the ward nurse for her opinion about problem cases and paid careful attention to her observations and chart notes. In his own days of intern training (perhaps partly under my mother's strong influence, I don't know) he developed a deep and lasting respect for the whole nursing profession.

I have spent all of my professional career in close association with, and close dependency on, nurses, and like many of my faculty colleagues, I've done a lot of worrying about the relationship between medicine and nursing. During most of this century the nursing profession has been having a hard time of it. It has been largely, although not entirely, an occupation for women, and sensitive issues of professional status, complicated by the special issue of the changing role of women in modern society, have led to a standoffish, often adversarial relationship between nurses and doctors. Already swamped by an increasing load of routine duties, nurses have been obliged to take on more and more purely administrative tasks: keeping the records in order; making sure the supplies are on hand for every sort of ward emergency; supervising the activities of the new paraprofessional group called LPNs (licensed practical nurses), who now perform much of the bedside work once done by RNs (registered nurses); overseeing ward maids, porters, and cleaners; seeing to it that patients scheduled for X rays are on their way to the X-ray department on time. Therefore, they have to spend more of their time at desks in the ward office and less time at the bedsides. Too late maybe, the nurses have begun to realize that they are gradually being excluded from the one duty which had previously been their most important reward but which had been so taken for granted that nobody mentioned it in listing the duties of a nurse: close personal contact with patients. Along with everything else nurses did in the long day's work, making up for all the tough and sometimes demeaning jobs assigned to them, they had the matchless opportunity to be useful friends to great numbers of human beings in trouble. They listened to their patients all day long and through the night, they gave comfort and reassurance to the patients and their families, they got to know them as friends, they were depended on. To contemplate the loss of this part of their work has been the deepest worry for nurses at large, and for the faculties responsible for the curricula of the nation's new and expanding nursing schools. The issue lies at the center of the running argument between medical school and nursing school administrators, but it is never clearly stated. Nursing education has been upgraded in recent years. Almost all the former hospital schools, which took in high-school graduates and provided an RN certificate after two or three years, have been replaced by schools attached to colleges and universities, with a four-year curriculum leading simultaneously to a bachelor's degree and an RN certificate.

The doctors worry that nurses are trying to move away from their historical responsibilities to medicine (meaning, really, to the doctors' orders). The nurses assert that they are their own profession, responsible for their own standards, coequal colleagues with physicians, and they do not wish to become mere ward administrators or technicians (although some of them, carrying the new and prestigious title of "nurse practitioner," are being trained within nursing schools to perform some of the most complex technological responsibilities in hospital emergency rooms and intensive care units). The doctors claim that what the nurses really want is to become substitute psychiatrists. The nurses reply that they have unavoidable responsibilities for the mental health and well-being of their patients, and that these are different from the doctors' tasks. Eventually the arguments will work themselves out, and some sort of agreement will be reached, but if it is to be settled intelligently, some way will have to be found to preserve and strengthen the traditional and highly personal nurse-patient relationship.

I have had a fair amount of firsthand experience with the issue, having been an apprehensive patient myself off and on over a three-year period on the wards of the hospital for which I work. I am one up on most of my physician friends because of this experience. I know some things they do not know about what nurses do.

One thing the nurses do is to hold the place together. It is an astonishment, which every patient feels from time to time, observing the affairs of a large, complex hospital from the vantage point of his bed, that the whole institution doesn't fly to pieces. A hospital operates by the constant interplay of powerful forces pulling away at each other in different directions, each force essential for getting necessary things done, but always at odds with each other. The intern staff is an almost irresistible force in itself, learning medicine by doing medicine, assuming all the responsibility within reach, pushing against an immovable attending and administrative staff, and frequently at odds with the nurses. The attending physicians are individual entrepreneurs trying to run small cottage industries at each bedside. The diagnostic laboratories are feudal fiefdoms, prospering from the insatiable demands for their services from the interns and residents. The medical students are all over the place, learning as best they can and complaining that they are not, as they believe they should be, at the epicenter of everyone's concern. Each individual worker in the place, from the chiefs of surgery to the dieticians to the ward maids, porters, and elevator operators, lives and works in the conviction that the whole apparatus would come to a standstill without his or her individual contribution, and in one sense or another each of them is right.

My discovery, as a patient first on the medical service and later in surgery, is that the institution is held together, *glued* together, enabled to function as an organism, by the nurses and by nobody else.

The nurses, the good ones anyway (and all the ones on my floor were good), make it their business to know everything that is going on. They spot errors before errors can be launched. They know everything written on the chart. Most important of all, they know their patients as unique human beings, and they soon get to know the close relatives and friends. Because of this knowledge, they are quick to sense apprehensions and act on them. The average sick person in a large hospital feels at risk of getting lost, with no identity left beyond a name and a string of numbers on a plastic wristband, in danger always of being whisked off on a litter to the wrong place to have the wrong procedure done, or worse still, *not* being whisked off at the right time. The attending physician or the house officer, on rounds and usually in a hurry, can murmur a few reassuring words on his way out the door, but it takes a confident, competent, and cheerful nurse, there all day long and in and out of the room on one chore or another through the night, to bolster one's confidence that the situation is indeed manageable and not about to get out of hand.

Knowing what I know, I am all for the nurses. If they are to continue their professional feud with the doctors, if they want their professional status enhanced and their pay increased, if they infuriate the doctors by their claims to be equal professionals, if they ask for the moon, I am on their side.

CHAPTER SIXTY-ONE

Olfaction and the

Tracking Mouse

I LEARNED A LITTLE ABOUT OLFACTION DURING MY RESIDENCY IN neurology at the Neurological Institute in the late 1930s. The former chief of neurosurgery, Dr. Joseph Elsberg, was still working at the institute then, and his scientific obsession was the use of olfactory acuity as a physical sign in the diagnosis of brain disease. He had worked out a complex system of glass vessels with blowers connected to tubes fitted into the nostrils with which he and his assistants were able to measure, with a rough degree of quantitation, the perception of tiny amounts of juniper, camphor, cinnamon, and the like in each side of the nose. The group had established the usefulness of the procedure in the localization of certain malignant brain tumors located in the deeper regions of the frontal and temporal lobes. The trouble with the procedure was that it required extreme patience and experience, and great skill, on the part of the technicians who carried it out, and the results were of significance in such a small proportion of the patients in the hospital that it was finally given up. None of the younger members of the neurosurgical staff was interested enough to continue the research work after Elsberg retired.

I did some reading in the field at the time, and found the literature on olfaction obscure and sparse. Nobody seemed to know much about the matter. The olfactory receptor cells were known to be bona fide brain cells, the only proper neurons in the brain that are exposed to the outside world and act as their own receptors of information from the environment. All the others, those concerned with the senses of touch, position, taste, hearing, and vision, depend upon relays of nerve impulses coming in from highly specialized receptor cells which pick up the appropriate stimuli at the periphery and send them along to centers in the interior of the brain which are set up to make sense of the sense. The most curious and remarkable thing about the olfactory neurons is that they come and go, replicating and replacing themselves in their positions at the surface of the olfactory mucosa, high up in the back of the nose. No other brain neurons have the property of multiplying or regenerating; once in place, the neurons of the rest of the brain are there for the duration of life, and those which age and die off are not replaced. But the olfactory receptor neurons keep coming; in the mouse they have been shown to have a turnover of the population every two to three weeks. Another peculiarity of these cells is that despite their exposure to the outside, and their location in a region of the air passages which is especially rich in bacteria and viruses of all sorts, the tissues in which they reside do not become infected. It was thought at one time that the poliomyelitis virus made its way into the brain by way of the olfactory neurons, but this was later proved wrong. It is now believed that the cells are somehow protected by the antimicrobial property of the mucus which is always present as a thin layer covering the cells.

From time to time, new information about olfaction appeared in the physiology literature, and a series of international conferences dealing with the phenomenon began in the 1950s. I kept in touch with this material as best I could, as an outsider, and one day about ten years ago I ran into some references to observations made much earlier — as far back as the 1920s — on the accomplishments of tracking hounds. A great deal of solid work had been done at that time, most of it sponsored by European police departments, on the capacity of trained dogs to track the footsteps of a single human being across fields marked at the same time by the tracks of other people.

Much of this was anecdotal, based on single observations made in the course of field trials and interdepartmental competitions, but the anecdotes were abundant and consistent, building a consensus accepted all round: a well-trained hound could distinguish with accuracy an odor of some kind arising from the track of a human being, for as long as forty-eight hours after the laying of the track, and could distinguish this particular track from all other tracks laid by other human beings.

If this was indeed true, it meant that the dog was able to smell a signal coming from the track which identified each human being as an individual self. But another elaborate and precise biological system was already known to exist for the same purpose: immunological markers that signal selfness are present at the surface of all cells in the body; the sensing of these chemical molecules is responsible for the fact that skin grafts are rejected with surgical precision when the grafts come from someone else, unless the foreign skin is taken from one identical twin and sewn into the skin of the other. This is believed to be a universal phenomenon: except for the exchange of tissues between identical twins, the skin of no one of the 4 billion human beings on the planet can be grafted successfully to any other. Grafting can be done these days with kidneys, even hearts, but only with the aid of drugs that incapacitate the lymphocytes responsible for immunologic rejection of non-self tissues.

It seemed to me strange that two different systems would have arisen for the same function in evolution, separately and unrelated to each other, and I began to speculate that they might indeed have evolved from a single ancestral system employed, early on in evolution, for enabling the first primitive organisms to make distinctions between their own cell surfaces and those of others. Such mechanisms are known to exist abundantly in the most ancient of metazoan creatures, sponges and corals for instance. Moscona showed some years ago that when the separated cells of two species of sponge are mixed together and rotated in a saline suspension, the two kinds of cells will reaggregate in clusters, each of which is made up exclusively of one or the other species. The cells can evidently recognize their own kind as self, and can at the same time avoid sticking to the non-self cells. Jacques Theodor placed together two pieces of soft coral of the same species, but from different colonies on the reef, and observed that, after first fusing to form a single frond of coral, the two bits would then separate from each other, precisely along the original line of apposition, with death of all the cells in the immediate vicinity of that line. Recently, Hildemann and his associates have observed the same sort of graft rejection in sponges: two sponges from the same colony will fuse together permanently, but when the sponges are of the same species but from different colonies, they will reject each other ten or twelve days after fusing. Moreover, the sponges seem to have a specific memory of the event; when the separated explants are again placed together, but with different surfaces confronting each other, the rejection reaction occurs in accelerated fashion, two to three days later. The phenomenon is remarkably like graft rejection in the mouse: the first skin graft from a foreign mouse is rejected in eight to ten days, but a second graft of the same tissue is rejected in three or four days.

In mice, the reaction of graft rejection is primarily a function of a particular class of lymphocytes, the so-called T-lymphocytes (so designated because of their origin in the thymus gland). The reaction is controlled by a special set of genes, called the H-2 locus, always situated together on a single chromosome. In man, the corresponding gene locus, governing the self–non-self distinction and the rejection of tissue grafts, is known as the HLA locus.

Several years ago, when invited to deliver an address before an Immunology Congress on possible future lines of immunologic research, I discussed the problem of self-marking and expressed the view that it would be remarkably unparsimonious of nature to set up two such elaborate and complex systems for individual self-marking— costly in terms of energy, one involving the immunologic markers of histocompatibility and the other using olfaction— and to have these two mechanisms evolving without being closely related to each other. I made at that time what I thought was a mild biological joke, predicting that the same set of genes would be found responsible for both systems of labeling, and that someday "man's best friend would be used for sniffing out histocompatible donors."

A while ago I was discussing this with Dr. Edward Boyse, whose research laboratory in Sloan-Kettering makes daily use of an extensive collection of meticulously inbred and sharply defined lines of mice. His wife, Jeanette Boyse, has the immediate responsibility for overseeing the breeding of various lines of congenic mice, in which the sole genetic difference between two lines lies in the H-2 locus on chromosome 17, the locus governing graft rejection and coding out the major histocompatibility complex (the MHC) of tissue antigens. The mice are contained in transparent boxes so that their mating behavior can be kept under close and constant observation. Mrs. Boyse had just noticed that the males of certain lines displayed a preference for mating with females of the opposite line possessing different H-2 genes. The possibility was raised that perhaps the male could smell the difference, and since these were two lines of genetically identical animals, except for the H-2 difference, it was obvious that the capacity of a male to smell such a difference would have to involve an olfactory distinction between self (in strict terms of individual self) and non-self.

It did not take long for the Boyses, together with two young postdoctoral fellows at Sloan-Kettering, Drs. Yamazaki and Yamaguchi, to establish with satisfactory statistical significance that the phenomenon of mating preference between H-2 congenic mice was real and consistent. We then moved on to a simpler system for getting at the same problem, which involved, at the outset, training a tracking mouse.

In brief, the technique was based on the classical Y-maze, with two different odors coming down the arms of the Y, one from the tracking mouse's own line, the other from the congenic line differing from himself only at the H-2 locus. The reward for selecting the correct arm was a drop of water, and the tracker was urged to seek the drop by being deprived of water for the preceding twenty-four hours. Training was begun by teaching the mouse to distinguish between the odor of cinnamon and juniper; then, when he'd got the idea, he was trained to discriminate between the smell of his own and a totally different breed of mouse, and finally to detect the odor of the congenic line, in this case the difference between B-6, his own line, and B-6 H-2^k, the other strain.

The experiments worked, and have continued to work, with a surprising degree of consistency and reproducibility. In all, eight smart tracking mice have been taught to smell H-2 during the past two years. Each experimental trial involves twenty-four runs toward the target, which is changed from one arm to the other at random, and the correct or incorrect choices are recorded by a third party who is himself unaware of the correctness of the choice. With a very high degree of statistical significance, each tracker has learned to distinguish between his own smell and the congenic smell when the odor box leading to the arm of the Y-maze contains mice of the proper genetic line. The odor is not detectable in homogenates of various mouse tissues, including spleen, liver, kidney, lung, or brain, nor can it be detected when mouse embryos are in the box. However, it is readily detected, with an accuracy even greater than when whole live mice are in the odor box, in samples of urine. The tracker can detect the odor of congenic urine when the urine is contained in a petri dish in the odor box, and the smell is still perceived when the urine has been diluted 1–40. The odorant is surprisingly stable, withstanding boiling for one hour. It is a small enough molecule to pass through a dialysis sac.

We have since learned that the same odorant can be detected in the urine of F-2 segregants derived from crosses between the two congenic lines, effectively ruling out smells derived from parental environment or family litter boxes.

It would be very nice to know which cells in the body are responsible for manufacturing the self-identifying odorant that ends up in the urine. The leading candidates for this role, in my view, are the lymphocytes themselves, because of the central role they play in mediating the homograft-rejection mechanism. An experiment still in progress at the Monell Institute has already produced suggestive evidence in favor of this idea. Yamazaki has transformed a mouse of one congenic line (B-6) into one of the other line (B-6 H-2^k), by irradiating B-6 mice to destroy all of their bone marrow cells and then transfusing them with lymphoid cells from the H-2^k line to repopulate the now-empty bone marrow. Thus, what used to be a pure-line B mouse was turned into a mouse with the K marker on its lymphocytes. Urine from such transformed mice was then tested in the Y-maze to see what it smelled like to the trained tracker. It was recognized as K urine, indicating that the odorant is secreted into the urine (and probably concentrated there) as the result of activity on the part of bone marrow cells — most likely the lymphocytes in the bone marrow.

The same odor is responsible for the phenomenon of pregnancy blocking, the so-called Bruce effect. This is the peculiar reaction that occurs when a newly impregnated mouse is placed in contact with a strange male: the pregnancy is promptly terminated and the female goes into estrus. She does not do so, of course, when the contact is with the original stud responsible for her pregnancy.

Using congenic lines of mice, differing only at H-2, Yamazaki and the group have found that replacing the original stud with a different male of the same line does not cause the Bruce effect, but when the new male is of the line with a different H-2 locus, the pregnancy stops and estrus resumes in the majority of females. The actual presence of the H-2 foreign male is not needed for this effect; the same results occur when the pregnant female is in the immediate vicinity of a sample of urine from the appropriate line.

The Bruce effect is not induced by exposure to *females* of the congenic line, or by urine from such females. Thus the Bruce effect must be caused by the perception by the pregnant female of two distinct and separate signals, one indicating maleness, the other announcing the presence of a male with a different H-2 locus.

I know of no satisfactory explanation for the Bruce effect, not anyway in teleological terms. Perhaps it represents a built-in response which tends to enhance heterozygosity and, to some extent, to impair close inbreeding. Or perhaps — and this is the teleology I prefer — the mere presence nearby of a strange male, differing in the odor of his H-2 from the original stud, signifies the departure of the father and the loss of protection to be expected from him for the forthcoming litter, and therefore it is time for the female to give it up and start over again. Our experiments have told us nothing about this, only that the smell of male strangeness is coded by the same string of genes that code for immunological strangeness.

Last year, Dr. Boyse and I had the opportunity of observing tracking dogs at work, first at the dog-training station of the Baltimore police department, then later at the Scotland Yard station just south of London. We saw enough to convince us that the specific and selective tracking of a man was a genuine and reproducible phenomenon, and that it ought to be entirely feasible to set up experiments to settle the question of whether identical twins leave identical tracks and even — although here I can envisage some formidably difficult technicalities — trying to correlate tracking accuracy with human HLA types. Needless to say, we have not set out on either of these lines, but some of the things we have already observed are perhaps of anecdotal interest even if not of scientific value. One curious thing we hadn't known: when a hound sets off on the track of a designated man, he does so not with his nose close to the ground, as in the movies, but rather tossing his head high, from side to side, as he goes. When the track turns at a sharp angle he overruns it, of course, but when he comes back to regain it he does so by sniffing the air well above the ground surface, getting clues not from the ground itself, or from footprints, but from something rising away from the ground.

In the Scotland Yard trials, we brought along several squares of gauze that had been placed in the bedding of various cages containing the two congenic groups of mice, differing from each other by only the genes for immunologic self-marking, and asked the trainer to see if his dog could learn to distinguish between the two. The squares were laid out at random, at intervals over a long slab of grass, the dog was given the scent of the one to be selected, and he trotted rapidly along with his head held several inches above the gauze squares until he reached the correct one, which he picked up neatly in his teeth and brought back to his master as though carrying the evening paper. The whole operation seemed so effortless as to be nearly automatic and, from the dog's point of view, the easiest of things. If we humans possess pheromones that label each of us as a person, I am glad to say that we cannot, as a rule anyway, smell them, social life being complicated enough as it is, but it would not surprise me at all if a Scotland Yard hound could do so, and could readily pick up the fragrance of any one urine sample and tell it from all the rest.

But even with the technical limitations of the tracking mouse and the Y-maze, it ought to become possible to learn something now about the chemical nature of the H-2 coded olfactant in mouse urine. Indeed, Drs. Yamazaki and Yamaguchi have recently transferred their laboratories to the Monell Institute in Philadelphia, where the chemistry of odorants is a high-technology specialty, for this purpose. There will surely be some interesting questions. What sort of heat-stable substance can it be, possessing enough variability in its structure to provide unique self-markers for the numberless individual mice, or, for that matter, 4 billion human beings? I imagine that it will turn out to be a *set* of chemicals, probably of the same class but with structural variations, arranged in infinite numbers of possible medleys, possibly very small changes in the intensity of one or another member of the group, and with each individual's odor sounding a unique chord.

Perhaps some similar arrangement of groups of molecular signals will account for the apparently infinite variability of cell markers in the immunologic system. It is conceivable that the tissue antigens are similar sets of different signals, displayed in varying concentrations to achieve uniqueness. It is not beyond imagining that the actual molecular configurations that fire off the olfactory receptor cells might turn out to be the same, or closely related to, the ones that, in the end, fire off a T-lymphocyte. And, to carry the matter as far as it can be stretched, it is even imaginable that some signal arrangement of this sort is at work in the homing of embryonic cells, the self-preservation of sponges, and the preservation of internal privacy within an amoeba. If so, it adds something more to the complexity of life for the single cell. It is not a simple life to be a single cell, although I have no right to say so, having been a single cell so long ago myself that I have no memory at all of that stage of my life.

CHAPTER SIXTY-TWO

Illness

ONE OF THE HARD THINGS TO LEARN IN MEDICINE, EVEN HARDER TO teach, is what it feels like to be a patient. In the old days, when serious illness was a more commonplace experience, shared round by everyone, the doctor had usually been through at least a few personal episodes on his own and had a pretty good idea of what it was like for his patient. A good many of the specialists in pulmonary disease who were brought up in the early years of this century had first acquired their interest in the field from having had tuberculosis themselves. Some of the leading figures in rehabilitation medicine had been crippled by poliomyelitis. And all physicians of those generations knew about pneumonia and typhoid at first hand, or at least once removed, in themselves or their immediate families.

It is very different today. The killing or near-killing illnesses are largely reserved for one's advancing years. No one goes through the six or eight perilous weeks of typhoid anymore, coming within sight of dying every day, getting through at the end with a stronger character perhaps, certainly with a different way of looking at life. The high technologies which are turned on to cope with serious disease—the electronic monitors in intensive care units, the chemotherapy drugs for cancer, the *tour de force* accomplishments of contemporary surgery, and the mobilization of increasingly complex procedures for diagnosis in medicine—are matters to be mastered only from lecture notes and books, and then by actual practice on patients, but very few doctors have more than an inkling of what it is actually like to go through such experiences. Even the childhood contagions are mostly gone, thanks to vaccines for measles, whooping cough, chicken pox, and the like, thanks especially to the easy control of streptococcal infections. Today's young doctors do not know what it is to have an earache, much less what it means to have an eardrum punctured.

The nearest thing to a personal education in illness is the grippe. It is almost all we have left in the way of on-the-job training, and I hope that somehow it can be spared as we proceed to eliminate so many other human diseases. Indeed, I would favor hanging on to grippe, and its cousin the common cold, for as long as possible. A case could be made, I think, for viewing the various viruses involved in these minor but impressive illnesses as a set of endangered species, essentially *good* for the human environment, something like snail darters.

Most people afflicted with grippe complain about it, and that is one of its virtues. It is a good thing for people to have, from time to time, something real to complain about, a genuine demon. It is also a good thing to be laid up once in a while, compelled by nature to stop doing whatever else and to take to bed. It is an especially good thing to have a fever and the malaise that goes along with fever, when you know that it will be gone in three or four days but meanwhile entitles you to all the privileges of the sick: bed rest, ice water on the bed table, aspirin, maybe an ice bag on the head or behind the neck, and the attentions of one's solicitous family. Sympathy: how many other opportunities turn up in a lifetime to engage the sympathy and concern of others for something that is not your fault and will surely be gone in a few days? Preserve the grippe, I say, and find some way to insert it into the practical curriculum of all medical students. Twice a year, say, the lecture hall in molecular biochemistry should be exposed to a silent aerosol of adenovirus, so that the whole class comes down at once. Schedules being what they are in medical school, this will assure that a good many students will be obliged to stay on their feet, working through the next days and nights with their muscle pains and fever, and learning what it is like *not* to be cared for. Good for them, and in a minor way good for their future as doctors.

The real problem is the shock of severe, dangerous illness, its unexpectedness and surprise. Most of us, patients and doctors alike, can ride almost all the way through life with no experience of real peril, and when it does come, it seems an outrage, a piece of unfairness. We are not used to disease as we used to be, and we are not at all used to being incorporated into a high technology.

I have learned something about this, but only recently, too late to do much for my skill at the bedside. On several occasions, starting around age sixty-four, I have had a close look from the bed itself at medicine and surgery and, as I shall relate, an even closer look at myself. On balance, I have very much liked what I have seen, but only in retrospect, once out of bed and home free. While there, I discovered that being a patient is hard work.

It is often said that people who have been precariously ill, especially those who have gone through surgical operations, love to talk about their trials and will do so at length to anyone ready to listen. I rather doubt this. Being ill is a peculiarly private experience, and most of the people I know who have gone through something serious tend to be reserved about it, changing the subject when it comes up. But here I am, about to talk about my times on the line and the things I learned. I only do so, I must say in advance, out of professional interest.

The first, and most surprising of all, was an obscure kind of pneumonia, chills, fever, prostration, and all, occurring suddenly on a Tuesday afternoon. I took to bed at home in good cheer, anticipating several days of warm soup, cold drinks, fluffed-up pillows, and ample family ministrations. But a week went by and I kept on with the chills and fever, so my wife called the doctor, a friend of mine and a real, house-calling doctor. He did the usual things, including taking samples of blood, murmured something about a virus "going around," and predicted that the fever would be gone in another day or two. But the next day I was in a hospital bed having more blood tests, being examined by platoons of interns and residents, and in and out of the X-ray department having pictures taken of all sites including bones. The laboratory tests had revealed a hemoglobin level of just under 8 grams percent, half the normal value, and it had become an urgent matter to discover where the blood had gone, or was going.

Within the next few days the pneumonia vanished, along with the chills and fever, and I had become a new sort of diagnostic problem.

To be worked up for anemia of unknown origin is strenuous exercise. The likeliest cause was blood loss, and the likeliest source was the intestinal tract—what is known, ominously, as silent bleeding. I received two transfusions, and then plunged headlong into technology. A bone marrow biopsy was, as I recall, the first piece of work, done neatly and quickly on a pelvic bone with rapid-fire explanations by the hematologist as he went along, telling me what I would feel and when it would hurt, but despite his reassurances I could not avoid the strong sense that having one's bone marrow sucked into a syringe was an unnatural act, no way for a human being to be treated. It did not in fact hurt much, but the small crunching of bone by the trocar followed by the peculiar and unfamiliar pain in the marrow itself were strange sensations, not at all nice.

I have performed bone marrow biopsies myself, long ago as an intern and from time to time since, and have always regarded the procedure as a minor one, almost painless, but it had never crossed my mind that it was, painless or not, so fundamentally unpleasant.

The rest of the workup was easy going, and at times engrossing. The walls of my stomach and upper intestinal tract were marvelously revealed by a barium meal, and those of my bowel by a similar enema, and all was well. But I continued to bleed, somewhere in that long channel, and more transfusions were needed.

It is not an easy task for doctors to look after doctors, and especially difficult when the doctor-patient is a colleague and close friend. It requires walking a fine line, making sure not to offend professional pride by talking down to the doctor-patient, but also making sure that the patient does what he is told to do. I was treated with great tact and firmness. The colleagues and friends who had me as a responsibility remained my good friends, but there was never a question as to my status: I was a patient and they expected me to behave like one. I was not to try making decisions about my own diagnosis and treatment. I was not allowed to go home for a few days, which I wanted very much to do at several times during what turned out to be a long period of hospitalization; it was explained very gently that the source of bleeding was still unknown and I might have a more massive hemorrhage at any time, rather less gently that if it happened I might suffer a lot of brain damage and I'd better not be doing that at home.

With negative X rays, my intestinal tract needed a different kind of look. On the possibility that I might have a polyp somewhere, bleeding freely but too small to show up by X ray, I was wheeled off to the endoscopy service for examination by the colonoscope, an incredibly long and flexible quartz fiber-optic tube through which all parts of the large intestine can be viewed under direct illumination by light sent in from outside. As a nice gesture of professional courtesy, the doctor stopped at frequent intervals during this procedure and passed the viewing end of the instrument over my shoulder and in front of my left eye. "Care to take a look?" he asked. I had never looked through this wonderful instrument before, although I had seen many photographs of the views to be had. It would have been interesting in any case, I suppose, but since it was the deep interior of my own intestine that I was looking at, I became totally absorbed. "What's that?" I cried, as something red moved into view. He took a look and said, "That's just you. Normal mucosa."

A few days after this fascinating but negative excursion, I had another episode of bleeding, my hemoglobin dropped to a disturbing level, more transfusions were given, and it was decided that I would probably need surgery in order to remove the part that was presumably bleeding. But without knowing the exact source, this could mean taking out a lot of intestine and, even then, missing it. The gastroenterologist who had me in charge, Dr. Paul Sherlock, knew of one obscure possibility not yet excluded, one that I had never heard about—a condition produced by an abnormal connection between an artery and vein in the intestinal wall— which had recently been reported as a cause of intestinal hemorrhage.

This was not, as it seemed to me at the time, a guess in the dark. The X rays and colonoscope had ruled out cancer of the colon (which is what I was pretty sure I had, at the outset), and diverticulosis (little cracks in the intestinal wall), and polyps had been excluded as well. The new syndrome of arteriovenous anomaly was about all that was left.

Finding out required close collaboration between the gastroenterologists and radiologists. A catheter was inserted in the femoral artery, high up in the right leg, and pushed up into the aorta until its tip reached the level of the main arteries branching off to supply the large intestine. At this point, an opaque dye was injected, to fill all those arteries. Just before pressing the syringe, Dr. Robin Watson, the X-ray chief, warned me that I would feel a sense of heat, not to worry. It was a brand-new sensory impression, perhaps never experienced except by patients undergoing this kind of arteriography: for about thirty seconds I felt as if the lower half of my body had suddenly caught fire, then the feeling was gone. Meanwhile, movies were being taken of the entire vascular bed reached by the dye, and the diagnosis was solidly confirmed. Dr. Watson came into the room a few minutes later with sample pictures displaying the lesion. "Care to take a look?" he asked. I was enchanted: there, in just one spot somewhere on the right side of my colon, was a spilled blur of dye, and the issue was settled. It struck me as a masterpiece of technological precision, also as a picture with a certain aesthetic quality, nice to look at. I could hear in the distance the voices of other doctors, quietly celebratory as doctors are when a difficult diagnosis is finally nailed down.

That evening I was visited by the anaesthesiologist for the brief but always reassuring explanation of the next day's events, and in the morning I rolled down the hall, into the elevator, and down to the operating room, pleasantly stoned from Valium. The next things I saw were the clock on the wall of the recovery room and the agreeable face of my friend the nurse in charge, who told me that it had gone very well. I have no memory of the operating room at all, only the sound of the wall switch and the hissing of the automatic doors as my litter entered the place.

That was my first personal experience with the kind of illness requiring hospital technology. Thinking back, I cannot find anything about it that I would want to change or try to improve, although it was indeed, parts of it anyway, like being launched personless on the assembly line of a great (but quiet) factory. I was indeed handled as an object needing close scrutiny and intricate fixing, procedure after procedure, test after test, carted from one part of the hospital to another day after day until the thing was settled. While it was going on I felt less like a human in trouble and more like a scientific problem to be solved as quickly as possible. What made it work, and kept such notions as "depersonalization" and "dehumanization" from even popping into my mind, was the absolute confidence I felt in the skill and intelligence of the people who had hold of me. In part this came from my own knowledge, beforehand, of their skill, but in larger part my confidence resulted from observing, as they went about their work, their own total confidence in themselves.

The next two course offerings were trauma. I'd never had real trauma before in all my life—or only once, when as a small boy in grammar school I'd been hit on the head by a pitched baseball and knocked out for a moment. The next day my head began to itch, and I went around the house and back and forth to school, scratching my head incessantly and complaining to everyone that the baseball had injured the nerves. My mother was skeptical of this, as she was about most self-diagnosis, and took a close look at my scalp. I was infested by dense families of head lice, caught perhaps from somebody's cap at school. In no time, but with a great deal of anguish caused by neat kerosene and larkspur shampoos, endless rakings with a fine-tooth comb, and finally a very short haircut, I was cured, although I'm not sure my mother ever thought of me again as quite the same boy. Anyway, that was all my trauma until I was sixty-six years old.

I was in the surf at Amagansett, floating in a high leisurely wave, and turned to catch it for a clean ride to the beach, when suddenly something went wrong with my right knee. After some floundering and swallowing a lot of water, I made the trip in under breakers and tried to stand. I couldn't, and had to wave for help. I was hoisted out and horsed along by friends, unable to place my weight on my right leg. On the way up the beach I was met by Dr. Herbert Chasis, a Bellevue colleague, and his wife, Barbara. Herbert knows more about kidney disease and hypertension than anyone I know, and Barbara had served as chief of the psychomedical wards during my years at Bellevue. They were sympathetic of course, but also to my surprise highly knowledgeable about knees and, like all good Bellevue people, ready to help. Indeed, Chasis had in his beach bag a proper knee brace, which he helped me put on, and explained to me that I had undoubtedly torn a knee cartilage (which he had done some years earlier; hence the equipment). Presently, crutches were provided as well, and off I went, home to get dressed and into Manhattan for a visit to the Hospital for Special Surgery. X rays again, and to my astonishment, another fiberoptics instrument, this time an arthroscope for looking into the interior of joints. In it went, moved around this part and that of the knee, and then it stopped. "Care to take a look?" asked the surgeon, handing me the eyepiece. I stared, transfixed, at the neat geometry of cartilage lining the joint, gray and glistening in the light, and then I saw what he had seen, a sizable piece of cartilage broken and dislodged. "Thank you," I thought to say, "what now?" "Out," he replied. So, Valium again, the unremembered operating room, and a long elliptical incision stitched with countless neat threads which I saw directly the next morning when the dressing was changed and I was commanded to get out of bed and stand on the leg, pain or no pain. Good for it, I was told, but I forget why. Teach it a lesson, maybe. Then on crutches for a few weeks, a single crutch for a few more, exercises thrice daily—lifting heavy weights by my foot (which I did for a few days and then began telling lies about)—and finally full recovery except for the odd pain now and then. Another triumph. I began to feel almost ready to write a textbook.

One more, and then I've finished, I trust. I was invited to give an evening lecture at the Cosmopolitan Club in New York, a place filled with dignity and intellectual women, including my wife. I prepared a talk on symbiosis, with a few lantern slides to illustrate one of my favorite models of insect behavior, the mimosa girdler. Halfway through the talk I called for the slides, the lights went out, I approached the screen to point to the location of the mandible-work of the beetle— and fell off the platform into the dark. Hauled to my feet, I found myself unable to move my left arm because of pain in the shoulder. I felt for the shoulder with my right hand and found an empty cavity. Someone brought a chair and sat me down while I caught my breath, and several sympathetic voices suggested that I cancel the evening. I wanted to finish the girdler story, however, and hunched back to the podium. It must have been a painful talk for the audience. I thought no one would notice the shoulder, and I droned on to finish the lecture, sweating into my eyeglasses and onto my manuscript, bracing my elbow against the podium, thinking that I was getting away with it nicely. Then I noticed that Dr. André Cournand, the great cardiologist from Bellevue, had moved from his seat in the front row and taken a chair alongside the podium, watching me carefully. I remembered the old anecdotes about that hospital, the car crash, the exploded street, and the figure of authority thrusting through the crowd: "Stand aside, I am a Bellevue man." If I topple, André will catch me, I thought.

Anyway, I finished it, although I'm not sure anyone was listening. An ambulance had been summoned, and I was carted off once more, on a litter, to Memorial. An X ray showed the shoulder dislocated and fractured ("Care to take a look?"), and my friends set about trying to get it back in place, me lying on my stomach buzzing with morphine, with the left arm hanging down, Ted Beattie (chief of surgery at Memorial) on the floor pulling down on my arm, but it wouldn't slip back in place. Finally, after a half hour of tugging, it was decided that I would have to be fixed under a general anaesthetic, and a call went out for the head of the anaesthesia department, Paul Goldiner. It was now 10 p.m., and Paul was at home in Westchester County. He hurried to his car and started the drive along the parkway to New York. Five minutes from home he passed the scene of a car crash and noticed a man lying prone on the grass. He stopped, went over to the man, found him pulseless and not breathing, and set about resuscitation. Anaesthesiologists are the best of all professionals at this skill, and shortly he had the man breathing again and conscious. He ran back to his car and set off again for New York. By this time, Beattie's maneuvers had snapped my humerus back into its joint, but it was too late to call Goldiner and tell him to stay home. He arrived at the door to be informed that his trip had been unnecessary, then told his own jubilant story; the trip had been the best he'd ever made. It is not often given to chiefs of anaesthesiology to save a life on the open highway, and Goldiner was a happy man. I have often wished I could locate his patient someday and have him take Paul Goldiner and me out to lunch.

That was the last of my trial runs as patient, up to now anyway. I know a lot more than I used to know about hospitals, medicine, nurses, and doctors, and I am more than ever a believer in the usefulness of technology, the higher the better. But I wish there were some easier way to come by this level of comprehension for medical students and interns, maybe a way of setting up electronic models like the simulated aircraft coming in for crash landings used for pilot training. Every young doctor should know exactly what it is like to have things go catastrophically wrong, and to be personally mortal. It makes for a better practice.

I have seen a lot of my inner self, more than most people, and you'd think I would have gained some new insight, even some sense of illumination, but I am as much in the dark as ever. I do not feel connected to myself in any new way. Indeed, if anything, the distance seems to have increased, and I am personally more a dualism than ever, made up of structure after structure over which I have no say at all. I have the feeling now that if I were to keep at it, looking everywhere with lenses and bright lights, even into the ventricles of my brain (which is a technical feasibility if I wanted to try it), or inside the arteries of the heart (another easy technique these days), I would be brought no closer to myself. I exist, I'm sure of that, but not in the midst of all that soft machinery. If I am, as I suppose is the case at bottom, an assemblage of electromagnetic particles, I now doubt that there is any center, any passenger compartment, any private green room where I am to be found in residence. I conclude that the arrangement runs itself, beyond my management, needing repairs by experts from time to time, but by and large running well, and I am glad I don't have to worry about the details. If I were really at the controls, in full charge, keeping track of everything, there would be a major train wreck within seconds.

And I do not at all resent any of the parts for going wrong. On the contrary, having seen what they are up against, I have more respect for them than I had before. I tip my hat to all of them, and I'm glad I'm here outside, wherever that is.

CHAPTER SIXTY-THREE

The Unforgettable

Fire

THE HARDEST OF ALL TASKS FOR THE MILITARY PEOPLE WHO ARE occupationally obliged to make plans for wars still to come must be to keep a comprehensive, up-to-date list of guesses as to what the other side might, in one circumstance or another, do. Prudence requires that all sorts of possibilities be kept in mind, including, above all, the "worst-case." In warfare, in this century, the record has already proved that the worst-case will turn out in the end to be the one that happens and, often enough, the one that hadn't been planned for. At the outset of World War I, the British didn't have in mind the outright loss of an entire generation of their best youth, nor did any of the Europeans count on such an unhinging of German society as would lead straight to Hitler. In World War II, when things were being readied, nobody forecast Dresden or Coventry as eventualities to be looked out for and planned against. In Vietnam, defeat at the end was not anywhere on the United States' list of possible outcomes, nor was what happened later in Cambodia and Laos part of the scenario.

We live today in a world densely populated by human beings living in close communication with one another all over the surface of the planet. Viewed from a certain distance it has the look of a single society, a community, the swarming of an intensely social species trying to figure out ways to become successfully interdependent. We obviously need, at this stage, to begin the construction of some sort of world civilization. The final worst-case for all of us has now become the destruction, by ourselves, of our species.

This will not be a novel event for the planet, if it does occur. The fossil record abounds with sad tales of creatures that must have seemed stunning successes in their heyday, wiped out in one catastrophe after another. The trilobites are everywhere, elegant fossil shells, but nowhere alive. The dinosaurs came, conquered, and then all at once went.

Epidemic disease, meteorite collisions, volcanoes, atmospheric shifts in the levels of carbon dioxide, earthquakes, excessive warming or chilling of the earth's surface are all on the worst-case list for parts of the biosphere, one time or another, but it is unlikely that these can ever be lethal threats to a species as intelligent and resourceful as ours. We will not be wiped off the face of the earth by hard times, no matter how hard; we are tough and resilient animals, good at hard times. If we are to be done in, we will do it ourselves by warfare with thermonuclear weaponry, and it will happen because the military planners, and the governments who pay close attention to them, are guessing at the wrong worst-case. At the moment there are really only two groups, the Russians and us, but soon there will be others, already lining up.

Each side is guessing that the other side will, sooner or later, fire first. To guard against this, each side is hell-bent on achieving a weapons technology capable of two objectives: to prevent the other from firing first by having enough missiles to destroy the first-strike salvo before it is launched (which means, of course, its own first strike) and, as a backup, to have for retaliation a powerful enough reserve to inflict what is called "unacceptable damage" on the other side's people. In today's urban world, this means the cities. The policy revision designated as Presidential Directive 59, issued by the Carter White House in August 1980, stipulates that enemy command and control networks and military bases would become the primary targets in a "prolonged, limited" nuclear war. Even so, *some* cities and towns would inevitably be blown away, then doubtless more, then perhaps all.

The term "unacceptable" carries the implication that there is an acceptable degree of damage from thermonuclear bombs. This suggests that we are moving into an era when the limited use of this kind of weaponry is no longer on the worst-case lists. Strategic weapons are those designed to destroy the whole enemy — armies, navies, cities, and all. Tactical nuclear bombs are something else again, smaller and neater, capable of taking out a fortified point, selectively and delicately removing, say, a tank division. Damage to one's country from strategic weapons may be unacceptable, in these terms, but tactical weapons do not raise this issue.

So it goes. The worst-case is clouds of missiles coming over the horizon, aimed at the cities. And another sort of merely bad-case might be to *neglect* the advantage of small-scale, surgically precise, tactical weapons, needed at crucial moments on conventional battlefields when things are going against one's side. So it seems.

Perhaps it really is the other way round. The worst of all possible scenarios might be the tactical use of a miniaturized thermonuclear bomb, a mere puff alongside the gigantic things stowed on MIRVs.

When we speak of mere puffs, it is useful to give a backward thought to Hiroshima and Nagasaki. We have gotten used to the notion that the two bombs dropped out of our B-29 bombers on August 6 and 9, 1945, were only primitive precursors of what we have at hand today, relatively feeble instruments, even rather quaint technological antiques, like Tiffany lamps. They were indeed nothing but puffs compared to what we now possess. If we and the Russians were to let everything fly at once, we could do, in a matter of minutes, a million times more damage than was done on those two August mornings long ago.

How do you figure a million times? You have to know, to begin with and in some detail, precisely what the Hiroshima and Nagasaki damage was like, and then try to imagine it a millionfold magnified. You don't even have to do that, if your imagination doesn't stretch that far. Any single one of today's best hydrogen bombs will produce at least one thousand times the lethal blast, heat, and radiation that resulted from the Hiroshima or Nagasaki bombs. Nothing would remain alive, no matter how shielded or "hardened," within an area twelve miles in diameter. Taking just one city—Boston, for example—you can begin to guess with some accuracy what just one modern bomb can do, say, tomorrow morning.

One thing for sure, such a bomb would not leave alive anyone to join a committee to prepare a book of sketches and paintings like those published several years ago in *Unforgettable Fire.* The people whose memories are contained in this book were residents of Hiroshima, most of them somewhere within a radius of two miles or so from the hypocenter, the Aioi bridge in the center of town. They survived, and made their drawings thirty years later. With one of today's bombs they would all have been vaporized within a fraction of a second after the explosion. What they recall most vividly, and draw most heartrendingly, are the deaths all around them, the collapsed buildings, and above all the long black strips of skin hanging from the arms and torsos of those still alive. They remember the utter hopelessness, the inability of anyone to help anyone else, the loneliness of the injured alongside the dying. Reading their accounts and wincing at the pictures, one gains the sure sense that no society, no matter how intricately structured, could have coped with that event. No matter how many doctors and hospitals might have been in place and ready to help with medical technology beforehand (as, for instance, in Boston or Baltimore today), at the moment of the fireball all of that help would have vanished in the new sun. As for the radioactivity, a single case of near-lethal radiation can occasionally be saved today by the full resources of a highly specialized, tertiary hospital unit, with endless transfusions and bone-marrow transplants. But what to do about a thousand such cases all at once, or a hundred thousand? Not to mention the more conventionally maimed and burned people, in the millions.

Words like "disaster" and "catastrophe" are too frivolous for the events that would inevitably follow a war with thermonuclear weapons. "Damage" is not the real term; the language has no word for it. Individuals might survive, but "survival" is itself the wrong word. As to the thought processes of the people in high perches of government who believe that they can hide themselves underground somewhere (they probably can) and emerge later on to take over again the running of society (they cannot, in the death of society) or, more ludicrous, the corporate executives who plan to come deranged out of their underground headquarters already installed in the mountains to reorganize the telephone lines or see to the oil business—these people cannot have thought at all.

Hiroshima and Nagasaki: The Physical, Medical and Social Effects of the Atomic Bombings is a 700-page, flatly written description of what happened in August 1945, containing a few photographs and a great many charts and tables to illustrate the abundant details in the text. Here and there, but in only a few paragraphs of the unemotional, factual text, are sentences that reveal the profundity of revulsion and disgust for this weapon and its use by the United States that still remain in the Japanese mind. It is briefly noted that Hiroshima had been spared the extensive fire-bombing to which most other Japanese cities were being subjected in the 1945 summer—there was an eagerly believed rumor that the Americans were sparing the city out of respect because it was known to be a Buddhist religious center—and then later, soon after the A-bombing, it was realized that the city had been preserved free of conventional damage in order to measure with exactitude the effects of the new bomb. It is tersely recalled that the first American journalists to arrive on the scene, a month after the bombing, were interested only in the extent of physical damage and the evidence of the instrument's great power, and it is further noted that no news about the injuries to the people, especially news about radiation sickness, was allowed by the Allied Occupation. "*On 6 September, 1945, the General Headquarters of the Occupational Forces issued a statement that made it clear that people likely to die from A-bomb afflictions should be left to die. The official attitude . . . was that people suffering from radiation injuries were not worth saving.*" The Japanese nation is of course now a friendly ally of the United States, peacefully linked to this country, but the people remember. The continuing bitterness of that memory runs far deeper than most Americans might guess. Apart from the 370,000 Hiroshima and Nagasaki survivors still alive, whose lasting evidences of physical and psychological damage are exhaustively documented in *Hiroshima and Nagasaki,* the Japanese people at large are appalled that other nations can still be so blind to the horror.

To get back to cases, worst-cases, what would you guess is the worst of all possibilities today, with the United States and the Soviet Union investing every spare dollar and ruble to build new and more powerful armaments, missiles enough to create artificial suns in every habitable place of both countries, and with France, Britain, India, China, South Africa, maybe Israel, and who knows what other country either stockpiling bombs of their own or preparing to build them? Of all the mistakes to be made, which is the worst?

A very bad one, although maybe not the worst of all, is a technical complication not much talked about in public but hanging over all the military scientists like a great net poised to fall at any moment. It is still a theoretical complication, not yet tested, or, for that matter, even testable, but very terrifying indeed. The notion is this: a good-sized nuclear bomb, say, ten megatons, exploded at a very high altitude, 250 miles or so over a country, or a set of several such bombs over a continent, might elicit such a surge of electromagnetic energy in the underlying atmosphere that all electronic devices on the earth below would be put out of commission—or destroyed outright—all computers, radios, telephones, television, all electric grids, all communications beyond the reach of a human shout. None of the buttons pressed in Moscow or Washington, if either lay beneath the rays, would function. The silos would not open on command, or fire their missiles. During this period the affected country would be, in effect, anaesthetized, and the follow-on missiles from the other side could pick off their targets like fruit from a tree. Only the submarine forces, roaming far at sea, would be able to fire back, and their only signal to fire would have to be the total absence of any signal from home. The fate of the aggressor's own cities would then lie at the fingertips of individual submarine commanders, out of touch with the rest of the world, forced to read the meaning of silence.

If the hypothesis is valid, it introduces a new piece of logic into the game. Metal shielding can be used to protect parts of the military communication lines, and fiber optics lines are already replacing some parts. Nuclear-power plants can be partially shielded, perhaps enough to prevent meltdowns everywhere. But no one can yet be certain of protection against this strange new threat.

Any first strike might have to involve this technical maneuver beforehand, with the risk of counterblows from somewhere in the oceans or from surviving intelligence in land-based missiles, but always with the tempting prospect of an enemy country sitting paralyzed like a rabbit in the headlights of a truck. Guessing wrong either way could be catastrophic, and I imagine the War College faculties on both sides are turning the matter over and over in their minds and on their computers, looking for new doctrine.

But all in all, looking ahead, it seems to me that the greatest danger lies in the easy assumption by each government that the people in charge of military policy in any adversary government are not genuine human beings. We make this assumption about the Russians all the time, and I have no doubt they hold the same belief about us. We know ourselves, of course, and take ourselves on faith: Who among us would think of sending off a cluster of missiles to do a million times more damage to a foreign country than was done at Hiroshima, for any reason? None of us, we would all affirm (some of us I fear with fingers crossed). But there are those people on the other side who do not think as we do, we think.

It may be that the road to the end is already being paved, right now, by those tactical "theater" bombs, the little ones, as small and precise as we can make them. If the other side's tanks are gaining on ours, and we are about to lose an action, let them have one! And when they send one of theirs back in retaliation, slightly larger, let them have another, bigger one. Drive them back, we will say, let them have it. A few such exchanges, and off will go the ICBMs, and down will go, limb by limb, all of mankind.

I hope these two books are widely translated, and then propped under the thoughtful, calculating, and expressionless eyes of all the officials in the highest reaches of all governments. They might then begin to think harder than they now think about the future, their own personal future, and about whether a one-time exchange of bombs between countries would leave any government still governing, or any army officer still in command of anything.

Maybe the military people should sit down together on neutral ground, free of politicians and diplomats, perhaps accompanied by their chief medical officers and hospital administrators, and talk together about the matter. They are, to be sure, a strange and unfamiliar lot, unworldly in a certain sense, but they know one another or could at least learn to know one another. After a few days of discussion, unaffectionately and coldly but still linked in a common and ancient professional brotherhood, they might reach the conclusion that the world is on the wrong track, that human beings cannot fight with such weapons and remain human, and that since organized societies are essential for the survival of the profession of arms it is time to stop. It is the generals themselves who should have sense enough to demand a freeze on the development of nuclear arms, and then a gradual, orderly, meticulously scrutinized reduction of such arms. Otherwise, they might as well begin to learn how spears are made, although their chances of living to use them are very thin, not much better than the odds for the rest of us.

Meanwhile, the preparations go on, the dreamlike rituals are rehearsed, and the whole earth is being set up as an altar for a burnt offering, a monstrous human sacrifice to an imagined god with averted eyes. Carved in the stone of the cenotaph in Hiroshima are the words: REST IN PEACE, FOR THE MISTAKE WILL NOT BE REPEATED. The inscription has a life of its own. Intended first as a local prayer and promise, it has already changed its meaning into a warning, and is now turning into a threat.

CHAPTER SIXTY-FOUR

The Corner of the Eye

THERE ARE SOME THINGS THAT HUMAN BEINGS CAN SEE ONLY OUT OF the corner of the eye. The niftiest examples of this gift, familiar to all children, are small, faint stars. When you look straight at one such star, it vanishes; when you move your eyes to stare into the space nearby, it reappears. If you pick two faint stars, side by side, and focus on one of the pair, it disappears and now you can see the other in the corner of your eye, and you can move your eyes back and forth, turning off the star in the center of your retina and switching the other one on. There is a physiological explanation for the phenomenon: we have more rods, the cells we use for light perception, at the periphery of our retinas, more cones, for perceiving color, at the center.

Something like this happens in music. You cannot really hear certain sequences of notes in a Bach fugue unless at the same time there are other notes being sounded, dominating the field. The real meaning in music comes from tones only audible in the corner of the mind.

I used to worry that computers would become so powerful and sophisticated as to take the place of human minds. The notion of Artificial Intelligence used to scare me half to death. Already, a large enough machine can do all sorts of intelligent things beyond our capacities: calculate in a split second the answers to mathematical problems requiring years for a human brain, draw accurate pictures from memory, even manufacture successions of sounds with a disarming resemblance to real music. Computers can translate textbooks, write dissertations of their own for doctorates, even speak in machine-tooled, inhuman phonemes any words read off from a printed page. They can communicate with one another, holding consultations and committee meetings of their own in networks around the earth.

Computers can make errors, of course, and do so all the time in small, irritating ways, but the mistakes can be fixed and nearly always are. In this respect they are fundamentally inhuman, and here is the relaxing thought: computers will not take over the world, they cannot replace us, because they are not designed, as we are, for ambiguity.

Imagine the predicament faced by a computer programmed to make language, not the interesting communication in sounds made by vervets or in symbols by brilliant chimpanzee prodigies, but real human talk. The grammar would not be too difficult, and there would be no problem in constructing a vocabulary of etymons, the original, pure, unambiguous words used to name real things. The impossibility would come in making the necessary mistakes we humans make with words instinctively, intuitively, as we build our kinds of language, changing the meanings to imply quite different things, constructing and elaborating the varieties of ambiguity without which speech can never become human speech.

Look at the record of language if you want to glimpse the special qualities of the human mind that lie beyond the reach of any machine. Take, for example, the metaphors we use in everyday speech to tell ourselves who we are, where we live, and where we come from.

The earth is a good place to begin. The word "earth" is used to name the ground we walk on, the soil in which we grow plants or dig clams, and the planet itself; we also use it to describe all of humanity ("the whole earth responds to the beauty of a child," we say to each other).

The earliest word for earth in our language was the Indo-European root *dhghem,* and look what we did with it. We turned it, by adding suffixes, into *humus* in Latin; today we call the complex polymers that hold fertile soil together "humic" acids, and somehow or other the same root became "humility." With another suffix the word became "human." Did the earth become human, or did the human emerge from the earth? One answer may lie in that nice cognate word "humble." "Humane" was built on, extending the meaning of both the earth and ourselves. In ancient Hebrew, *adamha* was the word for earth, *adam* for man. What computer could run itself through such manipulations as those?

We came at the same system of defining ourselves from the other direction. The word *wiros* was the first root for man; it took us in our vanity on to "virile" and "virtue," but also turned itself into the Germanic word *weraldh,* meaning the life of man, and thence in English to our word "world."

There is a deep hunch in this kind of etymology. The world of man derives from this planet, shares origin with the life of the soil, lives in humility with all the rest of life. I cannot imagine programming a computer to think up an idea like that, not a twentieth-century computer, anyway.

The world began with what it is now the fashion to call the "Big Bang." Characteristically, we have assigned the wrong words for the very beginning of the earth and ourselves, in order to evade another term that would cause this century embarrassment. It could not, of course, have been a bang of any sort, with no atmosphere to conduct the waves of sound, and no ears. It was something else, occurring in the most absolute silence we can imagine. It was the Great Light.

We say it had been chaos before, but it was not the kind of place we use the word "chaos" for today, things tumbling over each other and bumping around. Chaos did not have that meaning in Greek; it simply meant empty.

We took it, in our words, from chaos to cosmos, a word that simply meant order, cosmetic. We perceived the order in surprise, and our cosmologists and physicists continue to find new and astonishing aspects of the order. We made up the word "universe" from the whole affair, meaning literally turning everything into one thing. We used to say it was a miracle, and we still permit ourselves to refer to the whole universe as a marvel, holding in our unconscious minds the original root meaning of these two words, miracle and marvel—from the ancient root word *smei,* signifying a smile. It immensely pleases a human being to see something never seen before, even more to learn something never known before, most of all to think something never thought before. The rings of Saturn are the latest surprise. All my physicist friends are enchanted by this phenomenon, marveling at the small violations of the laws of planetary mechanics, shocked by the unaccountable braids and spokes stuck there among the rings like graffiti. It is nice for physicists to see something new and inexplicable; it means that the laws of nature are once again about to be amended by a new footnote.

The greatest surprise of all lies within our own local, suburban solar system. It is not Mars; Mars was surprising in its way but not flabbergasting; it was a disappointment not to find evidences of life, and there was some sadness in the pictures sent back to earth from the Mars Lander, that lonely long-legged apparatus poking about with its jointed arm, picking up sample after sample of the barren Mars soil, looking for any flicker of life and finding none; the only sign of life on Mars was the Lander itself, an extension of the human mind all the way from earth to Mars, totally alone.

Nor is Saturn the great surprise, nor Jupiter, nor Venus, nor Mercury, nor any of the glimpses of the others.

The overwhelming astonishment, the queerest structure we know about so far in the whole universe, the greatest of all cosmological scientific puzzles, confounding all our efforts to comprehend it, is the earth. We are only now beginning to appreciate how strange and splendid it is, how it catches the breath, the loveliest object afloat around the sun, enclosed in its own blue bubble of atmosphere, manufacturing and breathing its own oxygen, fixing its own nitrogen from the air into its own soil, generating its own weather at the surface of its rain forests, constructing its own carapace from living parts: chalk cliffs, coral reefs, old fossils from earlier forms of life now covered by layers of new life meshed together around the globe, Troy upon Troy.

Seen from the right distance, from the corner of the eye of an extraterrestrial visitor, it must surely seem a single creature, clinging to the round warm stone, turning in the sun.

CHAPTER SIXTY-FIVE

Making Science

Work

FOR ABOUT THREE CENTURIES WE HAVE BEEN DOING SCIENCE, TRYING science out, using science for the construction of what we call modern civilization. Every dispensable item of contemporary technology, from canal locks to dial telephones to penicillin to the Mars Lander, was pieced together from the analysis of data provided by one or another series of scientific experiments—also the technologies we fear the most for the threat they pose to civilization: radioactivity from the stored, stacked bombs or from leaking, flawed power plants, acid rain, pesticides, leached soil, depleted ozone, and increased carbon dioxide in the outer atmosphere.

Three hundred years seems a long time for testing a new approach to human interliving, long enough to settle back for critical appraisal of the scientific method, maybe even long enough to vote on whether to go on with it or not. There is an argument. Voices have been raised in protest since the beginning, rising in pitch and violence in the nineteenth century during the early stages of the industrial revolution, summoning urgent crowds into the streets any day these days on the issue of nuclear energy. Give it back, say some of the voices, it doesn't really work, we've tried it and it doesn't work, go back three hundred years and start again on something else less chancy for the race of man.

The scientists disagree, of course, partly out of occupational bias, but also from a different way of viewing the course and progress of science in the past fifty years. As they see it, science is just at its beginning. The principal discoveries in this century, taking all in all, are the glimpses of the depth of our ignorance about nature. Things that used to seem clear and rational, matters of absolute certainty—Newtonian mechanics, for example—have slipped through our fingers, and we are left with a new set of gigantic puzzles, cosmic uncertainties, ambiguities; some of the laws of physics are amended every few years, some are canceled outright, some undergo revised versions of legislative intent as if they were acts of Congress.

In biology, it is one stupefaction after another. Just thirty years ago we called it a biological revolution when the fantastic geometry of the DNA molecule was exposed to public view and the linear language of genetics was decoded. For a while things seemed simple and clear; the cell was a neat little machine, a mechanical device ready for taking to pieces and reassembling, like a tiny watch. But just in the last few years it has become almost imponderably complex, filled with strange parts whose functions are beyond today's imagining. DNA is itself no longer a straightforward set of instructions on a tape. There are long strips of what seem nonsense in between the genes, edited out for the assembly of proteins but essential nonetheless for the process of assembly; some genes are called jumping genes, moving from one segment of DNA to another, rearranging the messages, achieving instantly a degree of variability that we once thought would require eons of evolution. The cell membrane is no longer a simple skin for the cell; it is a fluid mosaic, a sea of essential mobile signals, an organ in itself. Cells communicate with one another, exchange messages like bees in a hive, regulate one another. Genes are switched on, switched off, by molecules from the outside whose nature is a mystery; somewhere inside are switches which, when thrown one way or the other, can transform any normal cell into a cancer cell, and sometimes back again.

It is not just that there is more to do, there is everything to do. Biological science, with medicine bobbing somewhere in its wake, is under way, but only just under way. What lies ahead, or what *can* lie ahead if the efforts in basic research are continued, is much more than the conquest of human disease or the amplification of agricultural technology or the cultivation of nutrients in the sea. As we learn more about the fundamental processes of living things in general we will learn more about ourselves, including perhaps the ways in which our brains, unmatched by any other neural structures on the planet, achieve the earth's awareness of itself. It may be too much to say that we will become wise through such endeavors, but we can at least come into possession of a level of information upon which a new kind of wisdom might be based. At the moment we are an ignorant species, flummoxed by the puzzles of who we are, where we came from, and what we are for. It is a gamble to bet on science for moving ahead, but it is, in my view, the only game in town.

The near views in our instruments of the dead soil of Mars, the bizarre rings of Saturn, and the strange surfaces of Saturn, Jupiter, Venus, and the rest, literally unearthly, are only brief glances at what is ahead for mankind in the exploration of our own solar system. In theory, there is no reason why human beings cannot make the same journeys in person, or out beyond into the galaxy.

We will solve our energy problems by the use of science, and in no other way. The sun is there, to be sure, ready for tapping, but we cannot sit back in the lounges of political lobbies and make guesses and wishes; it will take years, probably many years, of research. Meanwhile, there are other possibilities needing deeper exploration. Nuclear fission power, for all its present disadvantages, including where on earth to put the waste, can be made safer and more reliable by better research, while hydrogen fusion, inexhaustibly fueled from the oceans and much safer than fission, lies somewhere ahead. We may learn to produce vast amounts of hydrogen itself, alcohol or methane, when we have learned more about the changeable genes of single-celled microorganisms. If we are to continue to burn coal in large amounts, we will need research models for predicting how much more carbon dioxide we can inject into the planet's atmosphere before we run into the danger of melting the ice shelves of western Antarctica and flooding all our coasts. We will need science to protect us against ourselves.

It has become the fashion to express fear of computers—the machines will do our thinking, quicker and better than human thought, construct and replicate themselves, take over and eventually replace us—that sort of thing. I confess to apprehensions of my own, but I have a hunch that those are on my mind because I do not know enough about computers. Nor, perhaps, does anyone yet, not even the computer scientists themselves. For my comfort, I know for sure only one thing about the computer networks now being meshed together like interconnected ganglia around the earth: what they contain on their microchips are bits of information put there by human minds; perhaps they will do something like thinking on their own, but it will still be a cousin of human thought once removed and, because of newness, potentially of immense usefulness.

The relatively new term "earth science" is itself an encouragement. It is nice to know that our own dear planet has become an object of as much obsessive interest to large bodies of professional researchers as a living cell, and almost as approachable for discovering the details of how it works. Satellites scrutinize it all day and night, recording the patterns of its clouds, the temperatures at all parts of its surface, the distribution and condition of its forests, crops, waterways, cities, and barren places. Seismologists and geologists have already surprised themselves over and over again, probing the movement of crustal plates afloat on something or other, maybe methane, deep below the surface, meditating the evidences now coming in for the reality and continuing of continental drift, and calculating with increasing precision the data that describe the mechanisms involved in earthquakes. Their instruments are becoming as neat and informative as medicine's CAT scanners; the earth has deep secrets still, but they are there for penetrating.

The astronomers have long since become physicists, the physicists are astronomers; both are, as well, what we used to call chemists, examining the levels of ammonia or formaldehyde in clouds drifting billions of light-years away, measuring the concentrations of methane in the nearby atmosphere of Pluto, running into paradoxes. Contemporary physics lives off paradox. Niels Bohr said that a great truth is one for which the opposite is also a great truth. There are not so many neutrinos coming from our sun as there ought to be; something has gone wrong, not with the sun but with our knowledge. There are radioastronomical instruments for listening to the leftover sounds of the creation of the universe; the astronomers are dumbstruck, they can hardly hear themselves think.

The social scientists have a long way to go to catch up, but they may be up to the most important scientific business of all, if and when they finally get down to the right questions. Our behavior toward each other is the strangest, most unpredictable, and almost entirely unaccountable of all the phenomena with which we are obliged to live. In all of nature there is nothing so threatening to humanity as humanity itself. We need, for this most worrying of puzzles, the brightest and youngest of our most agile minds, capable of dreaming up ideas not dreamed before, ready to carry the imagination to great depths and, I should hope, handy with big computers but skeptical about long questionnaires and big numbers.

Fundamental science did not become a national endeavor in this country until the time of World War II, when it was pointed out by some influential and sagacious advisers to the government that whatever we needed for the technology of warfare could be achieved only after the laying of a solid foundation of basic research. During the Eisenhower administration a formal mechanism was created in the White House for the explicit purpose of furnishing scientific advice to the President, the President's Science Advisory Committee (PSAC), chaired by a new administration officer, the Science Adviser. The National Institutes of Health, which had existed before the war as a relatively small set of laboratories for research on cancer and infectious disease, expanded rapidly in the postwar period to encompass all disciplines of biomedical science. The National Science Foundation was organized specifically for the sponsorship of basic science. Each of the federal departments and agencies developed its own research capacity, relevant to its mission; the programs of largest scale were those in defense, agriculture, space, and atomic energy.

Most of the country's basic research has been carried out by the universities, which have as a result become increasingly dependent on the federal government for their sustenance, even their existence, to a degree now causing alarm signals from the whole academic community. The ever-rising costs of doing modern science, especially the prices of today's sophisticated and complex instruments, combined with the federal efforts to reduce all expenditures, are placing the universities in deep trouble. Meanwhile, the philanthropic foundations, which were the principal source of funds for university research before the war, are no longer capable of more than a minor contribution to science.

Besides the government's own national laboratories and the academic institutions there is a third resource for the country's scientific enterprise—industry. Up to very recently, industrial research has been conducted in relative isolation, unconnected with the other two. There are signs that this is beginning to change, and the change should be a source of encouragement for the future. Some of the corporations responsible for high technology, especially those involved in energy, have formed solid linkages with a few research universities—MIT and Cal Tech, for example—and are investing substantial sums in long-range research in physics and chemistry. Several pharmaceutical companies have been investing in fundamental biomedical research in association with medical schools and private research institutions.

There needs to be much more of this kind of partnership. The nation's future may well depend on whether we can set up within the private sector a new system for collaborative research. Although there are some promising partnership ventures now in operation, they are few in number; within industry the tendency remains to concentrate on applied research and development, excluding any consideration of basic science. The academic community tends, for its part, to stay out of fields closely related to the development of new products. Each side maintains adversarial and largely bogus images of the other, moneymakers on one side and impractical academics on the other. Meanwhile, our competitors in Europe and Japan have long since found effective ways to link industrial research to government and academic science, and they may be outclassing this country before long. In some fields, most conspicuously the devising and production of new scientific instruments, they have already moved to the front.

There are obvious difficulties in the behavior of the traditional worlds of research in the United States. Corporate research is obliged by its nature to concentrate on profitable products and to maintain a high degree of secrecy during the process; academic science, by its nature, must be carried out in the open and depends for its progress on the free exchange of new information almost at the moment of finding. But these are not impossible barriers to collaboration. Industry already has a life-or-death stake in what will emerge from basic research in the years ahead; there can be no more prudent investment for the corporate world, and the immediate benefit for any corporation in simply having the "first look" at a piece of basic science would be benefit enough in the long run. The university science community, for all the talk of ivory towers, hankers day and night for its work to turn out useful; a close working connection with industrial researchers might well lead to an earlier perception of potential applicability than is now the case.

The age of science did not really begin three hundred years ago. That was simply the time when it was realized that human curiosity about the world represented a deep wish, perhaps embedded somewhere in the chromosomes of human beings, to learn more about nature by experiment and the confirmation of experiment. The doing of science on a scale appropriate to the problems at hand was launched only in the twentieth century and has been moving into high gear only within the last fifty years. We have not lacked explanations at any time in our recorded history, but now we must live and think with the new habit of requiring reproducible observations and solid facts for the explanations. It is not as easy a time for us as it used to be: we are raised through childhood in skepticism and disbelief; we feel the need of proofs all around, even for matters as deep as the working of our own consciousness, where there is as yet no clear prospect of proof about anything. Uncertainty, disillusion, and despair are prices to be paid for living in an age of science. Illumination is the product sought, but it comes in small bits, only from time to time, not ever in broad, bright flashes of public comprehension, and there can be no promise that we will ever emerge from the great depths of the mystery of being.

Nevertheless, we have started to do science on a world scale, and to rely on it, and hope for it. Not just the scientists, everyone, and not for the hope of illumination, but for the sure predictable prospect of new technologies, which have always come along, like spray in the wake of science. We need better ways of predicting how a piece of new technology is likely to turn out, better measures available on an international level to shut off the ones that carry hazard to the life of the planet (including, but perhaps not always so much *first of all,* as is usually the only consideration, our own species' life). We will have to go more warily with technology in the future, for the demands will be increasing and the stakes will be very high. Instead of coping, or trying to cope, with the wants of four billion people, we will very soon be facing the needs, probably desperate, of double that number and, soon thereafter, double again. The real challenge to human ingenuity, and to science, lies in the century to come.

I cannot guess at the things we will need to know from science to get through the time ahead, but I am willing to make one prediction about the method: we will not be able to call the shots in advance. We cannot say to ourselves, we need this or that sort of technology, therefore we should be doing this or that sort of science. It does not work that way. We will have to rely, as we have in the past, on science in general, and on basic, undifferentiated science at that, for the new insights that will open up the new opportunities for technological development. Science is useful, indispensable sometimes, but whenever it moves forward it does so by producing a surprise; you cannot specify the surprise you'd like. Technology should be watched closely, monitored, criticized, even voted in or out by the electorate, but science itself must be given its head if we want it to work.

CHAPTER SIXTY-SIX

Alchemy

ALCHEMY BEGAN LONG AGO AS AN EXPRESSION OF THE DEEPEST AND oldest of human wishes: to discover that the world makes sense. The working assumption—that everything on earth must be made up from a single, primal sort of matter—led to centuries of hard work aimed at isolating the original stuff and rearranging it to the alchemists' liking. If it could be found, nothing would lie beyond human grasp. The transmutation of base metals to gold was only a modest part of the prospect. If you knew about the fundamental substance, you could do much more than make simple money: you could boil up a cure-all for every disease affecting humankind, you could rid the world of evil, and, while doing this, you could make a universal solvent capable of dissolving anything you might want to dissolve. These were heady ideas, and generations of alchemists worked all their lives trying to reduce matter to its ultimate origin.

To be an alchemist was to be a serious professional, requiring long periods of apprenticeship and a great deal of late-night study. From the earliest years of the profession, there was a lot to read. The documents can be traced back to Arabic, Latin, and Greek scholars of the ancient world, and beyond them to Indian Vedic texts as far back as the tenth century B.C. All the old papers contain a formidable array of information, mostly expressed in incantations, which were required learning for every young alchemist and, by design, incomprehensible to everyone else. The word "gibberish" is thought by some to refer back to Jabir ibn Hayyan, an eighth-century alchemist, who lived in fear of being executed for black magic and worded his doctrines so obscurely that almost no one knew what he was talking about.

Indeed, black magic was what most people thought the alchemists were up to in their laboratories, filled with the fumes of arsenic, mercury, and sulphur and the bubbling infusions of all sorts of obscure plants. We tend to look back at them from today's pinnacle of science as figures of fun, eccentric solitary men wearing comical conical hats, engaged in meaningless explorations down one blind alley after another. It was not necessarily so: the work they were doing was hard and frustrating, but it was the start-up of experimental chemistry and physics. The central idea they were obsessed with—that there is a fundamental, elementary particle out of which everything in the universe is made—continues to obsess today's physicists.

They never succeeded in making gold from base metals, nor did they find a universal elixir in their plant extracts; they certainly didn't rid the world of evil. What they did accomplish, however, was no small thing: they got the work going. They fiddled around in their laboratories, talked at one another incessantly, set up one crazy experiment after another, wrote endless reams of notes, which were then translated from Arabic to Greek to Latin and back again, and the work got under way. More workers became interested and then involved in the work, and, as has been happening ever since in science, one thing led to another. As time went on and the work progressed, error after error, new and accurate things began to turn up. Hard facts were learned about the behavior of metals and their alloys, the properties of acids, bases, and salts were recognized, the mathematics of thermodynamics were worked out, and, with just a few jumps through the centuries, the helical molecule of DNA was revealed in all its mystery.

The current anxieties over what science may be doing to human society, including the worries about technology, are no new thing. The third-century Roman emperor Diocletian decreed that all manuscripts dealing with alchemy were to be destroyed, on grounds that such enterprises were against nature. The work went on in secrecy, and, although some of the material was lost, a great deal was translated into other languages, passed around, and preserved.

The association of alchemy with black magic has persisted in the public mind throughout the long history of the endeavor, partly because the objective—the transmutation of one sort of substance to another— seemed magical by definition. Partly also because of the hybrid term: *al* was simply the Arabic article, but *chemy* came from a word meaning "the black land," *Khemia,* the Greek name for Egypt. Another, similar-sounding word, *khumeia,* meant an infusion or elixir, and this was incorporated as part of the meaning. The Egyptian origin is very old, extending back to Thoth, the god of magic (who later reappeared as Hermes Trismegistus, master of the hermetic seal required by alchemists for the vacuums they believed were needed in their work). The notion of alchemy may be as old as language, and the idea that language and magic are somehow related is also old. "Grammar," after all, was a word used in the Middle Ages to denote high learning, but it also implied a practicing familiarity with alchemy. *Gramarye,* an older term for grammar, signified occult learning and necromancy. "Glamour," of all words, was the Scottish word for grammar, and it meant, precisely, a spell, casting enchantment.

Medicine, from its dark origins in old shamanism millennia ago, became closely linked in the Middle Ages with alchemy. The preoccupation of alchemists with metals and their properties led to experiments—mostly feckless ones, looking back—with the therapeutic use of all sorts of metals. Paracelsus, a prominent physician of the sixteenth century, achieved fame from his enthusiastic use of mercury and arsenic, based on what now seems a wholly mystical commitment to alchemical philosophy as the key to understanding the universe and the human body simultaneously. Under his influence, three centuries of patients with all varieties of illness were treated with strong potions of metals, chiefly mercury, and vigorous purgation became standard medical practice.

Physics and chemistry have grown to scientific maturity, medicine is on its way to growing up, and it is hard to find traces anywhere of the earlier fumblings toward a genuine scientific method. Alchemy exists only as a museum piece, an intellectual fossil, so antique that we no longer need be embarrassed by the memory, but the memory is there. Science began by fumbling. It works because the people involved in it work, and *work together.* They become excited and exasperated, they exchange their bits of information at a full shout, and, the most wonderful thing of all, they keep *at* one another.

Something rather like this may be going on now, without realizing it, in the latest and grandest of all fields of science. People in my field, and some of my colleagues in the real "hard" sciences such as physics and chemistry, have a tendency to take lightly and often disparagingly the efforts of workers in the so-called social sciences. We like to refer to their data as soft. We do not acknowledge as we should the differences between the various disciplines within behavioral research—we speak of analytical psychiatry, sociology, linguistics, economics, and computer intelligence as though these inquiries were all of a piece, with all parties wearing the same old comical conical hats. It is of course not so. The principal feature that the social sciences share these days is the attraction they exert on considerable numbers of students, who see the prospect of exploring human behavior as irresistible and hope fervently that a powerful scientific method for doing the exploring can be worked out. All of the matters on the social-science agenda seem more urgent to these young people than they did at any other time in human memory. It may turn out, years hence, that a solid discipline of human science will have come into existence, hard as quantum physics, filled with deep insights, plagued as physics still is by ambiguities but with new rules and new ways of getting things done. Like, for instance, getting rid of thermonuclear weapons, patriotic rhetoric, and nationalism all at once. If anything like this does turn up we will be looking back at today's social scientists, and their close colleagues the humanists, as having launched the new science in a way not all that different from the accomplishment of the old alchemists, by simply working on the problem—this time, the fundamental, primal universality of the human mind.

CHAPTER SIXTY-SEVEN

Clever Animals

SCIENTISTS WHO WORK ON ANIMAL BEHAVIOR ARE OCCUPATIONALLY obliged to live chancier lives than most of their colleagues, always at risk of being fooled by the animals they are studying or, worse, fooling themselves. Whether their experiments involve domesticated laboratory animals or wild creatures in the field, there is no end to the surprises that an animal can think up in the presence of an investigator. Sometimes it seems as if animals are genetically programmed to puzzle human beings, especially psychologists.

The risks are especially high when the scientist is engaged in training the animal to do something or other and must bank his professional reputation on the integrity of his experimental subject. The most famous case in point is that of Clever Hans, the turn-of-the-century German horse now immortalized in the lexicon of behavioral science by the technical term, the "Clever Hans Error." The horse, owned and trained by Herr von Osten, could not only solve complex arithmetical problems, but even read the instructions on a blackboard and tap out infallibly, with one hoof, the right answer. What is more, he could perform the same computations when total strangers posed questions to him, with his trainer nowhere nearby. For several years Clever Hans was studied intensively by groups of puzzled scientists and taken seriously as a horse with something very like a human brain, quite possibly even better than human. But finally in 1911, it was discovered by Professor O. Pfungst that Hans was not really doing arithmetic at all; he was simply observing the behavior of the human experimenter. Subtle, unconscious gestures—nods of the head, the holding of breath, the cessation of nodding when the correct count was reached—were accurately read by the horse as cues to stop tapping.

Whenever I read about that phenomenon, usually recounted as the exposure of a sort of unconscious fraud on the part of either the experimenter or the horse or both, I wish Clever Hans would be given more credit than he generally gets. To be sure, the horse couldn't really do arithmetic, but the record shows that he was considerably better at observing human beings and interpreting their behavior than humans are at comprehending horses or, for that matter, other humans.

Cats are a standing rebuke to behavioral scientists wanting to know how the minds of animals work. The mind of a cat is an inscrutable mystery, beyond human reach, the least human of all creatures and at the same time, as any cat owner will attest, the most intelligent. In 1979, a paper was published in *Science* by B. R. Moore and S. Stuttard entitled "Dr. Guthrie and *Felis domesticus* or: Tripping over the Cat," a wonderful account of the kind of scientific mischief native to this species. Thirty-five years ago, E. R. Guthrie and G. P. Horton described an experiment in which cats were placed in a glass-fronted puzzle box and trained to find their way out by jostling a slender vertical rod at the front of the box, thereby causing a door to open. What interested these investigators was not so much that the cats could learn to bump into the vertical rod, but that before doing so each animal performed a long ritual of highly stereotyped movements, rubbing their heads and backs against the front of the box, turning in circles, and finally touching the rod. The experiment has ranked as something of a classic in experimental psychology, even raising in some minds the notion of a ceremony of superstition on the part of cats: before the rod will open the door, it is necessary to go through a magical sequence of motions.

Moore and Stuttard repeated the Guthrie experiment, observed the same complex "learning" behavior, but then discovered that it occurred only when a human being was visible to the cat. If no one was in the room with the box, the cat did nothing but take naps. The sight of a human being was all that was needed to launch the animal on the series of sinuous movements, rod or no rod, door or no door. It was not a learned pattern of behavior, it was a cat greeting a person.

The French investigator R. Chauvin was once engaged in a field study of the boundaries of ant colonies and enlisted the help of some enthusiastic physicists equipped with radioactive compounds and Geiger counters. The ants of one anthill were labeled and then tracked to learn whether they entered the territory of a neighboring hill. In the middle of the work the physicists suddenly began leaping like ballet dancers, terminating the experiment, while hundreds of ants from both colonies swarmed over their shoes and up inside their pants. To Chauvin's ethological eye it looked like purposeful behavior on both sides.

Bees are filled with astonishments, confounding anyone who studies them, producing volumes of anecdotes. A lady of our acquaintance visited her sister, who raised honeybees in northern California. They left their car on a side road, suited up in protective gear, and walked across the fields to have a look at the hives. For reasons unknown, the bees were in a furious mood that afternoon, attacking in platoons, settling on them from all sides. Let us walk away slowly, advised the beekeeper sister, they'll give it up sooner or later. They walked until bee-free, then circled the fields and went back to the car, and found the bees there, waiting for them.

There is a new bee anecdote for everyone to wonder about. It was reported from Brazil that male bees of the plant-pollinating euglossine species are addicted to DDT. Houses that had been sprayed for mosquito control in the Amazonas region were promptly invaded by thousands of bees that gathered on the walls, collected the DDT in pouches on their hind legs, and flew off with it. Most of the houses were virtually stripped of DDT during the summer months, and the residents in the area complained bitterly of the noise. There is as yet no explanation for this behavior. They are not harmed by the substance; while a honeybee is quickly killed by as little as six micrograms of DDT, these bees can cart away two thousand micrograms without being discommoded. Possibly the euglossine bees like the taste of DDT or its smell, or maybe they are determined to protect other insect cousins. Nothing about bees, or other animals, seems beyond imagining.

CHAPTER SIXTY-EIGHT

On Smell

THE VACUUM CLEANER TURNED ON IN THE APARTMENT'S BACK BED-room emits a high-pitched lament indistinguishable from the steam alarm on the teakettle in the kitchen, and the only way of judging whether to run to the stove is to consult one's watch: there is a time of day for the vacuum cleaner, another time for the teakettle. The telephone in the guest bedroom sounds like the back-door bell, so you wait for the second or third ring before moving. There is a random crunching sound in the vicinity of the front door, resembling an assemblage of people excitedly taking off galoshes, but when listened to carefully it is recognizable as a negligible sound, needing no response, made by the ancient elevator machinery in the wall alongside the door. So it goes. We learn these things from day to day, no trick to it. Sometimes the sounds around our lives become novel confusions, harder to sort out: the family was once given a talking crow named Byron for Christmas, and this animal imitated every nearby sound with such accuracy that the house-hold was kept constantly on the fly, answering doors and telephones, oiling hinges, looking out the window for falling bodies, glancing into empty bathrooms for the sources of flushing.

We are not so easily misled by vision. Most of the things before our eyes are plainly there, not mistakable for other things except for the illusions created for pay by professional magicians and, sometimes, the look of the lights of downtown New York against a sky so black as to make it seem a near view of eternity. Our eyes are not easy to fool.

Smelling is another matter. I should think we might fairly gauge the future of biological science, centuries ahead, by estimating the time it will take to reach a complete, comprehensive understanding of odor. It may not seem a profound enough problem to dominate all the life sciences, but it contains, piece by piece, all the mysteries. Smoke: tobacco burning, coal smoke, wood-fire smoke, leaf smoke. Most of all, leaf smoke. This is the only odor I can *will* back to consciousness just by thinking about it. I can sit in a chair, thinking, and call up clearly to mind the smell of burning autumn leaves, coded and stored away somewhere in a temporal lobe, firing off explosive signals into every part of my right hemisphere. But nothing else: if I try to recall the thick smell of Edinburgh in winter, or the accidental burning of a plastic comb, or a rose, or a glass of wine, I cannot do this; I can get a clear picture of any face I feel like remembering, and I can hear whatever Beethoven quartet I want to recall, but except for the leaf bonfire I cannot really remember a smell in its absence. To be sure, I know the odor of cinnamon or juniper and can name such things with accuracy when they turn up in front of my nose, but I cannot imagine them into existence.

The act of smelling something, anything, is remarkably like the act of thinking itself. Immediately, at the very moment of perception, you can feel the mind going to work, sending the odor around from place to place, setting off complex repertoires throughout the brain, polling one center after another for signs of recognition, old memories, connections. This is as it should be, I suppose, since the cells that do the smelling are themselves proper brain cells, the only neurons whose axons carry information picked up at first hand in the outside world. Instead of dendrites they have cilia, equipped with receptors for all sorts of chemical stimuli, and they are in some respects as mysterious as lymphocytes. There are reasons to believe that each of these neurons has its own specific class of receptors; like lymphocytes, each cell knows in advance what it is looking for; there are responder and nonresponder cells for different classes of odorant. And they are also the only brain neurons that replicate themselves; the olfactory receptor cells of mice turn over about once every twenty-eight days. There may be room for a modified version of the clonal-selection theory to explain olfactory learning and adaptation. The olfactory receptors of mice can smell the difference between self and nonself, a discriminating gift coded by the same H-2 gene locus governing homograft rejection. One wonders whether lymphocytes in the mucosa may be carrying along this kind of genetic information to donate to new generations of olfactory receptor cells as they emerge from basal cells.

The most medically wonderful of all things about these brain cells is that they do not become infected, not very often anyway, despite their exposure to all the microorganisms in the world of the nose. There must exist, in the mucus secretions bathing this surface of the brain, the most extraordinary antibiotics, including eclectic antiviral substances of some sort.

If you are looking about for things to even out the disparity between the brains of ordinary animals and the great minds of ourselves, the superprimate humans, this apparatus is a good one to reflect on in humility. Compared to the common dog, or any rodent in the field, we are primitive, insensitive creatures, biological failures. Heaven knows how much of the world we are missing.

I suppose if we tried we could improve ourselves. There are, after all, some among our species with special gifts for smelling—perfume makers, tea tasters, whiskey blenders—and it is said that these people can train themselves to higher and higher skills by practicing. Perhaps, instead of spending the resources of our huge cosmetic industry on chemicals for the disguising or outright destruction of odors we should be studying ways to enhance the smell of nature, facing up to the world.

In the meantime, we should be hanging on to some of the few great smells left to us, and I would vote for the preservation of leaf bonfires, by law if necessary. This one is pure pleasure, fetched like music intact out of numberless modular columns of neurons filled chockablock with all the natural details of childhood, firing off memories in every corner of the brain. An autumn curbside bonfire has everything needed for education: danger, surprise (you know in advance that if you poke the right part of the base of leaves with the right kind of stick, a blinding flare of heat and fragrance will follow instantly, but it is still an astonishment when it happens), risk, and victory over odds (if you jump across at precisely the right moment the flare and sparks will miss your pants), and above all the aroma of comradeship (if you smell that odor in the distance you know that there are friends somewhere in the next block, jumping and exulting in their leaves, maybe catching fire).

It was a mistake to change this, smoke or no smoke, carbon dioxide and the greenhouse effect or whatever; it was a loss to give up the burning of autumn leaves. Now, in our haste to protect the environment (which is us, when you get down to it), we rake them up and cram them into great black plastic bags, set out at the curb like wrapped corpses, carted away by the garbage truck to be buried somewhere or dumped in the sea or made into fuel or alcohol or whatever it is they do with autumn leaves these days. We should be giving them back to the children to burn.

CHAPTER SIXTY-NINE

My Magical

Metronome

I WOKE UP, LATE ONE FRIDAY NIGHT, FEELING LIKE THE LONG ISLAND Railroad thumping at top speed over a patch of bad roadbed. Doctor-fashion, I took my pulse and found it too fast to count accurately. I heaved out of bed and sat in a chair, gloomy, wondering what next. A while later the train slowed down, nearly stopped, and my pulse rate had suddenly dropped to 35. I decided to do some telephoning.

Next thing I knew, I was abed in the intensive care unit of the hospital down the street, intravenous tubes in place, wires leading from several places on my chest and from electrodes on my arms and legs, lights flashing from the monitor behind my bed. If I turned my head sharply I could see the bouncing lines of my electrocardiogram, a totally in-comprehensible graffito, dropped beats, long stretches of nothing fol-lowed by what looked like exclamation points. The handwriting on the wall, I thought. And illiterate at that.

Now it was Sunday, late afternoon, the monitor still jumpy, alarm lights still signaling trouble, all the usual drugs for restoring cardiac rhythm having been tried, and handwriting still a scrawl. The cardio-vascular surgeon at the foot of my bed was explaining that it would have to be a pacemaker, immediately, Sunday late afternoon. What did I think?

What I thought, and then said, was that this was one of the things about which a man is not entitled to his own opinion. Over to you, I said.

About an hour later I was back from the operating theater. Theater is right; the masked surgeon center stage, wonderfully lit, several colleagues as appreciative audience, me as the main prop. The denouement was that famous *deus ex machina* being inserted into the prop's chest wall, my gadget now, my metronome. Best of all, my heart rate an absolutely regular, dependable, reliable 70, capable of speeding up on demand but inflexibly tuned to keep it from dropping below 70. The battery guaranteed to last seven years or thereabouts before needing changing. Plenty of time to worry about that, later on.

Home in a couple of days, up and around doing whatever I felt like, up and down stairs, even pushing furniture from one place to another, then back to work.

Afterthought:

A new, unwarranted but irrepressible kind of vanity. I had come into the presence of a technological marvel, namely me. To be sure, the pacemaker is a wonderful miniature piece of high technology, my friend the surgeon a skilled worker in high technology, but the greatest of wonders is my own pump, my myocardium, capable of accepting electronic instructions from that small black box and doing exactly what it is told. I am exceedingly pleased with my machine-tooled, obedient, responsive self. I would never have thought I had it in me, but now that I have it in me, ticking along soundlessly, flawlessly, I am subject to waves of pure vanity.

Another surprise:

I do not want to know very much about my new technology. I do not even want to have the reasons for needing it fully explained to me. As long as it works, and it does indeed, I prefer to be as mystified by it as I can. This is a surprise. I would have thought that as a reasonably intelligent doctor-patient I would be filled with intelligent, penetrating questions, insisting on comprehending each step in the procedure, making my own decisions, even calling the shots. Not a bit of it. I turn out to be the kind of patient who doesn't want to have things explained, only to have things looked after by the real professionals. Just before I left the hospital, the cardiologist brought me a manila envelope filled with reprints, brochures, the pacemaker manufacturer's instructions for physicians listing all the indications, warnings, the things that might go wrong. I have the envelope somewhere, on a closet shelf I think, unexamined. I haven't, to be honest, the faintest idea how a pacemaker works, and I have even less curiosity.

This goes against the wisdom of the times, I know. These days one reads everywhere, especially in the popular magazines, that a patient should take more responsibility, be more assertive, insist on second and third opinions, and above all have everything fully explained by the doctor or, preferably, the doctors, before submitting to treatment. As a physician, I used to think this way myself, but now, as a successful patient, I feel different. Don't explain it to me, I say, go ahead and fix it.

I suppose I should be feeling guilty about this. In a way I do, for I have written and lectured in the past about medicine's excessive dependence on technology in general, and the resultant escalation in the cost of health care. I have been critical of what I called "halfway technologies," designed to shore things up and keep flawed organs functioning beyond their appointed time. And here I am, enjoying precisely this sort of technology, eating my words.

Pacemakers have had a bad press recently, with stories about overutilization, kited prices, kickbacks to doctors and hospitals, a scandal. Probably the stories, some of them anyway, are true. But I rise to the defense of the gadget itself, in which I now have so personal a stake. If anyone had tried to tell me, long ago when I was a medical student, that the day would come when a device the size of a cigarette lighter could be implanted permanently over the heart, with wires extending to the interior of the ventricle, dominating the heart's conduction system and regulating the rhythm with perfection, I would have laughed in his face. If then he had told me that this would happen one day to me, I would have gotten sore. But here it is, incomprehensible, and I rather like it.

CHAPTER SEVENTY

On Speaking of
Speaking

THERE IS NOTHING AT ALL WRONG WITH THE ENGLISH LANGUAGE, SO far as I can see, but that may only be because I cannot see ahead. If I were placed in charge of it, as chairman, say, of a National Academy for the Improvement of Language, I would not lay a finger on English. It suits every need that I can think of: flexibility, clarity, subtlety of metaphor, ambiguity wherever ambiguity is needed (which is more often than is generally acknowledged), and most of all changeability. I like the notion of a changing language. As a meliorist, I am convinced that all past changes were for the better; I have no doubt that today's English is a considerable improvement over Elizabethan or Chaucerian talk, and miles ahead of Old English. By now the language has reached its stage of ultimate perfection, and I'll be satisfied to have it this way forever.

But I know I'm wrong about this. English is shifting and changing before our eyes and ears, beyond the control of all individuals, committees, academies, and governments. The speakers of earlier versions undoubtedly felt the same satisfaction with their speech in their time. Chaucer's generation, and all the generations before, could not have been aware of any need to change or improve. Montaigne was entirely content with sixteenth-century French and obviously delighted by what he could do with it. Long, long ago, the furthermost ancestors of English speech must have got along nicely in Proto-Indo-European without a notion that their language would one day vanish.

"Vanish" is the wrong word anyway for what happened. The roots of several thousand Indo-European words are still alive and active, tucked up neatly like symbionts inside other words in Greek, Latin, and all the

Germanic tongues, including English. Much of what we say to each other today, in English, could be interpreted as Greek with an Indo-European accent. Three or four centuries from now, it is probable that today's English will be largely incomprehensible to everyone except the linguistic scholars and historians.

The ancient meanings of the Indo-European roots are sometimes twisted around, even distorted beyond recognition, but they are still there, resonating inside, reminding. The old root *gheue,* meaning simply to call, became *gudam* in Germanic and then "God" in English. *Meug* was a root signifying something damp and slippery, and thousands of years later it turned into "meek" in proper English and "mooch" in slang, also "schmuck." *Bha* was the Indo-European word for speaking, becoming *phanai* in Greek with the same meaning, then used much later for our most fundamental word indicating the inability to speak: "infancy." *Ster* was a root meaning to stiffen; it became *sterban* in Germanic and *steorfan* in Old English, meaning to die, and then turned into "starve" in our speech.

The changes in language will continue forever, but no one knows for sure who does the changing. One possibility is that children are responsible. Derek Bickerton, professor of linguistics at the University of Hawaii, explores this in his book *Roots of Language*. Sometime around 1880, a language catastrophe occurred in Hawaii when thousands of immigrant workers were brought to the islands to work for the new sugar industry. These people, speaking Chinese, Japanese, Korean, Portuguese, and various Spanish dialects, were unable to communicate with one another or with the native Hawaiians or the dominant English-speaking owners of the plantations, and they first did what such mixed-language populations have always done: they spoke Pidgin English (a corruption of "business English"). A pidgin is not really a language at all, more like a set of verbal signals used to name objects but lacking the grammatical rules needed for expressing thought and ideas. And then, within a single generation, the whole mass of mixed peoples began speaking a totally new tongue: Hawaiian Creole. The new speech contained ready-made words borrowed from all the original tongues, but bore little or no resemblance to the predecessors in the rules used for stringing the words together. Although generally regarded as a "primitive" language, Hawaiian Creole was constructed with a highly sophisticated grammar. Professor Bickerton's great discovery is that this brand-new speech could have been made only by the children. There wasn't time enough to allow for any other explanation. Soon after the influx of workers in 1880 the speech was Hawaiian Pidgin, and within the next twenty-five or thirty years the accepted language was Creole. The first immigrants, the parents who spoke Pidgin, could not have made the new language and then taught it to the children. They could not themselves understand Creole when it appeared. Nor could the adult English speakers in charge of the place either speak or comprehend Creole. According to Bickerton's research, it simply had to have been the work of children, crowded together, jabbering away at each other, playing.

Bickerton cites this historic phenomenon as evidence, incontrovertible in his view, for the theory that language is a biological, innate, genetically determined property of human beings, driven by a center or centers in the brain that code out grammar and syntax. His term for the gift of speech is "bioprogram." The idea confirms and extends the proposal put forward by Noam Chomsky, almost three decades ago, that human beings are unique in their possession of brains equipped for generating grammar. But the most fascinating aspect of the new work is its evidence that children—and probably very young children at that—are able to construct a whole language, working at it together, or more likely *playing* at it together.

It should make you take a different view of children, eliciting something like awe. We have always known that childhood is the period in which new languages as well as one's own can be picked up quickly and easily. The facility disappears in most people around the time of adolescence, and from then on the acquisition of a new language is hard, slogging labor. Children are gifted at it, of course. But it requires a different order of respect to take in the possibility that children make up languages, change languages, perhaps have been carrying the responsibility for evolving language from the first human communication to twentieth-century speech. If it were not for the children and their special gift we might all be speaking Indo-European or Hittite, but here we all are, speaking several thousand different languages and dialects, most of which would be incomprehensible to the human beings on earth just a few centuries back.

Perhaps we should be paying serious attention to the possible role played by children in the origin of speech itself. It is of course not known when language first appeared in our species, and it is pure guesswork as to how it happened. One popular guess is that at a certain stage in the evolution of the human skull, and of the brain therein, speech became a possibility in a few mutant individuals. Thereafter, these intellectual people and their genes outcompeted all their speechless cousins, and natural selection resulted in *Homo sapiens*. This notion would require the recurrence of the same mutation in many different, isolated communities all around the globe, or else one would have to assume that a lucky few speakers managed to travel with remarkable agility everywhere on earth, leaving their novel genes behind.

Another possibility, raised by the new view of children and speech, is that human language did not pop up as a special mutation, but came into existence as a latent property of all human brains at some point in the evolution of the whole species. The environment required for expression of the brain centers involved in the process was simply children, enough children crowded together in circumstances where they could spend a lot of time playing together. A critical mass of children in a sufficiently stable society could have been achieved whenever large enough numbers of families settled down to live in close quarters, as may have happened long ago in the tribal life of hunters and gatherers or in the earliest agricultural communities.

It makes an interesting scenario. The adults and wise elders of the tribe, sitting around a fire speaking a small-talk pidgin, pointing at one thing or another and muttering isolated words. No syntax, no strings of words, no real ideas, no metaphors. Somewhere nearby, that critical mass of noisy young children, gabbling and shouting at each other, their voices rising in the exultation of discovery, talking, talking, and forever thereafter never stopping.

CHAPTER SEVENTY-ONE

Seven Wonders

A WHILE AGO I RECEIVED A LETTER FROM A MAGAZINE EDITOR INVITING me to join six other people at dinner to make a list of the Seven Wonders of the Modern World, to replace the seven old, out-of-date Wonders. I replied that I couldn't manage it, not on short order anyway, but still the question keeps hanging around in the lobby of my mind. I had to look up the old biodegradable Wonders, the Hanging Gardens of Babylon and all the rest, and then I had to look up that word "wonder" to make sure I understood what it meant. It occurred to me that if the magazine could get any seven people to agree on a list of any such seven things you'd have the modern Seven Wonders right there at the dinner table.

Wonder is a word to wonder about. It contains a mixture of messages: something marvelous and miraculous, surprising, raising unanswerable questions about itself, making the observer wonder, even raising skeptical questions like, "I *wonder* about that." Miraculous and marvelous are clues; both words come from an ancient Indo-European root meaning simply to smile or to laugh. Anything wonderful is something to smile in the presence of, in admiration (which, by the way, comes from the same root, along with, of all telling words, "mirror").

I decided to try making a list, not for the magazine's dinner party but for this occasion: seven things I wonder about the most.

I shall hold the first for the last, and move along.

My Number Two Wonder is a bacterial species never seen on the face of the earth until 1982, creatures never dreamed of before, living violation of what we used to regard as the laws of nature, things literally straight out of Hell. Or anyway what we used to think of as Hell, the hot unlivable interior of the earth. Such regions have recently come into scientific view from the research submarines designed to descend twenty-five hundred meters or more to the edge of deep holes in the sea bottom, where open vents spew superheated seawater in plumes from chimneys in the earth's crust, known to oceanographic scientists as "black smokers." This is not just hot water, or steam, or even steam under pressure as exists in a laboratory autoclave (which we have relied upon for decades as the surest way to destroy all microbial life). This is extremely hot water under extremely high pressure, with temperatures in excess of 300 degrees centigrade. At such heat, the existence of life as we know it would be simply inconceivable. Proteins and DNA would fall apart, enzymes would melt away, anything alive would die instantaneously. We have long since ruled out the possibility of life on Venus because of that planet's comparable temperature; we have ruled out the possibility of life in the earliest years of this planet, four billion or so years ago, on the same ground.

B. J. A. Baross and J. W. Deming have recently discovered the presence of thriving colonies of bacteria in water fished directly from these deep-sea vents. Moreover, when brought to the surface, encased in titanium syringes and sealed in pressurized chambers heated to 250 degrees centigrade, the bacteria not only survive but reproduce themselves enthusiastically. They can be killed only by chilling them down in boiling water.

And yet they look just like ordinary bacteria. Under the electron microscope they have the same essential structure—cell walls, ribosomes, and all. If they were, as is now being suggested, the original archebacteria, ancestors of us all, how did they or their progeny ever learn to cool down? I cannot think of a more wonderful trick.

My Number Three Wonder is *oncideres,* a species of beetle encountered by a pathologist friend of mine who lives in Houston and has a lot of mimosa trees in his backyard. This beetle is not new, but it qualifies as a Modern Wonder because of the exceedingly modern questions raised for evolutionary biologists about the three consecutive things on the mind of the female of the species. Her first thought is for a mimosa tree, which she finds and climbs, ignoring all other kinds of trees in the vicinity. Her second thought is for the laying of eggs, which she does by crawling out on a limb, cutting a longitudinal slit with her mandible and depositing her eggs beneath the slit. Her third and last thought concerns the welfare of her offspring; beetle larvae cannot survive in live wood, so she backs up a foot or so and cuts a neat circular girdle all around the limb, through the bark and down into the cambium. It takes her eight hours to finish this cabinetwork. Then she leaves and where she goes I do not know. The limb dies from the girdling, falls to the ground in the next breeze, the larvae feed and grow into the next generation, and the questions lie there unanswered. How on earth did these three linked thoughts in her mind evolve together in evolution? How could any one of the three become fixed as beetle behavior by itself, without the other two? What are the odds favoring three totally separate bits of behavior—liking a particular tree, cutting a slit for eggs, and then girdling the limb—happening together by random chance among a beetle's genes? Does this smart beetle know what she is doing? And how did the mimosa tree enter the picture in its evolution? Left to themselves, unpruned, mimosa trees have a life expectancy of twenty-five to thirty years. Pruned each year, which is what the beetle's girdling labor accomplishes, the tree can flourish for a century. The mimosa-beetle relationship is an elegant example of symbiotic partnership, a phenomenon now recognized as pervasive in nature. It is good for us to have around on our intellectual mantelpiece such creatures as this insect and its friend the tree, for they keep reminding us how little we know about nature.

The Fourth Wonder on my list is an infectious agent known as the scrapie virus, which causes a fatal disease of the brain in sheep, goats, and several laboratory animals. A close cousin of scrapie is the C-J virus, the cause of some cases of senile dementia in human beings. These are called "slow viruses," for the excellent reason that an animal exposed to infection today will not become ill until a year and a half or two years from today. The agent, whatever it is, can propagate itself in abundance from a few infectious units today to more than a billion next year. I use the phrase "whatever it is" advisedly. Nobody has yet been able to find any DNA or RNA in the scrapie or C-J viruses. It may be there, but if so it exists in amounts too small to detect. Meanwhile, there is plenty of protein, leading to a serious proposal that the virus may indeed be *all* protein. But protein, so far as we know, does not replicate itself all by itself, not on this planet anyway. Looked at this way, the scrapie agent seems the strangest thing in all biology and, until someone in some laboratory figures out what it is, a candidate for Modern Wonder.

My Fifth Wonder is the olfactory receptor cell, located in the epithelial tissue high in the nose, sniffing the air for clues to the environment, the fragrance of friends, the smell of leaf smoke, breakfast, nighttime and bedtime, and a rose, even, it is said, the odor of sanctity. The cell that does all these things, firing off urgent messages into the deepest parts of the brain, switching on one strange unaccountable memory after another, is itself a proper brain cell, a certified neuron belonging to the brain but miles away out in the open air, nosing around the world. How it manages to make sense of what it senses, discriminating between jasmine and anything else non-jasmine with infallibility, is one of the deep secrets of neurobiology. This would be wonder enough, but there is more. This population of brain cells, unlike any other neurons of the vertebrate central nervous system, turns itself over every few weeks; cells wear out, die, and are replaced by brand-new cells rewired to the same deep centers miles back in the brain, sensing and remembering the same wonderful smells. If and when we reach an understanding of these cells and their functions, including the moods and whims under their governance, we will know a lot more about the mind than we do now, a world away.

Sixth on my list is, I hesitate to say, another insect, the termite. This time, though, it is not the single insect that is the Wonder, it is the collectivity. There is nothing at all wonderful about a single, solitary termite, indeed there is really no such creature, functionally speaking, as a lone termite, any more than we can imagine a genuinely solitary human being; no such thing. Two or three termites gathered together on a dish are not much better; they may move about and touch each other nervously, but nothing happens. But keep adding more termites until they reach a critical mass, and then the miracle begins. As though they had suddenly received a piece of extraordinary news, they organize in platoons and begin stacking up pellets to precisely the right height, then turning the arches to connect the columns, constructing the cathedral and its chambers in which the colony will live out its life for the decades ahead, air-conditioned and humidity-controlled, following the chemical blueprint coded in their genes, flawlessly, stone-blind. They are not the dense mass of individual insects they appear to be; they are an organism, a thoughtful, meditative brain on a million legs. All we really know about this new thing is that it does its architecture and engineering by a complex system of chemical signals.

The Seventh Wonder of the modern world is a human child, any child. I used to wonder about childhood and the evolution of our species. It seemed to me unparsimonious to keep expending all that energy on such a long period of vulnerability and defenselessness, with nothing to show for it, in biological terms, beyond the feckless, irresponsible pleasure of childhood. After all, I used to think, it is one sixth of a whole human life span! Why didn't our evolution take care of that, allowing us to jump catlike from our juvenile to our adult (and, as I thought) productive stage of life? I had forgotten about language, the single human trait that marks us out as specifically human, the property that enables our survival as the most compulsively, biologically, obsessively social of all creatures on earth, more interdependent and interconnected even than the famous social insects. I had forgotten that, and forgotten that children *do* that in childhood. Language is what childhood is for.

There is another related but different creature, nothing like so wonderful as a human child, nothing like so hopeful, something to worry about all day and all night. It is *us,* aggregated together in our collective, critical masses. So far, we have learned how to be useful to each other only when we collect in small groups—families, circles of friends, once in a while (although still rarely) committees. The drive to be useful is encoded in our genes. But when we gather in very large numbers, as in the modern nation-state, we seem capable of levels of folly and self-destruction to be found nowhere else in all of Nature.

As a species, taking all in all, we are still too young, too juvenile, to be trusted. We have spread across the face of the earth in just a few thousand years, no time at all as evolution clocks time, covering all livable parts of the planet, endangering other forms of life, and now threatening ourselves. As a species, we have everything in the world to learn about living, but we may be running out of time. Provisionally, but only provisionally, we are a Wonder.

And now the first on my list, the one I put off at the beginning of making a list, the first of all Wonders of the modern world. To name this one, you have to redefine the world as it has indeed been redefined in this most scientific of all centuries. We named the place we live in the *world* long ago, from the Indo-European root *wiros,* which meant man. We now live in the whole universe, that stupefying piece of expanding geometry. Our suburbs are the local solar system, into which, sooner or later, we will spread life, and then, likely, beyond into the galaxy. Of all celestial bodies within reach or view, as far as we can see, out to the edge, the most wonderful and marvelous and mysterious is turning out to be our own planet earth. There is nothing to match it anywhere, not yet anyway.

It is a living system, an immense organism, still developing, regulating itself, making its own oxygen, maintaining its own temperature, keeping all its infinite living parts connected and interdependent, including us. It is the strangest of all places, and there is everything in the world to learn about it. It can keep us awake and jubilant with questions for millennia ahead, if we can learn not to meddle and not to destroy. Our great hope is in being such a young species, thinking in language only a short while, still learning, still growing up.

We are not like the social insects. They have only the one way of doing things and they will do it forever, coded for that way. We are coded differently, not just for binary choices, *go* or *no-go.* We can go four ways at once, depending on how the air feels: *go, no-go,* but also *maybe,* plus *what the hell let's give it a try.* We are in for one surprise after another if we keep at it and keep alive. We can build structures for human society never seen before, thoughts never thought before, music never heard before.

Provided we do not kill ourselves off, and provided we can connect ourselves by the affection and respect for which I believe our genes are also coded, there is no end to what we might do on or off this planet.

At this early stage in our evolution, now through our infancy and into our childhood and then, with luck, our growing up, what our species needs most of all, right now, is simply a future.

CHAPTER SEVENTY-TWO

The Artificial Heart

A SHORT WHILE AGO, I WROTE AN ESSAY IN UNQUALIFIED PRAISE OF that technological marvel the pacemaker, celebrating the capacity of this small ingenious device to keep a flawed human heart working beyond what would otherwise have been its allotted time. I had no reservations about the matter: here was an item of engineering that ranks as genuine high technology, a stunning example of what may lie ahead for applied science in medicine.

And then, out of Salt Lake City, came the news of the artificial heart, a functioning replacement for the whole organ, far outclassing anything like my miniature metronome, a science-fiction fantasy come true.

My reaction to the first headlines, on the front pages of all the papers and in the cover stories of the newsmagazines, was all admiration and pleasure. A triumph, to be sure. No question about it.

But then the second thought, and the third and fourth thoughts, dragging their way in and out of my mind leaving one worry after another: What happens now? If the engineers keep at it, as they surely will, and this remarkable apparatus is steadily improved—as I'm sure it can be—so that we end up without the need for that cart with its compressors and all those hoses, an entirely feasible replacement for anyone's failing heart, what then? The heart disease called cardiomyopathy, for which the initial device was employed, is a relatively uncommon, obscure ailment, entailing very high cost, but for a limited number of patients; no great strain on the national economy. But who says that an artificial heart will be implanted only in patients with a single, rare form of intractable heart failure? What about the hundreds of thousands of people whose cardiac muscles have been destroyed by coronary atherosclerosis and who must otherwise die of congestive heart failure? Who will decide that only certain patients, within certain age groups, will be selected for this kind of lifesaving (or at least life-prolonging) technology? Will there be committees, sitting somewhere in Washington, laying out national policy? How can Congress stay out of the problem, having already set up a system for funding the artificial kidney (with runaway costs already far beyond the original expectations and no end in sight)? And where is the money to come from, at a time when every penny of taxpayers' money for the health-care system is being pinched out of shape?

I conclude that the greatest potential value of the successful artificial heart is, or ought to be, its power to convince the government as well as the citizenry at large that the nation simply must invest more money in basic biomedical research.

We do not really understand the underlying mechanism of cardiomyopathies at all, and we are not much better off at comprehending the biochemical events that disable the heart muscle or its valves in other more common illnesses. But there are clues enough to raise the spirits of people in a good many basic science disciplines, and any number of engrossing questions are at hand awaiting answers. The trouble is that most of the good questions that may lead, ultimately, to methods for prevention (for example, the metabolism and intimate pathologic changes in a failing myocardium, the possible roles of nutrition, viral infection, blood-clotting abnormalities, hypertension, life-style, and other unknown factors) are all long-range questions, requiring unguessable periods of time before the research can be completed. Nor can the outcome of research on any particular line be predicted in advance; whatever turns up as the result of science is bound to be new information. There can be no guarantee that the work will turn out to be useful. It can, however, be guaranteed that if such work is not done we will be stuck forever with this insupportably expensive, ethically puzzling, halfway technology, and it is doubtful that we can long afford it.

We are in a similar fix for the other major diseases, especially the chronic ones affecting the aging population. Although nothing so spectacular as the artificial heart has emerged for the treatment of stroke, or multiple sclerosis, or dementia, or arthritis, or diabetes, or cirrhosis, or advanced cancer, or the others on the list, the costs of whatever therapy we do possess continue to escalate at a terrifying rate. Soon we will be spending more than 10 percent of the GNP on efforts to cope with such chronic health problems. The diseases are all comparable in at least one respect: it cannot be promised that scientific research will solve them, but it can be firmly predicted that without research there is no hope at all of preventing or getting rid of them.

The artificial heart could, with better science and a lot of luck, turn out to be, one day or other, an interesting kind of antique, similar in its historical significance to the artificial lung and the other motor-driven prosthetic devices that were in the planning stage just before the development of the Salk vaccine and the virtual elimination of poliomyelitis. Or the complex and costly installations for lung surgery that were being planned for the state sanatoriums just before the institutions themselves were closed by the development of effective chemotherapy for tuberculosis.

The biological revolution of the past three decades has placed at the disposal of biomedical science an array of research techniques possessing a power previously unimaginable. It should be possible, henceforth, to ask questions about the normal and pathologic functions of cells and tissues at a very profound level, questions that could not even have been thought up as short a time ago as ten years. We should be thinking more about this new turn of events while meditating on the meaning of the artificial heart.

CHAPTER SEVENTY-THREE

Things Unflattened

by Science

IN ONE OF HER NORTON LECTURES AT HARVARD IN 1980, HELEN Gardner had some sharply critical things to say about criticism, particularly about the reductionist tendencies of contemporary literary criticism, and especially about the new New Criticism out of France known as deconstructionism, the reductionist fission of poetry, not line by line but word by word, particle by particle. She was worried about the new dogma that the poem itself cannot possess any meaning whatever, beyond the random insights brought to the words by the reader, the observer. The only reality to be perceived in a line of verse is a stochastic reality arranged by the observer, not by the creator of the line. Miss Gardner is dismayed by this affront to literature. "It marks," she writes, "a real loss of belief in the value of literature and of literary study, . . . dignified and partly justified by being linked with a universal skepticism about the possibility of any real knowledge of the universe we live in or any true understanding of the world of our daily experience." The "indeterminacy of literary texts," she says, "is part of the indeterminacy of the world."

Joan Peyser, in an introduction to the new edition of her ten-year-old book on modern music, expresses a similar level of dismay at what is happening to contemporary music. She writes, "The lessening of greatness in the music of modern times can be traced to Darwin, Marx, Einstein and Freud"; she adds, "the dissemination of their theories propelled everything hidden into the light; analysis annihilates mystery."

The geneticist C. H. Waddington asserted in his book on modern art that some of the earliest manifestations of abstract expression in modern painting, notably the work of Kandinsky and his followers, came from a feeling of hostility toward early-twentieth-century physics. Kandinsky believed that scientists were "capable only of recognizing those things that can be weighed and measured."

Annie Dillard, writing about the impact of modern physics on modern fiction, in a wonderful book on criticism entitled *Living by Fiction,* says, "nothing is more typical of modernist fiction than its shattering of narrative line. . . . The use of narrative collage is particularly adapted to twentieth-century treatments of time and space . . . a flattened landscape. . . . Events do not trigger other events at all; instead, any event is possible. . . . The world is an undirected energy; it is an infinite series of random possibilities." "This," she continues, "is the fiction of quantum mechanics," and she doesn't care much for it. She believes that there is meaning in the world, but concludes that the lyric poets are the best equipped of all of us to find it.

I wish the humanists, wherever they are—the artists, writers, poets, critics, and musicians (most of all the musicians)—would leave physics alone for a while and begin paying more attention to biology. Personally, having read my way through a long shelf of books written by physicists for nonmathematicians like me, I have given up looking for the meaning, any meaning at all, in the worlds of very small or very large events. I've become convinced that any effort to insert mysticism into quantum mechanics, or to get mysticism out of it, or indeed to try to force new meanings into the affairs of the everyday, middle-sized world, is not for me. There are some things about which it is not true to say that every man has a right to his own opinion. I do not have the right to an opinion about acausality in the small world, or about black holes or other universes beyond black holes in the large world, for I cannot do the mathematics. Physics, deep and beautiful physics, can be spoken only in pure, unaccented mathematics, and no other language exists for expressing its meaning, not yet anyway. Lacking the language, I concede that it is none of my business, and I am giving up on it.

Biology is something else again, another matter, quite another matter indeed, in fact very likely another form, or at least another aspect of matter, probably not glimpsed, or anyway not yet glimpsable, by the mathematics of quantum physics.

One big difference is that biology, being a more difficult science, has lagged behind, so far behind that we have not yet reached the stage of genuine theory—in the predictive sense in which theoretical physics drives that field along. Biologists are still principally engaged in making observations and collecting facts, trying wherever possible to relate one set of facts to another but still lacking much of a basis for grand unifying theories. Evolution is about as close as we have come, and it is certainly a grand and sweeping concept, but more like a wonderful puzzle, filled with bits of information waiting for more bits before the whole matter can be fitted together. It remains, necessarily, an intensely reductionist field in science, requiring the scrutiny of endless details, and then the details of the details, before it will become possible to see a large, clear picture of the whole orderly process, and it will need decades of work, perhaps centuries, before we can stand back for a long look. It may even be that some of the information lies forever beyond our grasp because of the sheer age and volume of planetary life and the disappearance from the record of so many crucial forms, crucial for comprehending the course of events.

In fact, we can look back only a relatively short distance. Up until the 1950s, the fossil record, on which the most solid parts of the structure of evolutionary theory were based, provided a fairly close look at only the last five hundred million years or so. We now know, from the work of Barghoorn, Cloud, Schopf, and others, that there is a period of at least three billion years of life about which we know very little, and for most of that time the sole occupants of the earth were the prokaryotes— bacteria and, I have no doubt, their resident viruses. We tend to use words such as "early" and "primitive" for such creatures, as though we members of the eukaryote world, possessing nucleated cells and on the way to making brains for ourselves, comprise a qualitatively different and vastly superior form of life. We tend sometimes even to dismiss four-fifths of the earth's life span as a long, dull prologue to the *real* events in evolution, nothing but featureless, aimless bacteria around, waiting for the real show to begin.

It was probably not like that at all. Leave aside the excitement when the very first successful cell appeared, membranes, nucleic acid, ribo-somes, proteins, and all, somewhere in a quiet pool, maybe in the aftermath of a lightning storm, maybe from a combination of energy sources: the sun, ionizing radiation and volcanic heat. It can be told as a plausible story, easy to imagine, for all the necessary chemical building blocks were at hand (or came to hand) during the first billion years, and it should no longer come as a surprise that beautifully formed bacterial fossils exist in rocks 3.5 billion years old. I wish, by the way, that we had set up a better term—a *nicer* term—than "primordial soup" for the nutrients and clay surfaces in those early waters of the earth. "Soup" is somehow too dismissive a word for a state of affairs so immensely important, more like the role of the yolk in a fertilized egg (although that doesn't sound much better). Maybe it is an unexplored tradition in the language of science to flatten out the prose for really huge events: what may be turning out to be the most profound and subtle of all

mechanisms in evolutionary genetics is now known, flatly and familiarly, as "jumping genes."

The first cell to appear on the planet was in all probability just that: a
single first cell, capable of replicating itself, and a creature of great
theoretical interest. But the events that followed over the next 2.5 billion
or so years seem to me even more fascinating. It is entirely possible that
the stretch of time was needed for the progeny of the first cell to learn
virtually everything essential for getting on in a closed ecosystem.
Long before the first great jump could be taken—the transformation of
prokaryotes to eukaryotes around a billion years ago—a great many
skills had to be acquired.

During those years, the life of the earth was of course made up of vast
numbers of individual cells, each one replicating on its own, but it
would have seemed to an outside observer more like a tissue, the
differentiated parts of a huge organism, than a set of discrete beings. In
most places, and in the algal mats that covered much of the earth's
surface for a very long time, the microorganisms arranged themselves
in neatly aligned layers, feeding one another in highly specialized ways
and developing the mechanisms for cooperation and coordination that,
I believe, have characterized the biosphere ever since.

Chemical messengers of precision and subtlety evolved during this
stage, used no doubt for the allocation of space and the encouragement
(or discouragement) of replication by neighboring microorganisms.
Some of these chemical signals are still with us, but now they are
emitted from specialized cells in the tissues of higher organisms, functioning as hormones. Insulin, for example, or a protein very similar to
insulin with similar properties, is produced by strains of that famous
and ancient bacterium, *E. coli*. Other bacteria are known to make a
substance similar to human chorionic gonadotropin. Later, when pro-
tozoa and fungi evolved from their ancestral prokaryotes, they came
equipped with ACTH, insulin, and growth hormone, all similar to
their modern counterparts.

Moreover, the life of the planet began the long, slow process of
modulating and regulating the physical conditions of the planet. The
oxygen in today's atmosphere is almost entirely the result of photosynthetic living, which had its start with the appearance of blue-green
algae among the microorganisms. It was very likely this first step—or
evolutionary jump—that led to the subsequent differentiation into
eukaryotic, nucleated cells, and there is almost no doubt that these new
cells were pieced together by the symbiotic joining up of prokaryotes.
The chloroplasts in today's green plants, which capitalize on the sun's
energy to produce the oxygen in our atmosphere, are the lineal descendants of ancient blue-green algae. The mitochondria in all our cells,

which utilize the oxygen for securing energy from plant food, are the progeny of ancient oxidative bacteria. Collectively, we are still, in a fundamental sense, a tissue of microbial organisms living off the sun, decorated and ornamented these days by the elaborate architectural structures that the microbes have constructed for their living quarters, including seagrass, foxes, and of course ourselves.

We can imagine three worlds of biology, corresponding roughly to the three worlds of physics: the very small world now being explored by the molecular geneticists and virologists, not yet as strange a place as quantum mechanics but well on its way to strangeness; an everyday, middle-sized world where things are as they are; and a world of the very large, which is the whole affair, the lovely conjoined biosphere, the vast embryo, the closed ecosytem in which we live as working parts, the place for which Lovelock and Margulis invented the term "Gaia" because of its extraordinary capacity to regulate itself. This world seems to me an even stranger one than the world of very small things in biology: it looks like the biggest organism I've ever heard of, and at the same time the most delicate and fragile, exactly the delicate and fragile creature it appeared to be in those first photographs taken from the surface of the moon. It is at this level of things that I find meaning in Wallace Stevens, although I haven't any idea that Stevens intended this in his "Man with the Blue Guitar": "they said, 'You have a blue guitar,/you do not play things as they are.'/The man replied, 'Things as they are/are changed upon the blue guitar.'" It is a long poem, alive with ambiguities, but it can be read, I think, as a tale of the earth itself.

Some biologists dislike the Lovelock-Margulis view of things, although they agree that the regulatory homeostasis of earth's life exists as a real phenomenon. They dislike the term "Gaia," for one thing, because of its possible religious undertones, and they dislike the notion of design that seems implicit—although one way out of that dilemma is to call the arrangement a "System" and then assert that this is the only way that complex "Systems" can survive, by endless chains of regulatory messages and intricate feedback loops. It is not necessary, in accounting for the evolution and now the stability of the earth's atmosphere, to suggest that evolution itself can plan ahead; all you need assume is the existence of close linkages of interdependency involving all existing forms of life, after the fashion of an organism. Finally, it is not a view of things, as has been claimed, that is likely to relieve human beings of any feeling of responsibility for the environment, backing them off from any concern for the whole place, on grounds that it runs itself and has done so, implacably, since long before we arrived on the scene. To the contrary, I should think it would have just the opposite effect, imposing a new feeling of anxiety for the environment everywhere. If you become convinced that you exist as a part of something that is itself alive, you are more likely to take pains not to do damage to the other vital parts around you.

Anyway, it seems to me a notion in biology not to be dismissed lightly, and requiring a great deal more thought and a lot more science. Part of the science can be done best by the technologies developed for space exploration. One thing discovered since NASA began its work, on which I should think almost everyone would now agree, is that by far the most interesting, engrossing, and puzzling object in the solar system — maybe in the whole galaxy — is our own planet. It needs more research, huge-scale and at the same time delicate, highly reductionist work, but in the meantime it is there for the humanists to think about, something new and amiable, a free gift from science and high technology, a nice piece of bewilderment for the poets, an instruction in humility for all the rest of us.

In the everyday middle-sized world where I live, biology has only begun to work. Medicine, the newest and youngest of all the sciences, bobs along in the wake of biology, indeed not yet sure that it *is* all that much a science, but certain that if there is to be a scientific future for medicine it can come only from basic biomedical research. I'm not sure who invented that convenient hybrid word "biomedical." I think it was someone from my professional side, wanting to lay claims on respectable science by the prefix "bio"; but it could as well have been a pure biologist wanting the suffix "medical" as a way to lay hands on NIH grants. Whichever, it is a nice word and it contains the truth: medicine is a branch of biological science for the long-term future.

This means that I am entitled, as a physician, to ask my biologist friends to answer a range of questions that are not yet perceived as an immediate part of my own bailiwick, just as they can expect me and my colleagues to turn up some quick answers to problems like cancer, coronary disease, schizophrenia, heartburn, whatever. Indeed, the only question I am inclined to turn aside as being impossible to respond to happens to be the one most often raised these days, not just by my biologist friends but by everyone: the question about stress, how to avoid stress, prevent stress, allay stress. I refuse to have anything to do with this matter, having made up my mind, from everything I have read or heard about it in recent years, that what people mean by stress is simply the condition of being human, and I will not recommend any meddling with that, by medicine or any other profession.

But I digress. What I wish to get at is an imaginary situation in which I am allowed three or four questions to ask the world of biomedical science to settle for me by research, as soon as possible. Can I make a short list of top-priority puzzles, things I am more puzzled by than anything else? I can.

First, I want to know what goes on in the mind of a honeybee. Is it true, as is often asserted, that a bee is simply a small, neatly assembled robot, capable only of behaving in ways for which the bee is programmed by instructions in bee DNA, or is something else going on? In short, does a bee know what is going on in its mind when it navigates its way to distant food sources and back to the hive, using polarized sunlight and the tiny magnet it carries as a navigational aid? Or is the bee just a machine, unable to do its mathematics and dance its language in any other way? To use Donald Griffin's term, does a bee have "awareness"; or to use a phrase I like better, can a bee think and imagine?

There is an experiment for this, or at least an observation made long ago by Karl von Frisch and more recently confirmed by James Gould at Princeton. Biologists who wish to study such things as bee navigation, language, and behavior in general have to train their bees to fly from the hive to one or another special place. To do this, they begin by placing a source of sugar very close to the hive so that the bees (considered by their trainers to be very dumb beasts) can learn what the game is about. Then, at regular intervals, the dish or whatever is moved progressively farther and farther from the hive, in increments of about 25 percent at each move. Eventually, the target is being moved a hundred feet or more at a jump, very far from the hive. Sooner or later, while this process is going on, the biologist shifting the dish of sugar will find that his bees are out there waiting for him, precisely where the next position had been planned. This is an uncomfortable observation to make, harder still to explain in conventional terms: Why would bees be programmed for such behavior in their evolution? Flowers do not walk away in regular, predictable leaps. One possible explanation, put forward by Gould but with deep reservations and some doubt, is that bees are very smart animals who know what the biologist is up to and can imagine where he will turn up next with his sugar. Another possibility favored by Gould is that we simply do not understand the matter and need to learn more about bees. I like this answer, and it is my reason for putting the bee question at the top of my list.

My second question, addressed at large to the world of biology, concerns music. Surely, music (along with ordinary language) is as profound a problem for human biology as can be thought of, and I would like to see something done about it. A few years ago the German government set a large advisory committee to work on the question of what the next Max Planck Institute should be taking on as its scientific mission. The committee worked for a very long time and emerged with the recommendation that the new Max Planck Institute should be dedicated to the problem of music—what music is, why it is indispensable for human existence, what music really means—hard questions like that. The government, in its wisdom, turned down the idea, muttering something in administrative language about relevance, and there the matter rests. I shall take it as a sign of growing-up in the United States when we can assemble a similar committee for the same purpose and have the idea of the National Institute of Music approved and funded. I will not wait up for this to happen, but I can imagine it starting on a very small scale and with a very limited mission and a modest budget: a narrow question, like Why is *The Art of Fugue* so important and what does this single piece of music do to the human mind? Later on, there will be other questions, harder to deal with.

And while you are on your feet, Science, I have one last question, this time one closer to medicine. Some years ago, Dr. Harold Wolff, professor of neurology at Cornell, conducted the following experiment. He hypnotized some healthy volunteer subjects, and while they were under deep hypnosis he touched their forearms with an ordinary pencil, which he told them was an extremely hot object; then he brought them out of the hypnotic state. In most cases, what happened was the prompt development of an area of redness and swelling at the skin site touched by the pencil, and in some subjects this went on to form a typical blister. I want to know all about that phenomenon. I also want to know how it happens that patients with intractable warts of long standing can have their warts instructed to drop off while under hypnosis.

Come to think of it, I would rather have a clear understanding of this phenomenon than anything else I can think of at the moment. The bees and the music can wait. If it is true, as it seems to be, that the human central nervous system can figure out how to go about creating a blister at a particular skin site, all on its own, or how to instruct its blood vessels, lymphocytes, and heaven knows what other participants in the tissues to eliminate a wart, then it is clear that the human nervous system has already evolved a vast distance beyond biomedical science. If I had a good wart I'd be happy to be a participant in this experiment, and I'll be glad any day to try my brain on a blister, but my motive for doing so would be less than worthy. If it worked I would feel gratified by the skill, excessively vain, and ready to dine out forever on the news that my own mind is so much smarter than I am.

CHAPTER SEVENTY-FOUR

Basic Science and the Pentagon

BASIC SCIENCE CAN BE DEFINED IN A NUMBER OF WAYS, BUT IT IS generally agreed that a central feature of the endeavor, which distinguishes it from other kinds of scholarship, is the absence of any predictable, usable product. In biology it has been immensely productive despite this apparent restriction; the discovery of mechanisms in nature has sometimes led, indirectly and often inadvertently, to methods for intervening in the same mechanisms. The control of infectious disease is only one example of the process at work.

In the last few years basic science has fallen on hard times in biology and medicine, even more so in physics and chemistry. Cosmology, perhaps the most basic of the sciences, is in the deepest trouble of all: the opportunities to pursue the exploration of our solar system, brilliantly begun, are being set aside because of the money shortage.

For the time being we seem to be stuck in a period of history when fundamental inquiry into matters of pure interest is being put off to the future. Most of what is going on in research today is aimed at clearly visible targets. It is applied science, intended to produce marketable products, capitalizing on the stores of basic knowledge that have accumulated thus far in a richly productive century.

I do not intend to quarrel here with this drift of things. If the nation has decided, through its elected leadership, to press ahead for practical applications and new technologies rather than to invest in pure inquiry for its own sake, I shall not argue here against that decision. I do not agree with it, I believe it to be unwise, but there it is. We live in a democracy.

But if that is to be the decision, I think it should be made fairly, cleanly, and unequivocally. This means that we should be scrutinizing all aspects of the national research effort in order to make sure that basic science *as a whole* is damped down. There should not be any exceptions.

Now, I will add to my definition of basic research in order to make clear the sort of science to be looked out for. It is not only the absence of a visible target and the lack of any imaginable product. It is the kind of research that depends on pure hunch, with nothing more than guesswork for the construction of the hypothesis to be tested. It is research carried out in an atmosphere of high uncertainty. The questions to be asked are in the nature of "What if?" questions, not the "How to?" questions that drive applied science along its even paths. It can be regarded as a dreamy sort of work, done by intelligent but highly impractical people, residents of an ivory tower, shielded from any contact with the realities of everyday human existence. Finally, it costs money, taxpayers' money, sometimes in very large amounts.

I wish I could report that research of this kind was being uniformly restrained, in accord with the perceived national policy, with equity all around for all fields of science. It is not so.

There is one large exception, an anomaly so enormous that it makes the whole policy look ridiculous.

The country, without seeming to notice that it is doing so, persists in one single venture of absolutely pure basic research, more basic in terms of the definitions described above than any other piece of research ever tried in all history. Moreover, the amount of public money being expended runs into many billions of dollars, enough to sustain all other fields of basic science for generations ahead, including the wildest imaginings of the astronomers and astrophysicists. With that kind of money we could be building Scarsdales on Mars if we had a mind to. We could be gardening out in the galaxy. We could free ourselves, our animals, and all our vegetation from disease. We could solve our energy problems and learn how to clean up after ourselves on our own suburban planet. We could begin paying attention to all our children, everywhere on the globe, and their children still to come. We could even begin learning enough about each other to begin growing up as a species, liking each other, on the way to loving each other.

The huge exception, the field of basic science that has been overlooked in all the cutbacks of funds, the area of fundamental inquiry that nobody seems to have noticed, is research on thermonuclear weapons.

I claim that this has to be classified as basic science on every count. It conforms to every item in any definition.

There is, to begin with, no usable product. To be sure, there are all those missiles, tucked away in their silos or riding through the underseas, but who would call those things a product? Who intends to use them, ever, for any purpose? Not us, we say. Not the Russians, they say. Not the Europeans, surely.

Moreover, an immense scientific establishment exists worldwide, with no research intention other than to make more of them, bigger and better, with more accurate systems for aiming them and guiding them to create new suns at whatever small spot on earth they choose. Worse, the new research programs to be added on, now that these nonproducts are in hand, are designed to protect this or that small spot against the other side's missiles. And underlying all the scientific questions is a deep, scientifically imponderable, central question. It is the paradigmatic "What if?" question of basic research: What if those things go off? Other imponderable questions: How do you protect a society against destruction if you have an *almost-perfect* antiballistic missile defense, one that will pick off with unfailing accuracy 950 out of 1000 missiles coming our way but will miss the other 50? Or if you have a system with unbelievable certainty, likely to miss only 10 of the 1000? What happens, then, when each missile is a ten- or twenty-megaton bomb, capable of vaporizing away whatever medium-sized city it happens to touch?

The present administration has no special fondness for the social and behavioral sciences, and the National Science Foundation is sharply reducing its funding—never generous at best—for these stepchildren of scholarship. Very well, the country will survive, and the disciplines of psychology, sociology, economics, and their siblings will have to eat grass until their time comes again. But the basic research enterprise involved in thermonuclear warfare contains a staggering array of behavioral research questions, the purest kind of social science, questions never before asked about human behavior, deep ambiguities approachable only in an atmosphere of almost total uncertainty. Should the country be providing the funding for these basic problems (I assume that the military must have the problems somewhere on its mind) if, at the same time, other fields in social science are to be put off? It is an unfairness, even a betrayal of principle.

But perhaps *I* am being unfair. Maybe these matters are not scheduled for study and do not exist in any line of the Pentagon budget. But then what? Who will be bringing in the data telling us what to expect when, say, five million of us vanish in twenty minutes and another five million are left behind with bone marrows burned out and skins in shreds, looking at what is left of the dead and waiting to die? Or, to magnify the problem to what will more likely be its true dimension, what will the few million survivors say to each other, or do to each other, at the moment when the other hundred millions are being transmuted back to the old interstellar dust? This, it seems to me, requires study, mandates study. Will no one be casting an anthropological eye at the dilemma to be faced when human beings cease being human?

The fundamental problem is the weaponry itself. Never mind the social sciences, for now. They can wait. If everyone agrees, as everyone seems to, that the weapons will never be let fly, never be used, never even be allowed out of the hatchways of their silos, and if, at the same time, everyone agrees, as everyone seems to agree, that they are indispensable not only for our security but for the security of the U.S.S.R. as well, then we are in the presence of a really great paradox.

Then there is the aspect of uncertainty, one of the rock-solid hallmarks for identifying basic science at its most basic. The problems raised by the mere existence of MIRVs, even more the questions raised by their presence in upper-space trajectories, are basic enough to pop the eyes. If they are flying over the North Pole, as they probably will, how good are the guidance data? Will the things wobble, yaw, shift course from Manhattan to the Sargasso Sea, to Yap, to wherever? Can we count on anything?

The dreamy, heavy-lidded, ivory-tower scientists at work on the weapons are also at work on nuclear defense, with all sorts of possibilities on their minds: laser beams to zap the intruding missiles while they are still safely aloft, anti-hydrogen-bomb hydrogen bombs, cities shielded by God knows what stealth armor, whole populations transported to safety under the hill, countries shielded by hope, by flags, by tears, by any old idea, by reassuring strings of words. Well, I claim this is basic research, and it should be stopped.

Or, if it is to be continued, and funded, I want in. As a citizen and a sometime scientist, I claim rights to a grant, part of the $200 billion or whatever it is. As it happens, I happen to have an idea, as good an idea as any of the thermonuclear notions I've heard about so far, worth a few billions. The United States now has around 300,000 American troops stationed in Europe, put there some years ago as a significant token of our determination to defend Europe. We assert, correctly I am sure, that if any nuclear bomb of any size down to the neatest, cleanest, most tactfully tactical "theater" bomb should ever be launched against those troops this country will surely let fly some of ours in return. We acknowledge, most of us, anyway, that that will lead to exchanges of the larger then still larger weapons, across the Atlantic, megaton after megaton, until everything is made dead.

To avoid this outcome (which in a *New York Times Magazine* article two military authorities, proponents of thermonuclear research, referred to in passing as a "dismal prospect"), I suggest that we use these hostages differently, and persuade the Russians to put up 300,000 troops as tokens of their good faith to be used symmetrically. Bring all the Russian troops to this country and put them on trains, different trains, different lines. Send all 300,000 Americans to the Soviet Union and put them on *their* trains, at random. Let the trains go off on their normal schedules. Once begun, the program will provide absolute assurance to each side that the other side can never know precisely where its 300,000 soldiers are at any given time. Hence, neither country will send off any missiles, for fear of killing a large number of its own people. American and Russian train schedules are both matters of public knowledge, well enough understood so that both sides can feel secure in their unpredictability.

It is, I grant, a little like the first plan for putting MX missiles on underground railways, but a real improvement, less expensive and far simpler than running those costly missiles around in Utah or Nevada. It would be the ultimate defense strategy. Enough money would be saved to provide real, old-fashioned Pullman accommodations for all the soldiers, good filling meals, marvelous views, movies, sleepers, the works. The entire railroad systems of both countries would be restored to solvency, maybe even enriched sufficiently to improve the roadbeds. Everyone would benefit, and no one would get hurt. And no one would fire from abroad, not a single missile, for fear of hitting them.

A side benefit, a spin-off, so to speak, might be the effect on the train-riding troops themselves. Looking out of the windows at the countryside views of both countries—the foreign scenery, the farms and gardens—they would catch glimpses, especially as their decoy trains entered the stations of various towns and cities, of something neither they nor their commanders may have realized before: there are people out there.

CHAPTER SEVENTY-FIVE

Science and

"Science"

I REMAIN PUZZLED OVER HOW TO CLASSIFY THE SCIENCE AND TECH-
nology underlying nuclear warfare. Because of the high degree of
uncertainty involved in this sort of research, as well as the ambiguity
and unpredictability of its outcome, I asserted earlier that it should be
classed as entirely basic science, by definition, and should therefore be
subject to the same budgetary constraints as all the rest of basic research
in the nation.

Since then I have changed my mind. I recant, partly under the
influence of the Defense Department's latest announced R & D plans for
fighting a "protracted" nuclear war. I take it back. This kind of military
research is not at all like any science I have ever heard of, basic or
applied. It is a new, peculiar kind of endeavor for which some other term
must be invented. It resembles, more closely, an endless game. I suppose
you could argue that scientific research is also a sort of game, but there is
a difference: ordinary games finish at some point; there are winners and
losers. Neither of these seems possible under the rules of nuclear "science," and the game seems designed to go on forever. I have placed the
word in quotation marks, provisionally, until I can think of a suitable
euphemism.

There are many differences, but one that is decisive and compelling.
In science in general, one characteristic feature is the awareness of error
in the selection and pursuit of a problem. This is the most commonplace
of criteria: if a scientist is going to engage in research of any kind, he has
to have it on his mind, from the outset, that he may be on to a dud. You
can tell a world-class scientist from the run-of-the-mill investigator by

the speed with which he recognizes that he is heading into a blind alley. Blind alleys and garden paths leading nowhere are the principal hazards in research.

Everyone in science knows about this, although it is not much talked about. Most scientific hypotheses, including what seem the brightest and best, turn out to be wrong. I would guess that the luckiest and most productive of investigators is right in his original notion, the guess with which he starts his work, about once out of a hundred tries, at his peak. What counts is his instinct for spotting wrongness, his willingness to give up on a favorite conviction, his readiness to quit and shift to a better project. Insoluble problems abound. It takes almost as much good judgment to recognize these when they turn up as to perceive quickly the ones that can be settled, solved, nailed down once and for all by research.

There are two ways of clouding the vision of a working scientist in making this discrimination (assuming that he is of average intellectual stature). One is money. If the funds for a particular research project are coming in over his head in cascades, the scientist may be misled into thinking that he is on to a good thing, no matter what his data show. I can only suspect this to be a possibility, having never seen it happen. Second, the researcher may be led down his garden path by his equipment. If he is in possession of sophisticated instruments of great power, and if he is being assured that whatever other new instruments he can think of will be delivered to the door of his laboratory tomorrow, he may find it difficult to stop himself on a dead road of inquiry, even if he knows it to be dead. I have long believed that there is no scientist alive whose career could not be terminated by an enemy, if the enemy were capable of increasing the laboratory's budget by tenfold or any-fold overnight and, as well, assuring access immediately to any instrument within reach of the victim's imagination.

Maybe one or the other or both of these things are responsible for what is going on in defense "science" today. Certainly, the cascades of money are out there, with more promised to come, enough to convince any individual researcher that the project must be a good one even if he doesn't understand why. And meanwhile, like enormous, irresistible, gleaming and spinning toys, there are the missiles and their warheads, each one more destructive than one thousand Hiroshima bombs, loaded with magnificent navigational equipment more fun to play with than anything else on earth or in space. Any technological whim can be promised instant gratification on demand. Toys indeed.

Still, the damned things are not going to work and the "science" is leading nowhere. Everyone who ought to know knows this, and almost everyone agrees, even in public. It is endgame, a dud, a piece of nonscience flawed enough to qualify as nonsense. There is no way to design or redesign these weapons so that they can ever be used to win a war or even to fight a war, and no technological fix within the grasp of human imagination that can assure defense against them—if what is to be defended is human society.

And yet the "science" goes on, one side adding an embellishment to its threat to devastate the cities of the other side, the other side then dangling a matching ornament; one side donning a new horrifying mask, the other waving a scary banner; a war dance on one side, a counter-dance on the other.

Lord Solly Zuckerman, a longtime science adviser to the British government on science in general and military science and technology in particular, has written a book on this, the best book on the problem that I have read in recent years: *Nuclear Illusion and Reality.* Zuckerman believes that the "technicians" are the main source of our trouble today. It is interesting that he uses the term as reservedly as do many proper scientists, even when, as in the case of physicists, they are talking about themselves. They do not refer to the workers in the field as scientists or engineers; they are the "technicians."

Well, Lord Zuckerman says, the technicians have been far too long in charge of the world's destiny, if you accept that the world's destiny will, in part, anyway, be determined by how we all come out in nuclear warfare. He maintains, as do most science advisers in most nations, that "nuclear weapons and nuclear weapons systems are not weapons of war." He says, rather more bluntly than most scientists seem willing to say, that the scientific community itself must carry a heavy burden of responsibility for today's dilemma. "The scientists who work in the defense departments of governments, or in defense industries, are not apostles of peace. Political and military leaders should cease seeking shelter behind the backs of those 'experts' who take what is usually called the harder line. . . . If the bridge itself is not to become sub-merged, the politicians will have to take charge of the technical men." There it is again, a scientist writing of the work of other scientists, now obliged to refer to them as "technical men."

It does not often happen that scientists come out with public declarations that an avenue of scientific research should be blocked by public action. Most of the time, the entire scientific community maintains that deep research is unpredictable because it is aimed at uncovering brand-new information about nature. To stop science at any point, in any field, risks a restriction on human knowledge, and scientists as a group believe in their hearts that knowledge and understanding of the world are what the world most needs. There have, of course, been a few exceptions: many eminent physicists and mathematicians were deeply opposed, back in the late 1940s, to any research that might lead to the development of the hydrogen bomb; more recently, a smaller group of biologists advised delay in the pursuit of recombinant-DNA techniques until the safety of the method could be assured.

But it is possible to oppose the kind of research involved in nuclear warfare on grounds that have nothing to do with the traditional openness and curiosity of the scientific mind. This is not an instance of scientists blocking science itself. What is to be blocked, if it can indeed be blocked, is not real science. It has a single objective that cannot conceivably be attained: national security, which lies as far beyond its reach as transmutation for the early alchemists. Indeed, as Zuckerman points out in his book, "the continued growth of nuclear arsenals not only fails to increase, but actually decreases, national security."

Zuckerman puts it in the coldest language. The development of nuclear weapons, he says, derives its momentum not from any notions of military science or national policy on either side but "from the minds of enthusiastic technicians plying their trade in the weapons laboratories." He is not talking about people he would be willing to call scientists.

It is hard to see how the nations possessing nuclear weaponry can come to an agreement on arms reduction by simply throwing away part of the arsenals now on hand, although this must somehow be accomplished, sooner or later. But it is even more important, in the interest of long-term stability, that all research efforts to devise better weapons and better defense systems be ended. The world needs a multilateral treaty under which all parties will agree to stop the flow of money into their nuclear R & D laboratories, to stop all testing of weapons systems, and, above all, to stop the "technicians" from cooking up new ideas.

CHAPTER SEVENTY-SIX

On the Need for Asylums

FROM TIME TO TIME, MEDICAL SCIENCE HAS ACHIEVED AN INDISPUTA-
ble triumph that is pure benefit for all levels of society and deserving of
such terms as "breakthrough" and "medical miracle." It is not a long
list, but the items are solid bits of encouragement for the future. The
conquests of tuberculosis, smallpox, and syphilis of the central nervous
system should be at the top of anyone's list. Rheumatic fever, the most
common cause of heart disease forty years ago, has become a rare,
almost exotic disorder, thanks to the introduction of antibiotics for
treating streptococcal sore throat. Some forms of cancer—notably
childhood leukemias, Hodgkin's disease, and certain sarcomas affecting young people—have become curable in a high proportion of patients. Poliomyelitis is no longer with us.

But there is still a formidable agenda of diseases for which there are no
cures, needing much more research before their underlying mechanisms can be brought to light. Among these diseases are some for which
we have only halfway technologies to offer, measures that turn out to be
much more costly than we had guessed and only partly, sometimes
marginally, effective. The transplantation of major organs has become
successful, but only for a relatively small number of patients with
damaged kidneys and hearts, and at a financial cost much too high for
applying the technologies on a wide scale. Very large numbers of
patients with these fatal illnesses have no access to such treatments.
Renal dialysis makes it possible to live for many months, even a few
years, with failed kidneys, but it is a hard life.

The overestimation of the value of an advance in medicine can lead to more trouble than anyone can foresee, and a lot of careful thought and analysis ought to be invested before any technology is turned loose on the marketplace. It begins to look as if coronary bypass surgery, for example, is an indispensable operation for a limited number of people, but it was probably not necessary for the large number in whom the expensive procedure has already been employed.

There are other examples of this sort of premature, sweeping adoption of new measures in medicine. Probably none has resulted in more untoward social damage than the unpredicted, indirect but calamitous effects of the widespread introduction twenty or so years ago of Thorazine and its chemical relatives for the treatment of schizophrenia. For a while, when it was first used in state hospitals for the insane, the new line of drugs seemed miraculous indeed. Patients whose hallucinations and delusions impelled them to wild, uncontrollable behavior were discovered to be so calmed by the treatment as to make possible the closing down of many of the locked wards in asylums. Patients with milder forms of schizophrenia could return, at least temporarily, to life outside the institutions. It was the first real advance in the treatment of severe mental disease, and the whole world of psychiatry seemed to have been transformed. Psychopharmacology became, overnight, a bright new discipline in medicine.

Then came the side effect. Not a medical side effect (although there were some of these) but a political one, and a disaster. On the assumption that the new drugs made hospitalization unnecessary, two social policies were launched with the enthusiastic agreement of both the professional psychiatric community and the governmental agencies responsible for the care of the mentally ill. Brand-new institutions, ambitiously designated "community mental health centers," were deployed across the country. These centers were to be the source of the new technology for treating schizophrenia, along with all other sorts of mental illness: in theory, patients would come to the clinics and be given the needed drugs, and, when necessary, psychotherapy. And at the same time orders came down that most of the patients living in the state hospitals be discharged forthwith to their homes or, lacking homes, to other quarters in the community.

For a while it looked like the best of worlds, on paper, anyway. Brochures with handsome charts were issued by state and federal agencies displaying the plummeting curves of state hospital occupancy, with the lines coinciding marvelously with the introduction of the new drugs. No one noted that the occupancy of private mental hospitals rose at the same time—though it could not rise very high, with the annual cost of such hospitalization running around $40,000 per bed. The term "breakthrough" was used over and over again, but after a little while it came to be something more like a breakout. The mentally ill were out of the hospital, but in many cases they were simply out on the streets, less agitated but lost, still disabled but now uncared for. The community mental health centers were not designed to take on the task of custodial care. They could serve as shelters only during the hours of appointment, not at night.

All this is still going on, and it is not working. To be sure, the drugs do work—but only to the extent of allaying some of the most distressing manifestations of schizophrenia. They do not turn the disease off. The evidences of the mind's unhinging are still there, coming and going in cycles of remission and exacerbation just as they have always done since schizophrenia was first described. Some patients recover spontaneously and for good, as some have always done. The chronically and permanently disabled are better off because they are in lesser degrees of mental torment when they have their medication; but they are at the same time much worse off because they can no longer find refuge when they are in need of it. They are, instead, out on the streets, or down in the subways, or wandering in the parks, or confined in shabby rooms in the shabbiest hotels, alone. Or perhaps they are living at home, but not many of them living happily; nor are many of their families happy to have them at home. One of the high risks of severe mental disease is suicide, and many of these abandoned patients choose this way out, with no one to stop them. It is an appalling situation.

It is claimed that the old state hospitals were even more appalling. They were called warehouses for the insane, incapable of curing anything, more likely to make it worse by the process known in psychiatric circles as "institutionalization," a steady downhill course toward total dependency on the very bleakness of the institution itself. The places were badly managed, always understaffed, repellent to doctors, nurses, and all the other people needed for the care of those with sick minds. Better off without them, it was said. Cheaper too, although this wasn't said so openly.

What never seems to have been thought of, or at least never discussed publicly, was changing the state hospitals from bad to good institutions, given the opportunity for vastly improved care that came along with the drugs. It was partly the history of such places that got in the way. For centuries the madhouses, as they were called, served no purpose beyond keeping deranged people out of the public view. Despite efforts at reform in the late nineteenth and early twentieth centuries, they remained essentially lockups.

But now it is becoming plain that life in the state hospitals, bad as it was, was better than life in the subways or in the doorways of downtown streets, late on cold nights with nothing in the shopping bag to keep a body warm, and no protection at all against molestation by predators or the sudden urge for self-destruction. What now?

We should restore the state hospital system, improve it, expand it if necessary, and spend enough money to ensure that the patients who must live in these institutions will be able to come in off the streets and live in decency and warmth, under the care of adequately paid, competent professionals and compassionate surrogate friends.

If there is not enough money, there are ways to save. There was a time when many doctors were glad to volunteer their services on a part-time basis, indeed competed to do so, unpaid by state or federal funds and unreimbursed by insurance companies, in order to look after people unable to care for themselves. We should be looking around again for such doctors, not necessarily specialists in psychiatric medicine, but well-trained physicians possessing affection for people in trouble—a quality on which recruitment to the profession of medicine has always, we hope, been based. We cannot leave the situation of insane human beings where it is today.

A society can be judged by the way it treats its most disadvantaged, its least beloved, its mad. As things now stand, we must be judged a poor lot, and it is time to mend our ways.

CHAPTER SEVENTY-SEVEN

Altruism

ALTRUISM HAS ALWAYS BEEN ONE OF BIOLOGY'S DEEP MYSTERIES. WHY should any animal, off on its own, specified and labeled by all sorts of signals as its individual self, choose to give up its life in aid of someone else? Nature, long viewed as a wild, chaotic battlefield swarmed across by more than ten million different species, comprising unnumbered billions of competing selves locked in endless combat, offers only one sure measure of success: survival. Survival, in the cool economics of biology, means simply the persistence of one's own genes in the generations to follow.

At first glance, it seems an unnatural act, a violation of nature, to give away one's life, or even one's possessions, to another. And yet, in the face of improbability, examples of altruism abound. When a worker bee, patrolling the frontiers of the hive, senses the nearness of a human intruder, the bee's attack is pure, unqualified suicide; the sting is barbed, and in the act of pulling away the insect is fatally injured. Other varieties of social insects, most spectacularly the ants and higher termites, contain castes of soldiers for whom self-sacrifice is an everyday chore.

It is easy to dismiss the problem by saying that "altruism" is the wrong technical term for behavior of this kind. The word is a human word, pieced together to describe an unusual aspect of human behavior, and we should not be using it for the behavior of mindless automata. A honeybee has no connection to creatures like us, no brain for figuring out the future, no way of predicting the inevitable outcome of that sting.

But the meditation of the 50,000 or so connected minds of a whole hive is not so easy to dismiss. A multitude of bees can tell the time of day, calculate the geometry of the sun's position, argue about the best location for the next swarm. Bees do a lot of close observing of other bees; maybe they know what follows stinging and do it anyway.

Altruism is not restricted to the social insects, in any case. Birds risk their lives, sometimes lose them, in efforts to distract the attention of predators from the nest. Among baboons, zebras, moose, wildebeests, and wild dogs there are always stubbornly fated guardians, prepared to be done in first in order to buy time for the herd to escape.

It is genetically determined behavior, no doubt about it. Animals have genes for altruism, and those genes have been selected in the evolution of many creatures because of the advantage they confer for the continuing survival of the species. It is, looked at in this way, not the emotion-laden problem that we feel when we try to put ourselves in the animal's place; it is just another plain fact of life, perhaps not as hard a fact as some others, something rather nice, in fact, to think about.

J. B. S. Haldane, the eminent British geneticist, summarized the chilly arithmetic of the problem by announcing, "I would give up my life for two brothers or eight cousins." This calculates the requirement for ultimate self-interest: the preservation and survival of an individual's complement of genes. Trivers, Hamilton, and others have constructed mathematical models to account nicely for the altruistic behavior of social insects, quantifying the self-serving profit for the genes of the defending bee in the act of tearing its abdomen apart. The hive is filled with siblings, ready to carry the *persona* of the dying bee through all the hive's succeeding generations. Altruism is based on kinship; by preserving kin, one preserves one's self. In a sense.

Haldane's prediction has the sound of a beginning sequence: two brothers, eight (presumably) first cousins, and then another series of much larger numbers of more distant relatives. Where does the influence tail off? At what point does the sharing of the putative altruist's genes become so diluted as to be meaningless? Would the line on a graph charting altruism plummet to zero soon after those eight cousins, or is it a long, gradual slope? When the combat marine throws himself belly-down on the live grenade in order to preserve the rest of his platoon, is this the same sort of altruism, or is this an act without any technically biological meaning? Surely the marine's genes, most of them, will be blown away forever; the statistical likelihood of having two brothers or eight cousins in that platoon is extremely small. And yet there he is, belly-down as if by instinct, and the same kind of event has been recorded often enough in wartime to make it seem a natural human act, normal enough, even though rare, to warrant the stocking of medals by the armed services.

At what point do our genetic ties to each other become so remote that we feel no instinctual urge to help? I can imagine an argument about this, with two sides, but it would be a highly speculative discussion, not by any means pointless but still impossible to settle one way or the other. One side might assert, with total justification, that altruistic behavior among human beings has nothing at all to do with genetics, that there is no such thing as a gene for self-sacrifice, not even a gene for helpfulness, or concern, or even affection. These are attributes that must be learned from society, acquired by cultures, taught by example. The other side could maintain, with equal justification, since the facts are not known, precisely the opposite position: we get along together in human society because we are genetically designed to be social animals, and we are obliged, by instructions from our genes, to be useful to each other. This side would argue further that when we behave badly, killing or maiming or snatching, we are acting on misleading information learned from the wrong kinds of society we put together; if our cultures were not deformed, we would be better company, paying attention to what our genes are telling us.

For the purposes of the moment I shall take the side of the sociobiologists because I wish to carry their side of the argument a certain distance afield, beyond the human realm. I have no difficulty in imagining a close enough resemblance among the genomes of all human beings, of all races and geographic origins, to warrant a biological mandate for all of us to do whatever we can to keep the rest of us, the species, alive. I maintain, despite the moment's evidence against the claim, that we are born and grow up with a fondness for each other, and we have genes for that. We can be talked out of it, for the genetic message is like a distant music and some of us are hard-of-hearing. Societies are noisy affairs, drowning out the sound of ourselves and our connection. Hard-of-hearing, we go to war. Stone-deaf, we make thermonuclear missiles. Nonetheless, the music is there, waiting for more listeners.

But the matter does not end with our species. If we are to take seriously the notion that the sharing of similar genes imposes a responsibility on the sharers to sustain each other, and if I am right in guessing that even very distant cousins carry at least traces of this responsibility and will act on it whenever they can, then the whole world becomes something to be concerned about on solidly scientific, reductionist, genetic grounds. For we have cousins more than we can count, and they are all over the place, run by genes so similar to ours that the differences are minor technicalities. All of us, men, women, children, fish, sea grass, sandworms, dolphins, hamsters, and soil bacteria, everything alive on the planet, roll ourselves along through all our generations by replicating DNA and RNA, and although the alignments of nucleotides within these molecules are different in different species, the molecules themselves are fundamentally the same substance. We make our proteins in the same old way, and many of the enzymes most needed for cellular life are everywhere identical.

This is, in fact, the way it should be. If cousins are defined by common descent, the human family is only one small and very recent addition to a much larger family in a tree extending back at least 3.5 billion years. Our common ancestor was a single cell from which all subsequent cells derived, most likely a cell resembling one of today's bacteria in today's soil. For almost three-fourths of the earth's life, cells of that first kind were the whole biosphere. It was less than a billion years ago that cells like ours appeared in the first marine invertebrates, and these were somehow pieced together by the joining up and fusion of the earlier primitive cells, retaining the same blood lines. Some of the joiners, bacteria that had learned how to use oxygen, are with us still, part of our flesh, lodged inside the cells of all animals, all plants, moving us from place to place and doing our breathing for us. Now there's a set of cousins!

Even if I try to discount the other genetic similarities linking human beings to all other creatures by common descent, the existence of these beings in my cells is enough, in itself, to relate me to the chestnut tree in my backyard and to the squirrel in that tree.

There ought to be a mathematics for connections like this before claiming any kinship function, but the numbers are too big. At the same time, even if we wanted to, we cannot think the sense of obligation away. It is there, maybe in our genes for the recognition of cousins, or, if not, it ought to be there in our intellects for having learned about the matter. Altruism, in its biological sense, is required of us. We have an enormous family to look after, or perhaps that assumes too much, making us sound like official gardeners and zookeepers for the planet, responsibilities for which we are probably not yet grown-up enough. We may need new technical terms for concern, respect, affection, substitutes for altruism. But at least we should acknowledge the family ties and, with them, the obligations. If we do it wrong, scattering pollutants, clouding the atmosphere with too much carbon dioxide, extinguishing the thin carapace of ozone, burning up the forests, dropping the bombs, rampaging at large through nature as though we owned the place, there will be a lot of paying back to do and, at the end, nothing to pay back with.

CHAPTER SEVENTY-EIGHT

Falsity and Failure

TWO FRIENDS OF MINE, EMINENT SCIENTISTS WITH HIGH RESPON-
sibilities for science management and policy, were recently called before
a congressional committee to testify in defense of the morals of American research. Why is it, they were asked, that there have been so many
instances of outright fraud and plagiarism in recent years, so many
publications of experiments never actually performed, so much fudging
of data?

At about the same time, articles about falsification of research—
particularly in biomedical science—appeared in *The New York Times*
and in two respected and widely read technical periodicals, *Nature*
(published in London) and *Science* (in Washington). The general drift of
the thoughtful, worried essays was that the reported instances of deliberate mistruth on the part of scientists seem to be on the increase, and
the self-monitoring system, traditionally relied upon to spot and immediately expose all cases of faked data, appears to be malfunctioning.

The list of fraudulent research reports is not a long one, but several of
the studies were carried out within the walls of the country's most
distinguished scientific institutions, long regarded as models of scientific probity. *Science* stated flat out, in its April 10, 1981, issue: "There is
little doubt that a dark side of science has emerged during the past
decade. . . . Four major cases of cheating in biomedical research came
to light in 1980 alone with some observers in the lay press calling it a
'crime wave.'" It is the same list in all the reports: the case of a
pathologist knowingly employing a contaminated cell-culture line,
two junior researchers who plagiarized work already done by others, a
clinical investigator found to have inserted bogus data on cancer chemotherapy into the project's computer. None of these studies involved
crucial issues of science; the papers in question dealt with relatively
minor matters, unlikely to upheave any field but requiring, nonetheless,
a significant waste of time and money in other laboratories attempting

to confirm the unconfirmable. The real damage has been done to the public confidence in the scientific method, and there are apprehensions within the scientific community itself that someone, somewhere, perhaps in Washington, will begin framing new regulations to ensure exactitude and honesty in an endeavor that has always prided itself, and depended for its very progress, on these two characteristics.

Now that the issue has surfaced so publicly it is likely that story will lead to story, and there will be more speculations and skepticism about any piece of science that seems to carry surprising or unorthodox implications. Indeed, a number of old stories are being exhumed and revived, as though to reveal a pattern of habitual falsehood in the process of science: Ptolemy and his unearthly second-century A.D. data establishing the sun's movement around the earth, supposed examples of seventeenth-century fudging in Newton's calculations, even some small questions about the perfection of Gregor Mendel's classical (and absolutely solid) generalizations about plant genetics one hundred years ago. Lumped in with these are some outright examples of bent science: Cyril Burt's 1930s data on the inheritance of intelligence in identical twins, the falsified synthesis of a cellular protein by a postdoctoral student at the Rockefeller Institute twenty years ago, and the notorious episode of skin-graft fabrication at Sloan-Kettering in 1974. These can, if you like, be made to seem all of a piece, a constantly spreading blot on the record of science. Or, if you prefer (and I do prefer), they can be viewed as anomalies, the work of researchers with unhinged minds or, as in the cases of Newton and Mendel, gross exaggerations of the fallibility of even superb scientists.

It is an impossibility for a scientist to fake his results and get away with it, unless he is lucky enough to have the faked data conform, in every fine detail, to a guessed-at truth about nature (the probability of this kind of luck is exceedingly small), or unless the work he describes is too trivial to be of interest to other investigators. Either way, he cannot win. If he reports something of genuine significance, he knows for a certainty that other workers will repeat his experiments, or try to, and if he has cooked his data the word will soon be out, to the ruin of his career. If he has plagiarized someone else's paper, the computer retrieval systems available to scientific libraries everywhere will catch him at it, sooner or later, with the same result.

In short, the system does indeed work, and the fact that only four instances of scientific malfeasance have been identified in a year during which some 18,000 research projects were sponsored by the National Institutes of Health means just what the fact says: such events are extremely rare. This is not a claim that scientists are necessarily, by nature, an impeccably honest lot, although I am convinced that all the best ones are. It says, simply, that people are not inclined to try cheating in a game where cheating leads almost inevitably to losing.

You have only to glance through other pages of the same issue of *Nature* in which the editorial comment on fraud appears to catch a sense of how the system really works, and works at its very best. There are two extensive papers dealing with an important and fascinating question raised last year by a Canadian group of immunologists, who had found evidence suggesting, cautiously but not conclusively, that mice can inherit through the male line an acquired abnormality in their immune cells known technically as "tolerance." If true, the claim would support nothing less than Lamarckianism, long since jettisoned from biology; it would be an upheaval indeed to face again, as an open problem, the question of the inheritance of acquired characteristics. The two new papers explore the matter in elegantly designed and meticulously executed experiments, with the conclusion that the Canadian work could not be confirmed. There is, in this instance, no question at all of contrived data or even the misguided reading of results; it is a typical instance of disagreement in science, something that happens whenever major ideas are under exploration. It will, in this case, lead to more work in the three laboratories now caught up in the problem and no doubt in others not yet involved. It may also lead to new knowledge, a deeper comprehension of immunology, and conceivably to something surprising, even if the Canadians turn out at the end to have been totally wrong.

In the same journal there are three marvelous papers—one from the University of Cambridge, two from Cal Tech—that will cause even more of a stir in biomedical science, generating surprise, argument, and new bursts of research in laboratories around the world. The genetic composition of human mitochondria has been elucidated, and these structures, long believed to be the descendants of bacteria living as permanent lodgers inside all nucleated cells, are turning out to have an arrangement of their genes like nothing else on earth: they display an astonishing economy in their circles of DNA, and in some respects the genetic code is different from what has, up to now, been regarded as a universal code. It is something quite new, unorthodox, unexpected, and therefore certain to be challenged but also likely to be repeated, confirmed, and extended. Molecular genetics may then be moved on to new ground, new explanations for the origin of mitochondria will be thought up and tested, and science itself will be off and running in a new direction.

With work like this going on in the pages of a single issue of *Nature,* and with similar things to be read in *Science,* week after week these days, I cannot find time to worry so much about falsity and fraud. Only to reflect that my dictionary gives the Latin root for "falsity" as *fallere,* which is the same root for the word "failure."

CHAPTER SEVENTY-NINE

On Medicine and the Bomb

IN THE COMPLICATED BUT STEADILY ILLUMINATING AND LINKED fields of immunology, genetics, and cancer research, it has become a routine technical maneuver to transplant the bone-marrow cells of one mouse to a mouse of a different line. This can be accomplished by irradiating the recipient mouse with a lethal dose of X rays, enough to destroy all the immune cells and their progenitors, and replacing them with the donor's marrow cells. If the new cells are close enough in their genetic labels to the recipient's own body cells, the marrow will flourish and the mouse will live out a normal life span. Of course, if the donor cells are not closely matched, they will recognize the difference between themselves and the recipient's tissues, and the result, the so-called graft-versus-host reaction, will kill the recipient in the same way that a skin graft from a foreign mouse is destroyed by the lymphocytes of a recipient.

It is a neat biological trick, made possible by detailed knowledge of the genetics involved in graft rejection. Any new bone-marrow cells can survive and repopulate the recipient's defense apparatus provided the markers on the cell surfaces are the same as those of the donor, and precise techniques are now available for identifying these markers in advance.

Something like this can be done in human beings, and the technique of bone-marrow transplantation is now becoming available for patients whose marrows are deficient for one reason or another. It is especially useful in the treatment of leukemia, where the elimination of leukemic cells by X ray and chemotherapy sometimes causes the simultaneous destruction of the patient's own immune cells, which must then be replaced if the patient is to survive. It is a formidable procedure, requiring the availability of tissue-match donors (usually members of the patient's family), and involving extremely expensive and highly specialized physical facilities—rooms equipped for absolute sterility to prevent infection while the new cells are beginning to propagate. Not many hospitals are outfitted with units for this kind of work, perhaps twenty or twenty-five in the United States, and each of them can take on only a few patients at a time. The doctors and nurses who work in such units are among the most specialized of clinical professionals, and there are not many of them. All in all, it is an enormously costly venture, feasible in only a few places but justifiable by the real prospect of new knowledge from the associated research going on in each unit, and of course by the lifesaving nature of the procedure when it works.

This, then, is the scale on which contemporary medicine possesses a technology for the treatment of lethal X-irradiation.

The therapy of burns has improved considerably in recent years. Patients with extensively burned skin who would have died ten years ago are now, from time to time, being saved from death. The hospital facilities needed for this accomplishment are comparable, in their technical complexity and cost, to the units used for bone-marrow transplantation. Isolation rooms with special atmospheric controls to eliminate all microbes from the air are needed, plus teams of trained professionals to oversee all the countless details of management. It is still a discouraging undertaking, requiring doctors and nurses of high spirit and determination, but it works often enough to warrant the installation of such units in a limited number of medical centers. Some of these places can handle as many as thirty or forty patients at a time, but no more than that number.

The surgical treatment of overwhelming trauma underwent a technological transformation during the Korean and Vietnam wars, and it is now possible to do all sorts of things to save the lives of injured people— arteries and nerves can be successfully reconnected, severed limbs sewn back in place, blood substitutes infused, shock prevented, massive damage to internal organs repaired. Here also, special units with highly trained people are essential, elaborate facilities for rapid transport to the hospital are crucial, and the number of patients that can be handled by a unit is minimal.

These are genuine advances in medical science. The medical profession can be proud of them, and the public can be confident that work of this kind will steadily improve in the future. The prospects for surviving various kinds of injury that used to be uniformly fatal are better now than at any other time in history.

If there were enough money, these things could be scaled up to meet the country's normal everyday needs with tailor-made centers for the treatment of radiation injury, burns, and massive trauma spotted here and there in all major urban centers, linked to outlying areas by helicopter ambulances. It would cost large sums to build and maintain, but the scores, maybe hundreds, of lives saved would warrant the cost.

The Department of Defense ought to have a vested interest in enhancing this array of technologies, and I suppose it does. I take it for granted that substantial sums are being spent from the R & D funds of that agency to improve matters still further. In any conventional war, the capacity to rescue injured personnel from death on the battlefield does more than simply restore manpower to the lines: its effect on troop morale has traditionally been incalculable.

But I wonder if the hearts of the long-range planners in DOD can really be in it.

Military budgets have to be put together with the same analytic scrutiny of potential costs versus benefits that underlies the construction of civilian budgets, allowing for the necessarily different meanings assigned by the military to the terms "cost" and "benefit." It is at least agreed that money should not be spent on things that will turn out to be of no use at all. The people in the Pentagon offices and their counterparts in the Kremlin where the questions of coping with war injuries are dealt with must be having a hard time of it these days, looking ahead as they must look to the possibility of thermonuclear war. Any sensible analyst in such an office would be tempted to scratch off all the expense items related to surgical care of the irradiated, burned, and blasted, the men, women, and children with empty bone marrows and vaporized skin. What conceivable benefit can come from sinking money in hospitals subject to instant combustion, only capable of salvaging, at their intact best, a few hundred of the victims who will be lying out there in the hundreds of thousands? There exists no medical technology that can cope with the certain outcome of just one small, neat, so-called tactical bomb exploded over a battlefield. As for the problem raised by a single large bomb, say a twenty-megaton missile (equivalent to approximately two thousand Hiroshimas) dropped on New York City or Moscow, with the dead and dying in the millions, what would medical technology be good for? As the saying goes, forget it. Think of something else. Get a computer running somewhere in a cave, to estimate the likely numbers of the lucky dead.

The doctors of the world know about this, of course. They have known about it since the 1945 Hiroshima and Nagasaki "episodes," but it has dawned on them only in the last few years that the public at large may not understand. Some of the physicians in this country and abroad are forming new organizations for the declared purpose of making it plain to everyone that modern medicine has nothing whatever to offer, not even a token benefit, in the event of thermonuclear war. Unlike their response to other conceivable disasters, they do not talk of the need for more research or ask for more money to expand existing facilities. What they say is, in effect, count us out.

It is not a problem that has any real connection to politics. Doctors are not necessarily pacifists, and they come in all sorts of ideological stripes. What they have on their minds and should be trying to tell the world, in the hope that their collective professional opinion will gain public attention and perhaps catch the ears of political and military leaders everywhere, is simply this: if you go ahead with this business, the casualties you will instantly produce are beyond the reach of any health-care system. Since such systems here and abroad are based in urban centers, they will vanish in the first artificial suns, but even if they were miraculously to survive they could make no difference, not even a marginal difference.

I wish the psychiatrists and social scientists were further along in their fields than they seem to be. We need, in a hurry, some professionals who can tell us what has gone wrong in the minds of statesmen in this generation. How is it possible for so many people with the outward appearance of steadiness and authority, intelligent and convincing enough to have reached the highest positions in the governments of the world, to have lost so completely their sense of responsibility for the human beings to whom they are accountable? Their obsession with stockpiling nuclear armaments and their urgency in laying out detailed plans for using them have, at the core, aspects of what we would be calling craziness in other people, under other circumstances. Just before they let fly everything at their disposal, and this uniquely intelligent species begins to go down, it would be a small comfort to understand how it happened to happen. Our descendants, if there are any, will surely want to know.

CHAPTER EIGHTY

The Problem of

Dementia

I HAVE ALWAYS TENDED TO AGREE WITH THOSE WHO CRITICIZE THE government for legislating special funds for individual diseases (the "disease-of-the-month" syndrome, as it is termed) at cost to the country's broader and, on balance, more productive programs in basic, undifferentiated science. The evidence is convincing enough: we have been learning more ways into the center of human disease mechanisms by studying normal biological processes than by mounting frontal, targeted assaults on one disease after another. When, for example, we have found our way to the epicenter of the cancer problem, as sooner or later we shall, armed with enough deep information to switch a neoplastic cell back to the normal mode of life, it will be because the crucial information will have emerged in its own time from basic research on normal cells, most of it likely to be coming from applications of the recombinant-DNA technique to fundamental cell biology.

I would, however, make one exception to the nontargeting rule, and push for special consideration and high priority for one particular human disease, not a disease-of-the-month but a disease-of-the-century, the brain disease that afflicts increasing members of our population because of the increasing population of older people in the society—senility, or, as it is now termed, senile dementia. The major form of the disorder, Alzheimer's disease, affects more than 500,000 people over the age of fifty, most of them in their seventies and eighties. It is responsible for most of the beds in the country's nursing homes, at a cost exceeding $10 billion now and scheduled to rise to $40 billion or more within the next few years.

It is the worst of all diseases, not just for what it does to the patient, but for its devastating effects on families and friends. It begins with the loss of learned skills—arithmetic and typing, for instance—and progresses inexorably to a total shutting down of the mind. It is not in itself lethal, unmercifully; patients go on and on living, essentially brainless but otherwise healthy, into advanced age, unless lucky enough to be saved by pneumonia.

It is not, as we used to think, simply an aspect of aging or a natural part of the human condition, nor is it due to hardening of the arteries or anything else we know about. It remains an unsolved mystery.

One acceptable guess, but pure guess, is that it could be due to a virus of the strange class known as the "slow" viruses. One such agent was isolated some years back from the brain tissue of demented patients in a landlocked tribe in New Guinea, where most members of the group lost their minds by the age of forty to a disease known locally as "kuru." It was learned that ritual cannibalism had been a long tradition in this tribe, involving the eating of the brain of each deceased by others, including young children, and Gajdusek and his colleagues succeeded in transmitting the disease to chimpanzees by intracerebral inoculations of brain tissue. Later on, it was learned that a similar disease occurs sporadically but rarely elsewhere in the world, under the names of its discoverers, Creutzfeld and Jakob, and a similar virus has been recovered from the brain tissue of such patients.

The virus is itself the most peculiar of all forms of life. It is in the first place almost impossible to kill, resisting such traditional sterilizing procedures as boiling and exposure to alcohol, formaldehyde, and other disinfectants; indeed, the agent was recovered intact from several specimens of brain tissue that had been placed in formalin and stored in pathological museums for a decade or longer. When injected into susceptible laboratory animals (chimpanzees, guinea pigs, mice, hamsters) it produces no evidence of disease for periods of eighteen months or longer, after which the brain undergoes rapid destruction. Unlike other viruses it cannot be shown—or hasn't yet been shown—to consist of particles visible by electron microscopy, nor has anyone found nucleic acid to account for its ability to multiply many times over in the affected brain, even when the brain is known to contain a trillion infectious "units." If it is *not* made up of nucleic acid, and can nonetheless replicate itself, it will surely be the strangest of all creatures on this planet, but this is not yet known for sure; perhaps it possesses its own DNA or RNA, hidden away where it cannot be found, or it may be similar to a class of naked, very small viruses seen in plants. At present, it is a mystery.

Creutzfeld-Jakob disease is rare, accounting for only a small minority of cases of dementia in this country, but it could well be that it is not so unique as it seems. The idea that it may be related in its causative mechanism to the larger group of brain diseases labeled Alzheimer's is not outlandish. But it would still be a considerable gamble to launch a new laboratory on the hypothesis that Alzheimer's is caused by a similar slow virus, and very few such projects are planned or under way.

But quite apart from a general reluctance to take on such a long shot, there is another reason for reluctance. Even if it should turn out to be a valid notion, the work would require more time, and more money, than most biomedical scientists believe they have at their disposal these days. If you were planning to inject samples of suspected virus into an array of experimental animals, the thought of an interval of a year and a half or two years before you could reasonably expect even a preliminary, tentative answer would stay your hand, especially if you were a scientist just beginning a career. By the time you finished your first experiment you would be near the end of your first grant, most likely with nothing to show for it: no annual report, no publications, nothing to put before a faculty committee charged with considering your eligibility for promotion.

The climate is wrong for research problems like this one. Most NIH grants are awarded for periods of two to three years, most young investigators have their personal salaries paid from such grants, and there is a general, feverish sense that the research projects have to be absolutely sure things, bound to result in published papers and grant renewals by the end of the first year.

Even if an investigator decided to take a safer (and perhaps more productive) route into the problem by studying, say, the detailed characteristics of some of the already known slow viruses—"scrapie," a disease of sheep transmissible to mice, or a similar disease affecting mink brains—in hopes of learning something new about the structure or function of such viruses (if that is what they are) that might then be applied to the human disease, there is still the barrier of time and money. Each experiment requires many months of waiting, and the cost of maintaining mice or guinea pigs in good health over such long periods of time is formidable. Scientists, even those consumed by curiosity over intriguing and engrossing puzzles, tend to stay away from problems like these.

What is needed is a new kind of research support mechanism, designed specifically and selectively for the problem of senile dementia. Such a mechanism must provide money, of course, and a good deal of money, but it must also take care of the problem of time, which is peculiar to this particular biological puzzle, and it must do so in a way not available—or anyway not yet available—within the research support mechanisms of the NIH. Something of the order of ten years of guaranteed support for each laboratory is necessary, with assured increments annually indexed for inflation. At least six new laboratories should be organized and launched within the country's major research universities.

Ten years may seem an extraordinarily long period of commitment for a scientific program, and indeed it is. But it may not be long enough, and I would not argue against fifteen, or even twenty.

Now, who should foot that bill, and assume all that responsibility? Not the federal government, obviously. Governmental agencies cannot obligate themselves for such a stretch of time; they are good at thinking two years ahead, sometimes four, but no further. Who then?

I believe this is a task for the several large private foundations that have staked their mission in what is called the Health-Care Delivery System. Senile dementia is, or should be, high on their agenda of concerns, nagging away at their staffs because of the present high cost, the predictable escalation of cost in the coming decades (enough to swamp all other parts of any health-care system), and, above all, the plain fact that nothing at all can be done to alleviate this disease problem by reorganizing existing medical-care facilities or by building new ones. No training programs, no enlistment of new professionals or non-professionals, no rearrangements of payment mechanisms, nothing based on today's level of information about the disease can possibly be useful. The only hope lies in research, and the research will not be done — not on the scale appropriate to the problem — unless the foundations step in.

The trustees of some of the largest foundations have resolved to stay away from any involvement in basic biomedical science, in the belief that the federal government should shoulder that responsibility, and up to now they have held to that resolve, spending many millions each year on wholly commendable efforts to improve the delivery of health care. Now they have done that, and good for them. I would be glad to contribute to a banquet in their honor, to celebrate their achievements, and all my friends would come, provided that on the occasion the trustees would announce that henceforth, for the next fifteen years, one-half of their endowment income would be committed to research on dementia.

As a personal footnote, I must confess to another motive in pressing for more work on the slow virus of Creutzfeld-Jakob disease. Scientifically, it *ought* to be irresistible. The only reason it is being resisted is that too few people have had adequate long-term support to set out on such new and shifting ground. But think of the intellectual reward. To be able to catch hold of, and inspect from all sides, a living, self-replicating form of life that nobody has so far been able to see or detect by chemical methods, and one that may turn out to have its own private mechanisms for producing progeny, novel to the earth's life, should be the chance of a lifetime for any investigator. To have such a biological riddle, sitting there unsolved and neglected, is an embarrassment for biological science.

CHAPTER EIGHTY-ONE

The Lie Detector

EVERY ONCE IN A WHILE THE REASONS FOR DISCOURAGEMENT ABOUT the human prospect pile up so high that it becomes difficult to see the way ahead, and it is then a great blessing to have one conspicuous and irrefutable good thing to think about ourselves, something solid enough to step onto and look beyond the pile.

Language is often useful for this, and music. A particular painting, if you have the right receptors, can lift the spirits and hold them high enough to see a whole future for the race. The sound of laughter in the distance in the dark can be a marvelous encouragement. But these are chancy stimuli, ready to work only if you happen to be ready to receive them, which takes a bit of luck.

I have been reading magazine stories about the technology of lie detection lately, and it occurs to me that this may be the thing I've been looking for, an encouragement propped up by genuine, hard scientific data. It is promising enough that I've decided to take as given what the articles say, uncritically, and to look no further. For a while, anyway.

As I understand it, a human being cannot tell a lie, even a small one, without setting off a kind of smoke alarm somewhere deep in a dark lobule of the brain, resulting in the sudden discharge of nerve impulses, or the sudden outpouring of neurohormones of some sort, or both. The outcome, recorded by the lie-detector gadgetry, is a highly reproducible cascade of changes in the electrical conductivity of the skin, the heart rate, and the manner of breathing, similar to the responses to various kinds of stress.

Lying, then, is stressful, even when we do it for protection, or relief, or escape, or profit, or just for the pure pleasure of lying and getting away with it. It is a strain, distressing enough to cause the emission of signals to and from the central nervous system warning that something has gone wrong. It is, in a pure physiological sense, an unnatural act.

Now I regard this as a piece of extraordinarily good news, meaning, unless I have it all balled up, that we are a moral species by compulsion, at least in the limited sense that we are biologically designed to be truthful to each other. Lying doesn't hurt, mind you, and perhaps you could tell lies all day and night for years on end without being damaged, but maybe not—maybe the lie detector informs us that repeated, inveterate untruthfulness will gradually undermine the peripheral vascular system, the sweat glands, the adrenals, and who knows what else. Perhaps we should be looking into the possibility of lying as an etiologic agent for some of the common human ailments still beyond explaining, recurrent head colds, for instance, or that most human of all unaccountable disorders, a sudden pain in the lower mid-back.

It makes a sort of shrewd biological sense, and might therefore represent a biological trait built into our genes, a feature of humanity as characteristic for us as feathers for birds or scales for fish, enabling us to live, at our best, the kinds of lives we are designed to live. This is, I suppose, the "sociobiological" view to take, with the obvious alternative being that we are brought up this way as children in response to the rules of our culture. But if the latter is the case, you would expect to encounter, every once in a while, societies in which the rule does not hold, and I have never heard of a culture in which lying was done by everyone as a matter of course, all life through, nor can I imagine such a group functioning successfully. Biologically speaking, there is good reason for us to restrain ourselves from lying outright to each other whenever possible. We are indeed a social species, more interdependent than the celebrated social insects; we can no more live a solitary life than can a bee; we are obliged, as a species, to rely on each other. Trust is a fundamental requirement for our kind of existence, and without it all our linkages would begin to snap loose.

The restraint is a mild one, so gentle as to be almost imperceptible. But it is there; we know about it from what we call guilt, and now we have a neat machine to record it as well.

It seems a trivial thing to have this information, but perhaps it tells us to look again, and look deeper. If we had better instruments, designed for profounder probes, we might see needles flipping, lines on charts recording quantitative degrees of meanness of spirit, or a lack of love. I do not wish for such instruments, I hope they will never be constructed; they would somehow belittle the issues involved. It is enough, quite enough, to know that we cannot even tell a plain untruth, betray a trust, without scaring some part of our own brains. I'd rather guess at the rest.

There is, of course, one problem that will have to be straightened out sooner or later by medicine, duty-bound. It concerns placebos. The sugar pill is sometimes indispensable in therapy, powerfully reassuring, but it is essentially a little white lie. If you wired up the average good internist in the act of writing a prescription, would the needles go flying?

Let others go to work on the scientific side issues, of which there are probably many. Is there a skin secretion, a pheromone, secreted in the process? Can a trained tracking hound smell the altered skin of a liar? Is the total absence of this secretion the odor of sanctity? I can think of any number of satisfying experiments that someone ought to be doing, but I confess to a serious misgiving about the possible misuses of the sort of knowledge I have in mind. Supposing it were found that there is indeed a special pentapeptide released into the blood on the telling of a lie, or some queer glycolipid in the sweat of one's palms, or, worst of all, something chemically detectable in balloons of exhaled breath. The next thing to happen would surely be new industries in Texas and Japan for the manufacture of electronic sensing devices to be carried in one's pocket, or perhaps worn conspicuously on one's sleeve depending on the consumer's particular need. Governments would become involved, sooner or later, and the lawyers and ethicists would have one field day after another. Before long we would stop speaking to each other, television would be abolished as a habitual felon, politicians would be confined by house arrest, and civilization would come to a standstill.

Come to think of it, you might not have to do any of the research on human beings after all, which I find a relaxing thought. Animals, even plants, lie to each other all the time, and we could restrict the research to them, putting off the real truth about ourselves for the several centuries we need to catch our breath. What is it that enables certain flowers to resemble nubile insects, or opossums to play dead, or female fireflies to change the code of their flashes in order to attract, and then eat, males of a different species? What about those animals that make their livings by deception—the biological mimics, the pretenders, the fish dangling bits of their flesh as bait in front of their jaws, the malingering birds limping along to lie about the location of their nests, the peacock, who is surely not conceivably all that he claims to be? It is a rich field indeed, open to generations of graduate students in the years ahead, risk-free. All we need is to keep telling ourselves that this is not a human problem, to understand that we have evolved beyond mendacity except under extraordinary conditions, and to stay clear of the instruments.

It would be safe enough for the scientists themselves, of course, because good science depends on truth-telling, and we should be willing to wear detectors on the lapels of our white coats all day long. I have only one small reservation about this. Scientists do have a tendency to vanity—some of the best ones are vanity-prone—and there is probably a mechanism at work here with a fundamental connection to lying. Perhaps this is one kind of human experimentation that ought to be done early on, if it can pass review by the local ethics review board: catch hold of an eminent researcher at the moment when he is involved in a press conference, looking and sounding for all the world like the greatest thing since the invention of the nucleated cell, and hook him up to the machine, or stick a sensor on his necktie. Then we could learn how to control the work for background noise, and move on to the insects.

I don't want to go over this again. I didn't write any of the above.

CHAPTER EIGHTY-TWO

Some Scientific

Advice

IT WAS GOOD NEWS WHEN A SCIENCE ADVISER WAS APPOINTED AND installed in the White House, put there with the explicit understanding that his job is not to represent the scientific community as an advocate but to provide the President with the best-informed and most objective counsel available for the formulation of a national science policy. We have had Science Advisers in the White House before, but never a recognizable science policy. It is an ambitious undertaking, and the Adviser will need all the advice he can get. No single scientist, or any full-time staff assigned to his office, can possibly appraise and evaluate the progress and problems all along the immense frontier of today's science in this country, let alone in the rest of the world. He will need the services of expert committees and panels representing the various broad fields of science, industry, and education. He will need as well good advice from thoughtful, sagacious citizens who have no connection at all with science or scientists. Something like the structure of the President's Scientific Advisory Committee (PSAC), in useful existence until evicted in the late Nixon years, will be indispensable for the Science Adviser's work, and it is probable that sooner or later such a body will be created politically neutral, one hopes, made up of people who can agree not to act as special pleaders for the constituencies of science and technology, but to provide unbiased advice for the country's research effort in the years ahead.

Having served as a member of PSAC for four years in the late 1960s and early 1970s, I am aware of the difficulties involved in objectivity. The biologists will want more biomedical science, the physicists will want more physics and more big instruments, the social scientists will hope at least to ensure the survival of their disciplines in hard times, the industrialists will demand more applied research, and the citizens-at-large will want to make sure that the health, safety, and well-being of ordinary people are enhanced by science and not, as some apprehend, placed more in jeopardy. Somewhere offstage, the military and intelligence communities will be wanting things to go their way in research.

But it begins already to look like an entirely new set of puzzles for which the administration will be seeking advice. In the old days, the early 1970s, the main task for the Science Adviser and his advisers was to identify the most important national problems for which a better kind of scientific study might be useful, and then to press for expansion of that sort of research, whatever. There were opportunities all over the place, and the PSAC panels fired off one report after another, always recommending more research. Now things are different. Nobody in the upper reaches of government is likely to be looking around for new ways to spend money. It is much more probable that the Science Adviser will look over the country's scientific endeavor with an eye out for expenditures that can be reduced or eliminated.

The word is out that the United States cannot do all the science that needs doing. Instead of trying to explore all aspects of biology or physics or chemistry or behavioral science, we are told that a more limited agenda must be arranged. The problem will be to identify a finite number of surefire areas of science, and concentrate our efforts on these in hopes of achieving prompt and profitable payoffs. Energy is an obvious candidate, agriculture another, biological engineering another.

If this is the way things are to go, the Adviser and his committees are likely to have a dreary time of it. Trying to make guesses at the future in research is an easy enough job if you are talking about matters of some certainty — the likelihood of getting certain proteins more cheaply from bacteria by the recombinant-DNA technique, for example — but trying to guess which lines of fundamental science are *unlikely* to yield profitable knowledge is quite another matter. I cannot imagine a more depressing undertaking for a committee, no matter how bright and stimulating its members.

What branches of science should we now give up on, or turn over to the rising generations of increasingly adept investigators in Europe or the United Kingdom or Japan or the Soviet Union? Or, within those branches, which particular lines of investigation should we set aside on grounds that their prospects for a short-term payoff are too marginal for an investment? I can see ways of answering questions like these in applied research: obviously solar energy versus nuclear fusion versus conservation versus fossil fuels versus hydrogen are items that can be argued over in terms of the dollars and years needed for research, and reasonably intelligent appraisals can be arrived at.

But what can be said about the future yields from *basic* research, in any field of science? No Science Adviser, nor any committee, has ever succeeded in forecasting the future outcome of this kind of scientific endeavor. It is in the nature of basic research that the future is unknowable until it happens. No committee could have sat around a table in the early 1950s and predicted that the pursuit of work in solid-state physics would produce the microchip. All the world's molecular biologists of the 1960s, assembled in any conference hall, could not have imagined that the strings of genes of one species could soon be inserted into the DNA of a totally different species for manufacturing salable products. Nor can any group of our best cell biologists, hot on the trail of mechanisms responsible for cancer, predict with any confidence which particular line of research carries a higher probability of success than another line.

What are we talking about, anyway? Is this an argument over costs, and is the country so near to being broke that the President must be advised to reduce the national effort in science? I cannot imagine it. This is a special intellectual knack, a sort of national, natural gift, in which the United States excels. It is one of the things that Americans and their institutions—mainly their talented universities—are really good at. And, if I may say so at a time when every federal penny is to be watched and pinched, good basic science comes relatively cheap. As a percentage of the gross national product, the amount being spent now on basic science is so small that it would go undiscovered if incorporated into the budget of the Department of Defense. We can afford to spend more than we spend today.

My unsolicited and perhaps unwelcome advice to the Adviser would be to plunge, to splurge, to cut back nowhere, to encourage the doing of basic research wherever the questions seem engrossing and fascinating, and not to *think* of excluding any field, never mind the cost. It is the best investment, short-term or long-term, that the country can make.

CHAPTER EIGHTY-THREE

The Attic of the Brain

MY PARENTS' HOUSE HAD AN ATTIC, THE DARKEST AND STRANGEST part of the building, reachable only by placing a stepladder beneath the trapdoor and filled with unidentifiable articles too important to be thrown out with the trash but no longer suitable to have at hand. This mysterious space was the memory of the place. After many years all the things deposited in it became, one by one, lost to consciousness. But they were still there, we knew, safely and comfortably stored in the tissues of the house.

These days most of us live in smaller, more modern houses or in apartments, and attics have vanished. Even the deep closets in which we used to pile things up for temporary forgetting are rarely designed into new homes.

Everything now is out in the open, openly acknowledged and displayed, and whenever we grow tired of a memory, an old chair, a trunkful of old letters, they are carted off to the dump for burning.

This has seemed a healthier way to live, except maybe for the smoke—everything out to be looked at, nothing strange hidden under the roof, nothing forgotten because of no place left in impenetrable darkness to forget. Openness is the new life-style, no undisclosed belongings, no private secrets. Candor is the rule in architecture. The house is a machine for living, and what kind of a machine would hide away its worn-out, obsolescent parts?

But it is in our nature as human beings to clutter, and we hanker for places set aside, reserved for storage. We tend to accumulate and outgrow possessions at the same time, and it is an endlessly discomforting mental task to keep sorting out the ones to get rid of. We might, we think, remember them later and find a use for them, and if they are gone for good, off to the dump, this is a source of nervousness. I think it may be one of the reasons we drum our fingers so much these days.

We might take a lesson here from what has been learned about our brains in this century. We thought we discovered, first off, the attic, although its existence has been mentioned from time to time by all the people we used to call great writers. What we really found was the trapdoor and a stepladder, and off we clambered, shining flashlights into the corners, vacuuming the dust out of bureau drawers, puzzling over the names of objects, tossing them down to the floor below, and finally paying around fifty dollars an hour to have them carted off for burning.

After several generations of this new way of doing things we took up openness and candor with the febrile intensity of a new religion, everything laid out in full view, and as in the design of our new houses it seemed a healthier way to live, except maybe again for smoke.

And now, I think, we have a new kind of worry. There is no place for functionless, untidy, inexplicable notions, no dark comfortable parts of the mind to hide away the things we'd like to keep but at the same time forget. The attic is still there, but with the trapdoor always open and the stepladder in place we are always in and out of it, flashing lights around, naming everything, unmystified.

I have an earnest proposal for psychiatry, a novel set of therapeutic rules, although I know it means waiting in line.

Bring back the old attic. Give new instructions to the patients who are made nervous by our times, including me, to make a conscious effort to hide a reasonable proportion of thought. It would have to be a gradual process, considering how far we have come in the other direction talking, talking all the way. Perhaps only one or two thoughts should be repressed each day, at the outset. The easiest, gentlest way might be to start with dreams, first by forbidding the patient to mention any dream, much less to recount its details, then encouraging the outright forgetting that there was a dream at all, remembering nothing beyond the vague sense that during sleep there had been the familiar sound of something shifting and sliding, up under the roof.

We might, in this way, regain the kind of spontaneity and zest for ideas, things popping into the mind, uncontrollable and ungovernable thoughts, the feel that this notion is somehow connected unaccountably with that one. We could come again into possession of real memory, the kind of memory that can come only from jumbled forgotten furniture, old photographs, fragments of music.

It has been one of the great errors of our time to think that by thinking about thinking, and then talking about it, we could possibly straighten out and tidy up our minds. There is no delusion more damaging than to get the idea in your head that you understand the functioning of your own brain. Once you acquire such a notion, you run the danger of moving in to take charge, guiding your thoughts, shepherding your mind from place to place, *controlling* it, making lists of regulations. The human mind is not meant to be governed, certainly not by any book of rules yet written; it is supposed to run itself, and we are obliged to follow it along, trying to keep up with it as best we can. It is all very well to be aware of your awareness, even proud of it, but never try to operate it. You are not up to the job.

I leave it to the analysts to work out the techniques for doing what now needs doing. They are presumably the professionals most familiar with the route, and all they have to do is turn back and go the other way, session by session, step by step. It takes a certain amount of hard swallowing and a lot of revised jargon, and I have great sympathy for their plight, but it is time to reverse course.

If after all, as seems to be true, we are endowed with unconscious minds in our brains, these should be regarded as normal structures, installed wherever they are for a purpose. I am not sure what they are built to contain, but as a biologist, impressed by the usefulness of everything alive, I would take it for granted that they are useful, probably indispensable organs of thought. It cannot be a bad thing to own one, but I would no more think of meddling with it than trying to exorcise my liver, an equally mysterious apparatus. Until we know a lot more, it would be wise, as we have learned from other fields in medicine, to let them be, above all not to interfere. Maybe, even—and this is the notion I wish to suggest to my psychiatric friends—to stock them up, put more things into them, make *use* of them. Forget whatever you feel like forgetting. From time to time, practice *not* being open, discover new things *not* to talk about, learn reserve, hold the tongue. But above all, develop the human talent for forgetting words, phrases, whole unwelcome sentences, all experiences involving wincing. If we should ever lose the loss of memory, we might lose as well that most attractive of signals ever flashed from the human face, the blush. If we should give away the capacity for embarrassment, the touch of fingertips might be the next to go, and then the suddenness of laughter, the unaccountable sure sense of something gone wrong, and, finally, the marvelous conviction that being human is the best thing to be.

Attempting to operate one's own mind, powered by such a magical instrument as the human brain, strikes me as rather like using the world's biggest computer to add columns of figures, or towing a Rolls-Royce with a nylon rope.

I have tried to think of a name for the new professional activity, but each time I think of a good one I forget it before I can get it written down. Psychorepression is the only one I've hung on to, but I can't guess at the fee schedule.

CHAPTER EIGHTY-FOUR

Humanities and

Science

LORD KELVIN WAS ONE OF THE GREAT BRITISH PHYSICISTS OF THE LATE nineteenth century, an extraordinarily influential figure in his time, and in some ways a paradigm of conventional, established scientific leadership. He did a lot of good and useful things, but once or twice he, like Homer, nodded. The instances are worth recalling today, for we have nodders among our scientific eminences still, from time to time, needing to have their elbows shaken.

On one occasion, Kelvin made a speech on the overarching importance of numbers. He maintained that no observation of nature was worth paying serious attention to unless it could be stated in precisely quantitative terms. The numbers were the final and only test, not only of truth but about meaning as well. He said, "When you can measure what you are speaking about, and express it in numbers, you know something about it. But when you cannot—your knowledge is of a meagre and unsatisfactory kind."

But, as at least one subsequent event showed, Kelvin may have had things exactly the wrong way round. The task of converting observations into numbers is the hardest of all, the last task rather than the first thing to be done, and it can be done only when you have learned, beforehand, a great deal about the observations themselves. You can, to be sure, achieve a very deep understanding of nature by quantitative measurement, but you must know what you are talking about before you can begin applying the numbers for making predictions. In Kelvin's case, the problem at hand was the age of the earth and solar system. Using what was then known about the sources of energy and the loss of energy from the physics of that day, he calculated that neither the earth nor the sun were older than several hundred million years. This caused a considerable stir in biological and geological circles, especially among the evolutionists. Darwin himself was distressed by the numbers; the time was much too short for the theory of evolution. Kelvin's figures were described by Darwin as one of his "sorest troubles."

T. H. Huxley had long been aware of the risks involved in premature extrapolations from mathematical treatment of biological problems. He said, in an 1869 speech to the Geological Society concerning numbers, "This seems to be one of the many cases in which the admitted accuracy of mathematical processes is allowed to throw a wholly inadmissible appearance of authority over the results obtained by them. . . . As the grandest mill in the world will not extract wheat flour from peascods, so pages of formulas will not get a definite result out of loose data."

The trouble was that the world of physics had not moved fast enough to allow for Kelvin's assumptions. Nuclear fusion and fission had not yet been dreamed of, and the true age of the earth could not even be guessed from the data in hand. It was not yet the time for mathematics in this subject.

There have been other examples, since those days, of the folly of using numbers and calculations uncritically. Kelvin's own strong conviction that science could not be genuine science without measuring things was catching. People in other fields of endeavor, hankering to turn their disciplines into exact sciences, beset by what has since been called "physics envy," set about converting whatever they knew into numbers and thence into equations with predictive pretensions. We have it with us still, in economics, sociology, psychology, history, even, I fear, in English-literature criticism and linguistics, and it frequently works, when it works at all, with indifferent success. The risks of untoward social consequences in work of this kind are considerable. It is as important—and as hard—to learn *when* to use mathematics as *how* to use it, and this matter should remain high on the agenda of considera-tion for education in the social and behavioral sciences.

Of course, Kelvin's difficulty with the age of the earth was an exceptional, almost isolated instance of failure in quantitative measure-ment in nineteenth-century physics. The instruments devised for ap-proaching nature by way of physics became increasingly precise and powerful, carrying the field through electromagnetic theory, triumph after triumph, and setting the stage for the great revolution of twentieth-century physics. There is no doubt about it: measurement works when the instruments work, and when you have a fairly clear idea of what it is that is being measured, and when you know what to do with the numbers when they tumble out. The system for gaining information and comprehension about nature works so well, indeed, that it carries another hazard: the risk of convincing yourself that you know everything.

Kelvin himself fell into this trap toward the end of the century. (I don't mean to keep picking on Kelvin, who was a very great scientist; it is just that he happened to say a couple of things I find useful for this discussion.) He stated, in a summary of the achievements of nineteenth-century physics, that it was an almost completed science; virtually everything that needed knowing about the material universe had been learned; there were still a few anomalies and inconsistencies in electromagnetic theory, a few loose ends to be tidied up, but this would be done within the next several years. Physics, in these terms, was not a field any longer likely to attract, as it previously had, the brightest and most imaginative young brains. The most interesting part of the work had already been done. Then, within the next decade, came radiation, Planck, the quantum, Einstein, Rutherford, Bohr, and all the rest—quantum mechanics—and the whole field turned over and became a brand-new sort of human endeavor, still now, in the view of many physicists, almost a full century later, a field only at its beginnings.

But even today, despite the amazements that are turning up in physics each year, despite the jumps taken from the smallest parts of nature—particle physics—to the largest of all—the cosmos itself—the impression of science that the public gains is rather like the impression left in the nineteenth-century public mind by Kelvin. Science, in this view, is first of all a matter of simply getting all the numbers together. The numbers are sitting out there in nature, waiting to be found, sorted and totted up. If only they had enough robots and enough computers, the scientists could go off to the beach and wait for their papers to be written for them. Second of all, what we know about nature today is pretty much the whole story: we are very nearly home and dry. From here on, it is largely a problem of tying up loose ends, tidying nature up, getting the files in order. The only real surprises for the future—and it is about those that the public is becoming more concerned and apprehensive—are the technological applications that the scientists may be cooking up from today's knowledge.

I suggest that the scientific community is to blame. If there are disagreements between the world of the humanities and the scientific enterprise as to the place and importance of science in a liberal-arts education, and the role of science in twentieth-century culture, I believe that the scientists are themselves responsible for a general misunderstanding of what they are really up to.

Over the past half century, we have been teaching the sciences as though they were the same academic collection of cut-and-dried subjects as always, and—here is what has really gone wrong—as though they would always be the same. The teaching of today's biology, for example, is pretty much the same kind of exercise as the teaching of Latin was when I was in high school long ago. First of all, the fundamentals, the underlying laws, the essential grammar, and then the reading of texts. Once mastered, that is that: Latin is Latin and forever after will be Latin. And biology is precisely biology, a vast array of hard facts to be learned as fundamentals, followed by a reading of the texts.

Moreover, we have been teaching science as though its facts were somehow superior to the facts in all other scholarly disciplines, more fundamental, more solid, less subject to subjectivism, immutable. English literature is not just one way of thinking, it is all sorts of ways. Poetry is a moving target. The facts that underlie art, architecture, and music are not really hard facts, and you can change them any way you like by arguing about them, but science is treated as an altogether different kind of learning: an unambiguous, unalterable, and endlessly useful display of data needing only to be packaged and installed somewhere in one's temporal lobe in order to achieve a full understanding of the natural world.

And it is, of course, not like this at all. In real life, every field of science that I can think of is incomplete, and most of them—whatever the record of accomplishment over the past two hundred years—are still in the earliest stage of their starting point. In the fields I know best, among the life sciences, it is required that the most expert and sophisticated minds be capable of changing those minds, often with a great lurch, every few years. In some branches of biology the mind-changing is occurring with accelerating velocities. The next week's issue of any scientific journal can turn a whole field upside down, shaking out any number of immutable ideas and installing new bodies of dogma, and this is happening all the time. It is an almost everyday event in physics, in chemistry, in materials research, in neurobiology, in genetics, in immunology. The hard facts tend to soften overnight, melt away, and vanish under the pressure of new hard facts, and the interpretations of what appear to be the most solid aspects of nature are subject to change, now more than at any other time in history. The conclusions reached in science are always, when looked at closely, far more provisional and tentative than are most of the assumptions arrived at by our colleagues in the humanities.

The running battle now in progress between the sociobiologists and the antisociobiologists is a marvel for students to behold, close up. To observe, in open-mouthed astonishment, the polarized extremes, one group of highly intelligent, beautifully trained, knowledgeable, and imaginative scientists maintaining that all sorts of behavior, animal and human, are governed exclusively by genes, and another group of equally talented scientists saying precisely the opposite and asserting that all behavior is set and determined by the environment, or by culture, and both sides brawling in the pages of periodicals such as *The New York Review of Books,* is an educational experience that no college student should be allowed to miss. The essential lesson to be learned has nothing to do with the relative validity of the facts underlying the argument, it is the argument itself that is the education: we do not yet know enough to settle such questions.

It is true that at any given moment there is the appearance of satisfaction, even self-satisfaction, within every scientific discipline. On any Tuesday morning, if asked, a good working scientist will gladly tell you that the affairs of the field are nicely in order, that things are finally looking clear and making sense, and all is well. But come back again, on another Tuesday, and he may let you know that the roof has just fallen in on his life's work, that all the old ideas—last week's ideas in some cases—are no longer good ideas, that something strange has happened.

It is the very strangeness of nature that makes science engrossing. That ought to be at the center of science teaching. There are more than seven-times-seven types of ambiguity in science, awaiting analysis. The poetry of Wallace Stevens is crystal-clear alongside the genetic code.

I prefer to turn things around in order to make precisely the opposite case. Science, especially twentieth-century science, has provided us with a glimpse of something we never really knew before, the revelation of human ignorance. We have been used to the belief, down one century after another, that we more or less comprehend everything bar one or two mysteries like the mental processes of our gods. Every age, not just the eighteenth century, regarded itself as the Age of Reason, and we have never lacked for explanations of the world and its ways. Now, we are being brought up short, and this has been the work of science. We have a wilderness of mystery to make our way through in the centuries ahead, and we will need science for this but not science alone. Science will, in its own time, produce the data and some of the meaning in the data, but never the full meaning. For getting a full grasp, for perceiving real significance when significance is at hand, we shall need minds at work from all sorts of brains outside the fields of science, most of all the brains of poets, of course, but also those of artists, musicians, philosophers, historians, writers in general.

It is primarily because of this need that I would press for changes in the way science is taught. There is a need to teach the young people who will be doing the science themselves, but this will always be a small minority among us. There is a deeper need to teach science to those who will be needed for thinking about it, and this means pretty nearly everyone else, in hopes that a few of these people—a much smaller minority than the scientific community and probably a lot harder to find—will, in the thinking, be able to imagine new levels of meaning that are likely to be lost on the rest of us.

In addition, it is time to develop a new group of professional thinkers, perhaps a somewhat larger group than the working scientists, who can create a discipline of scientific criticism. We have had good luck so far in the emergence of a few people ranking as philosophers of science and historians and journalists of science, and I hope more of these will be coming along, but we have not yet seen a Ruskin or a Leavis or an Edmund Wilson. Science needs critics of this sort, but the public at large needs them more urgently.

I suggest that the introductory courses in science, at all levels from grade school through college, be radically revised. Leave the fundamentals, the so-called basics, aside for a while, and concentrate the attention of all students on the things that are *not* known. You cannot possibly teach quantum mechanics without mathematics, to be sure, but you can describe the strangeness of the world opened up by quantum theory. Let it be known, early on, that there are deep mysteries, and profound paradoxes, revealed in their distant outlines, by the quantum. Let it be known that these can be approached more closely, and puzzled over, once the language of mathematics has been sufficiently mastered.

Teach at the outset, before any of the fundamentals, the still imponderable puzzles of cosmology. Let it be known, as clearly as possible, by the youngest minds, that there are some things going on in the universe that lie beyond comprehension, and make it plain how little is known.

Do not teach that biology is a useful and perhaps profitable science; that can come later. Teach instead that there are structures squirming inside all our cells, providing all the energy for living, that are essentially foreign creatures, brought in for symbiotic living a billion or so years ago, the lineal descendants of bacteria. Teach that we do not have the ghost of an idea how they got there, where they came from, or how they evolved to their present structure and function. The details of oxidative phosphorylation and photosynthesis can come later.

Teach ecology early on. Let it be understood that the earth's life is a system of interliving, interdependent creatures, and that we do not understand at all how it works. The earth's environment, from the range of atmospheric gases to the chemical constituents of the sea, has been held in an almost unbelievably improbable state of regulated balance since life began, and the regulation of stability and balance is accomplished solely by the life itself, like the internal environment of an immense organism, and we do not know how *that* one works, even less what it means. Teach that.

Go easy, I suggest, on the promises sometimes freely offered by science. Technology relies and depends on science these days, more than ever before, but technology is nothing like the first justification for doing research, nor is it necessarily an essential product to be expected from science. Public decisions about what to have in the way of technology are totally different problems from decisions about science, and the two enterprises should not be tangled together. The central task of science is to arrive, stage by stage, at a clearer comprehension of nature, but this does not mean, as it is sometimes claimed to mean, a search for mastery over nature. Science may provide us, one day, with a better understanding of ourselves, but never, I hope, with a set of technologies for doing something or other to improve ourselves. I am made nervous by assertions that human consciousness will someday be unraveled by research, laid out for close scrutiny like the workings of a computer, and then, *and then*! I hope with some fervor that we can learn a lot more than we now know about the human mind, and I see no reason why this strange puzzle should remain forever and entirely beyond us. But I would be deeply disturbed by any prospect that we might use the new knowledge in order to begin doing something about it, to improve it, say. This is a different matter from searching for information to use against schizophrenia or dementia, where we are badly in need of technologies, indeed likely one day to be sunk without them. But the ordinary, everyday, more or less normal human mind is too marvelous an instrument ever to be tampered with by anyone, science or no science.

The education of humanists cannot be regarded as complete, or even adequate, without exposure in some depth to where things stand in the various branches of science, and particularly, as I have said, in the areas of our ignorance. This does not mean that I know how to go about doing it, nor am I unaware of the difficulties involved. Physics professors, most of them, look with revulsion on assignments to teach their subject to poets. Biologists, caught up by the enchantment of their new power, armed with flawless instruments to tell the nucleotide sequences of the entire human genome, nearly matching the physicists in the precision of their measurements of living processes, will resist the prospect of broad survey courses; each biology professor will demand that any student in his path must master every fine detail within that professor's research program. The liberal-arts faculties, for their part, will continue to view the scientists with suspicion and apprehension. "What do the scientists want?" asked a Cambridge professor in Francis Cornford's wonderful *Microcosmographia Academica*. "Everything that's going," was the quick answer. That was back in 1912, and universities haven't much changed.

The worst thing that has happened to science education is that the great fun has gone out of it. A very large number of good students look at it as slogging work to be got through on the way to medical school. Others look closely at the premedical students themselves, embattled and bleeding for grades and class standing, and are turned off. Very few see science as the high adventure it really is, the wildest of all explorations ever undertaken by human beings, the chance to catch close views of things never seen before, the shrewdest maneuver for discovering how the world works. Instead, they become baffled early on, and they are misled into thinking that bafflement is simply the result of not having learned all the facts. They are not told, as they should be told, that everyone else—from the professor in his endowed chair down to the platoons of postdoctoral students in the laboratory all night—is baffled as well. Every important scientific advance that has come in looking like an answer has turned, sooner or later—usually sooner—into a question. And the game is just beginning.

An appreciation of what is happening in science today, and of how great a distance lies ahead for exploring, ought to be one of the rewards of a liberal-arts education. It ought to be a good in itself, not something to be acquired on the way to a professional career but part of the cast of thought needed for getting into the kind of century that is now just down the road. Part of the intellectual equipment of an educated person, however his or her time is to be spent, ought to be a feel for the queernesses of nature, the inexplicable things.

And maybe, just maybe, a new set of courses dealing systematically with ignorance in science might take hold. The scientists might discover in it a new and subversive technique for catching the attention of students driven by curiosity, delighted and surprised to learn that science is exactly as Bush described it: an "endless frontier." The humanists, for their part, might take considerable satisfaction watching their scientific colleagues confess openly to not knowing everything about everything. And the poets, on whose shoulders the future rests, might, late nights, thinking things over, begin to see some meanings that elude the rest of us. It is worth a try.

CHAPTER EIGHTY-FIVE

On Matters of Doubt

THE "TWO-CULTURES" CONTROVERSY OF SEVERAL DECADES BACK HAS quieted down some, but it is still with us, still unsettled because of the polarized views set out by C. P. Snow at one polemical extreme and by F. R. Leavis at the other; these remain as the two sides of the argument. At one edge, the humanists are set up as knowing, and wanting to know, very little about science and even less about the human meaning of contemporary science; they are, so it goes, antiscientific in their prejudice. On the other side, the scientists are served up as a bright but illiterate lot, well-read in nothing except science, even, as Leavis said of Snow, incapable of writing good novels. The humanities are presented in the dispute as though made up of imagined unverifiable notions about human behavior, unsubstantiated stories cooked up by poets and novelists, while the sciences deal parsimoniously with lean facts, hard data, incontrovertible theories, truths established beyond doubt, the unambiguous facts of life.

   The argument is shot through with bogus assertions and false images, and I have no intention of becoming entrapped in it here, on one side or the other. Instead, I intend to take a stand in the middle of what seems to me a muddle, hoping to confuse the argument by showing that there isn't really any argument in the first place. To do this, I must try to show that there is in fact a solid middle ground to stand on, a shared common earth beneath the feet of all the humanists and all the scientists, a single underlying view of the world that drives all scholars, whatever their discipline—whether history or structuralist criticism or linguistics or quantum chromodynamics or astrophysics or molecular genetics.

There is, I think, such a shared view of the world. It is called *bewilderment*. Everyone knows this, but it is not much talked about; bewilderment is kept hidden in the darkest closets of all our institutions of higher learning, repressed whenever it seems to be emerging into public view, sometimes glimpsed staring from attic windows like a mad cousin of learning. It is the family secret of twentieth-century science, and of twentieth-century arts and letters as well. Human knowledge doesn't stay put. What we have been learning in our time is that we really do not understand this place or how it works, and we comprehend our own selves least of all. And the more we learn, the more we are—or ought to be—dumbfounded.

It is the greatest fun to be bewildered, but only when there lies ahead the sure certainty of having things straightened out, and soon. It is like a marvelous game, provided you have some way of keeping score, and this is what seems to be lacking in our time. It is confusing, and too many of us are choosing not to play, settling back with whatever straws of fixed knowledge we can lay hands on, denying bewilderment, pretending one conviction or another, nodding our heads briskly at whatever we prefer to believe, staying away from the ambiguity of being.

We would be better off if we had never invented the terms "science" and "humanities" and then set them up as if they represented two different kinds of intellectual enterprise. I cannot see why we ever did this, but we did. Now, to make matters worse, we have these two encampments not only at odds but trying to swipe problems from each other. The historians, some of them anyway, want to be known as social scientists and solve the ambiguities of history by installing computers in all their offices; the deconstructionists want to become the ultimate scientists of poetry, looking at every word in a line with essentially the reductionist attitude of particle physicists in the presence of atoms, but still unaware of the uncertainty principle that governs any good poem: not only can the observer change the thing observed, he can even destroy it. The biologists have invaded all aspects of human behavior with equations to explain away altruism and usefulness by totting up the needs of genes; the sociobiologists are becoming humanists manqué, swept off their feet by ants. The physicists, needing new terms for their astonishments, borrow "quarks" from Joyce and label precisely quantitative aspects of matter almost dismissively with poetically allusive words like "strangeness," "color," and "flavor"; soon some parts of the universe will begin to "itch."

We have, to be sure, learned enough to know better than to say some things, about letters and about science, but we are still too reticent about our ignorance. Most things in the world are unsettling and bewildering, and it is a mistake to try to explain them away; they are there for marveling at and wondering at, and we should be doing more of this.

I do not mean to suggest that we are surrounded by unknowable things. Indeed, I cannot imagine any sorts of questions to be asked about ourselves or about nature that cannot sooner or later be answered, given enough time. I do admit to worrying, late at night, about that matter of time: obviously we will have to get rid of modern warfare and quickly, or else we will end up, with luck, throwing spears and stones at each other. We could, without luck, run out of time in what is left of this century and then, by mistake, finish the whole game off by upheaving the table, ending life for everything except the bacteria, maybe—with enough radiation, even them. If you are given to fretting about what is going on in the minds of the young people in our schools, or on the streets of Zurich or Paris or Sydney or Tokyo or wherever, give a thought to the idea of impermanence for a whole species—*ours*—and the risk of earthly incandescence; it is a brand-new idea, never before confronted as a reality by any rising generation of human beings.

I have an idea, as an aside. Why not agree with the Russians about just one technological uniformity to be installed, at small cost, in all the missiles, theirs and ours: two small but comfortable chambers added to every vehicle before firing, one for a prominent diplomat selected by the other side, one for a lawyer selected at random? It might be a beginning.

Here's a list of things, taken more or less at random, that we do not understand:

I am entitled to say, if I like, that awareness exists in all the individual creatures on the planet—worms, sea urchins, gnats, whales, subhuman primates, superprimate humans, the lot. I can say this because we do not know what we are talking about; consciousness is so much a total mystery for our own species that we cannot begin to guess about its existence in others. I can say that bird song is the music made by songbirds for their own pleasure, pure fun, also for ours, and it is only a piece of good fortune that the music turns out to be handy for finding mates for breeding or setting territorial markers. I can say, if I like, that social insects behave like the working parts of an immense central nervous system: the termite colony is an enormous brain on millions of legs; the individual termite is a mobile neuron. This would mean that there is such a phenomenon as collective thinking, which goes on whenever sufficient numbers of creatures are sufficiently connected to one another, and it would also mean that we humans could do the same trick if we tried, and perhaps we've already done it, over and over again, in the making of language and the meditative making (for which the old Greek word *poesis* is best) of metaphors. I can even assert out loud that we are, as a species, held together by something like affection (what the physicists might be calling a "weak force") and by something like love (a "strong force"), and nobody can prove that I'm wrong. I can dismiss all the evidence piling up against such an idea, all our destructiveness and cantankerousness, as error, error-proneness, built into our species to allow more flexibility of choice, and nobody can argue me out of this unless I choose to wander off to another point of view.

I am inclined to assert, unconditionally, that there is one central, universal aspect of human behavior, genetically set by our very nature, biologically governed, driving each of us along. Depending on how one looks at it, it can be defined as the urge to be useful. This urge drives society along, sets our behavior as individuals and in groups, invents all our myths, writes our poetry, composes our music.

It is not easy to be a social species and, at the same time, such a juvenile, almost brand-new species, milling around in groups, trying to construct a civilization that will last. Being useful is easy for an ant: you just wait for the right chemical signal, at the right stage of the construction of the hill, and then you go looking for a twig of exactly the right size for that stage and carry it back, up the flank of the hill, and put it in place, and then you go and do that thing again. An ant can dine out on his usefulness, all his life, and never get it wrong.

It is a different problem for us, carrying such risks of doing it wrong, getting the wrong twig, losing the hill, not even recognizing, yet, the outline of the hill. We are beset by strings of DNA, immense arrays of genes, instructing each of us to be helpful, impelling us to try our whole lives to be useful, but never telling us how. The instructions are not coded out in anything like an operator's manual; we have to make guesses all the time. The difficulty is increased when groups of us are set to work together; I have seen, and sat on, numberless committees, not one of which intended anything other than great merit, feckless all. Larger collections of us—cities, for instance—hardly ever get anything right. And, of course, there is the modern nation, probably the most stupefying example of biological error since the age of the great reptiles, wrong at every turn, but always felicitating itself loudly on its great value. It is a biological problem, as much so as a coral reef or a rain forest, but such things as happen to human nations could never happen in a school of fish. It is, when you think about it, a humiliation, but then "humble" and "human" are cognate words. We are smarter than the fish, but their instructions come along in their eggs; ours we are obliged to figure out, and we are, in this respect, slow learners.

The sciences and the humanities are all of a piece, one and the same kind of work for the human brain, done by launching guesses and finding evidence to back up the guesses. The methods and standards are somewhat different, to be sure. It is easier to prove that something is so in science than it is to make an assertion about Homer or Cézanne or

Wallace Stevens and have it stand up to criticism from all sides, harder still to *be* Homer or Cézanne or Stevens, but the game is the same game. The hardest task for the scientists, hardly yet begun, is to find out what their findings may mean, deep inside, and how one piece of solid information, firmly established by experimentation and confirmation, fits with that unlike piece over there. The natural world is all of a piece, we all know this in our bones, but we have a long, long way to go before we will see how the connections are made.

If you are looking about for really profound mysteries, essential aspects of our existence for which neither the sciences nor the humanities can provide any sort of explanation, I suggest starting with music. The professional musicologists, tremendous scholars all, for whom I have the greatest respect, haven't the ghost of an idea about what music is, or why we make it and cannot be human without it, or even—and this is the telling point—how the human mind makes music on its own, before it is written down and played. The biologists are no help here, nor the psychologists, nor the physicists, nor the philosophers, wherever they are these days. Nobody can explain it. It is a mystery, and thank goodness for that. The Brandenburgs and the late quartets are not there to give us assurances that we have arrived; they carry the news that there are deep centers in our minds that we know nothing about except that they are there.

The thing to do, to get us through the short run, the years just ahead, is to celebrate our ignorance. Instead of presenting the body of human knowledge as a mountainous structure of coherent information capable of explaining everything about everything if we could only master all the details, we should be acknowledging that it is, in real life, still a very modest mound of puzzlements that do not fit together at all. As a species, the thing we are biologically good at is learning new things, thanks to our individual large brains and thanks above all to the gift of speech that connects them, one to another. We can take some gratification at having come a certain distance in just the few thousand years of our existence as language users, but it should be a deeper satisfaction, even an exhilaration, to recognize that we have such a distance still to go. Get us through the next few years, I say, just get us safely out of this century and into the next, and then watch what we can do.

CHAPTER EIGHTY-SIX

Late Night Thoughts on Listening to Mahler's Ninth Symphony

I CANNOT LISTEN TO MAHLER'S NINTH SYMPHONY WITH ANYTHING like the old melancholy mixed with the high pleasure I used to take from this music. There was a time, not long ago, when what I heard, especially in the final movement, was an open acknowledgment of death and at the same time a quiet celebration of the tranquillity connected to the process. I took this music as a metaphor for reassurance, confirming my own strong hunch that the dying of every living creature, the most natural of all experiences, has to be a peaceful experience. I rely on nature. The long passages on all the strings at the end, as close as music can come to expressing silence itself, I used to hear as Mahler's idea of leave-taking at its best. But always, I have heard this music as a solitary, private listener, thinking about death.

Now I hear it differently. I cannot listen to the last movement of the Mahler Ninth without the door-smashing intrusion of a huge new thought: death everywhere, the dying of everything, the end of humanity. The easy sadness expressed with such gentleness and delicacy by that repeated phrase on faded strings, over and over again, no longer comes to me as old, familiar news of the cycle of living and dying. All through the last notes my mind swarms with images of a world in which the thermonuclear bombs have begun to explode, in New York and San Francisco, in Moscow and Leningrad, in Paris, in Paris, in Paris. In Oxford and Cambridge, in Edinburgh. I cannot push away the thought of a cloud of radioactivity drifting along the Engadin, from the Moloja Pass to Ftan, killing off the part of the earth I love more than any other part.

I am old enough by this time to be used to the notion of dying, saddened by the glimpse when it has occurred but only transiently knocked down, able to regain my feet quickly at the thought of continuity, any day. I have acquired and held in affection until very recently another sideline of an idea which serves me well at dark times: the life of the earth is the same as the life of an organism: the great round being possesses a mind: the mind contains an infinite number of thoughts and memories: when I reach my time I may find myself still hanging around in some sort of midair, one of those small thoughts, drawn back into the memory of the earth: in that peculiar sense I will be alive.

Now all that has changed. I cannot think that way anymore. Not while those things are still in place, aimed everywhere, ready for launching.

This is a bad enough thing for the people in my generation. We can put up with it, I suppose, since we must. We are moving along anyway, like it or not. I can even set aside my private fancy about hanging around, in midair.

What I cannot imagine, what I cannot put up with, the thought that keeps grinding its way into my mind, making the Mahler into a hideous noise close to killing me, is what it would be like to be young. How do the young stand it? How can they keep their sanity? If I were very young, sixteen or seventeen years old, I think I would begin, perhaps very slowly and imperceptibly, to go crazy.

There is a short passage near the very end of the Mahler in which the almost vanishing violins, all engaged in a sustained backward glance, are edged aside for a few bars by the cellos. Those lower notes pick up fragments from the first movement, as though prepared to begin everything all over again, and then the cellos subside and disappear, like an

exhalation. I used to hear this as a wonderful few seconds of encouragement: we'll be back, we're still here, keep going, keep going.

Now, with a pamphlet in front of me on a corner of my desk,
published by the Congressional Office of Technology Assessment,
entitled *MX Basing,* an analysis of all the alternative strategies for
placement and protection of hundreds of these missiles, each capable of
creating artificial suns to vaporize a hundred Hiroshimas, collectively
capable of destroying the life of any continent, I cannot hear the same
Mahler. Now, those cellos sound in my mind like the opening of all the
hatches and the instant before ignition.

If I were sixteen or seventeen years old, I would not feel the cracking
of my own brain, but I would know for sure that the whole world was
coming unhinged. I can remember with some clarity what it was like to
be sixteen. I had discovered the Brahms symphonies. I knew that there
was something going on in the late Beethoven quartets that I would
have to figure out, and I knew that there was plenty of time ahead for all
the figuring I would ever have to do. I had never heard of Mahler. I was
in no hurry. I was a college sophomore and had decided that Wallace
Stevens and I possessed a comprehensive understanding of everything
needed for a life. The years stretched away forever ahead, forever. My
great-great grandfather had come from Wales, leaving his signature in
the family Bible on the same page that carried, a century later, my
father's signature. It never crossed my mind to wonder about the
twenty-first century; it was just there, given, somewhere in the sure
distance.

The man on television, Sunday midday, middle-aged and solid, nice-
looking chap, all the facts at his fingertips, more dependable looking
than most high-school principals, is talking about civilian defense, his
responsibility in Washington. It can make an enormous difference, he is
saying. Instead of the outright death of eighty million American citizens in twenty minutes, he says, we can, by careful planning and
practice, get that number down to only forty million, maybe even
twenty. The thing to do, he says, is to evacuate the cities quickly and
have everyone get under shelter in the countryside. That way we can
recover, and meanwhile we will have retaliated, incinerating all of
Soviet society, he says. What about radioactive fallout? he is asked. Well,
he says. Anyway, he says, if the Russians know they can only destroy
forty million of us instead of eighty million, this will deter them. Of
course, he adds, they have the capacity to kill all two hundred and
twenty million of us if they were to try real hard, but they know we can
do the same to them. If the figure is only forty million this will deter
them, not worth the trouble, not worth the risk. Eighty million would

be another matter, we should guard ourselves against losing that many all at once, he says.

If I were sixteen or seventeen years old and had to listen to that, or read things like that, I would want to give up listening and reading. I would begin thinking up new kinds of sounds, different from any music heard before, and I would be twisting and turning to rid myself of human language.